THE

# SPORT QUIZ BOOK

# THE SPORT QUIZ BOOK

**THOUSANDS OF BRAIN-TEASING QUESTIONS TO TEST YOUR KNOWLEDGE TO THE LIMIT**

**COMPILED BY PHILIP REED AND MARC BREMAN**

This edition published and distributed by Siena

This edition published 1999
Siena is an imprint of Parragon

Parragon
Queen Street House
4-5 Queen Street
Bath BA1 1HE



Printed and bound in the UK

Compiled by Philip Reed and Marc Breman

Design by Zeta @ Moo



ISBN 0 75252 983 8

# CONTENTS

# ATHLETICS

# • ATHLETICS - QUIZ 1 •

*Answers on page 10*

1 Which Ethiopian won his third successive 10,000m World Championship title in 1997?

2 What were the Commonwealth Games called when they began in 1930?

3 Who won her second World Cup 3000m title in 1994?

4 Where were the 1997 World Championships held?

5 What is the height of the hurdles in the women's 400m?

6 At which distance was Rob Denmark 1994 Commonwealth Games champion?

7 Who won the men's 800m at the 1993 World Indoor Championships?

8 Who has held the world record for the women's 400m since 1985?

9 Which New Zealander won both the men's 880yds and the Mile at the 1962 Commonwealth Games?

10 Which event has Lars Riedel won in the last three World Championships?

11 Who assumed Linford Christie's Commonwealth Games 100m title in 1998?

12 What is the maximum depth of the waterjump in the steeplechase?

13 In what is Bill 'Bojangles' Robinson the record holder?

14 Who won their second Commonwealth Games 4x100m title in 1998?

15 At which event did Nick A'Hern win his second consecutive Commonwealth Games title in 1998?

## *Answers to page 10*

**1** 220yds, **2** 3ft, **3** Mike Powell, **4** John Regis, **5** 5000m, **6** Trevor Bickle, **7** Marion Jones, **8** 2.5m, **9** 1993, **10** Marathon, **11** Dan O'Brien, **12** Kuala Lumpur, **13** 1968, **14** Liz McColgan, **15** Steve Cram.

# • ATHLETICS - QUIZ 2 •

*Answers on page 11*

1 Who won the women's 400m hurdles at the 1994 World Cup?

2 Which year saw Jamaica win their first Commonwealth Games men's 4x400m title?

3 Which field event has styles called scissors, straddle and Western roll?

4 Who succeeded Carl Lewis as long jump world champion, also winning twice in a row?

5 Where were the first Commonwealth Games, then called the British Empire Games, held in 1930?

6 Who won the 1983 World Championship men's 1500m title?

7 Which country's athletes hold the world records for the women's 1500m, 3000m, 5000m and 10,000m?

8 During which 1954 competition did Roger Bannister run the first sub-four-minute mile in a major championship?

9 What is the longest race in the decathlon?

10 Which Romanian was overall Grand Prix women's champion in 1988 and 1989?

11 At what distance was Daniel Komen 1998 Commonwealth Games champion?

12 Which Scot won the men's 100m in the 1982 Commonwealth Games?

13 Who set a long-standing men's 200m world record in September 1979?

14 Who won both the women's 100m and 200m at the 1990 Commonwealth Games?

15 What is the height of the hurdles in the women's 100m?

---

## *Answers to page 11*

**1** 50k walk, **2** Marion Jones, **3** Don Quarrie, **4** Stuttgart, **5** Sonia O'Sullivan, **6** Ron Hill, **7** 10,000m, **8** Uwe Hohn, **9** Petra Felke, **10** Peter Elliott, **11** 2kg, **12** 5000m walk, **13** Canada, **14** Riaan Botha, **15** Sally Gunnell.

# • ATHLETICS - QUIZ 3 •

*Answers on page 8*

1. What was the 200m called in the Commonwealth Games prior to 1970?
2. What is the height of the hurdles in the men's 400m?
3. Who set a men's long jump world record in August 1991?
4. Who won the men's 200m at the 1989 World Indoor Championships?
5. At which distance was Ismael Kirui 1993 and 1995 world champion?
6. Which Australian won consecutive Commonwealth Games pole vault titles in 1962 and 1966?
7. Who won both the women's 100m and 200m at the 1998 World Cup?
8. What is the diameter of the discus circle?
9. In which year was Linford Christie men's 100m world champion?
10. At which event did Rob de Castella successfully defend his Commonwealth Games title in 1986?
11. Who won his third successive World Championship decathlon title in 1995?
12. Where were the 1998 Commonwealth Games held?
13. In which year did Dick Fosbury win Olympic gold with his new high jump technique?
14. Under what name did Liz Lynch successfully defend her Commonwealth Games 10,000m title in 1990?
15. Who successfully defended his Commonwealth Games men's 1500m title in 1986?

## *Answers to page 8*

**1** Haile Gebresilasie, **2** British Empire Games, **3** Yvonne Murray, **4** Athens, **5** 2ft 6in, **6** 5000m, **7** Tom McKean, **8** Marita Koch, **9** Peter Snell, **10** Discus, **11** Ato Boldon, **12** 2.5ft, **13** Running backwards, **14** England, **15** 30k road walk.

# • ATHLETICS - QUIZ 4 •

*Answers on page 9*

**1** In which event was Robert Korzeniowski the first Pole to become world champion in 1997?

**2** Who was the overall 1998 Grand Prix women's champion ?

**3** Who successfully defended his 200m title at the 1974 Commonwealth Games?

**4** Where were the World Championships held in 1993?

**5** Who won the women's 5000m at the 1998 World Cup?

**6** Who, in 1970, was the last Englishman to win the Commonwealth Games marathon?

**7** At which distance was Alberto Cova the first Commonwealth Games champion?

**8** Who, in 1984, was the first to throw a javelin over 100m?

**9** Who set a women's javelin world record in September 1988?

**10** Who won the men's 1500m title at the 1990 Commonwealth Games?

**11** What is the weight of the men's discus?

**12** Which discontinued event did Mikhail Shchennikov win at its last four World Championships?

**13** Which was the first country to host the Commonwealth Games twice?

**14** Who became, in 1998, the second South African Commonwealth Games pole vault champion?

**15** Who won her second successive 400m hurdles title at the 1994 Commonwealth Games?

***Roger Bannister first ran the four minute mile on May 6th 1954 in 3 mins 59.4 seconds.***

---

*Answers to page 9*

**1** Sally Gunnell, **2** 1998, **3** High jump, **4** Mike Powell, **5** Hamilton, **6** Steve Cram, **7** China, **8** Empire Games, **9** 1500m, **10** Paula Ivan, **11** 5000m, **12** Allan Wells, **13** Pietro Mennea, **14** Merlene Ottey, **15** 2ft 9in.

# • ATHLETICS - QUIZ 5 •

*Answers on page 14*

**1** Who retained his World Cup javelin title in 1998?

**2** Who won the 100yds in the 1930 Commonwealth Games?

**3** Where was the 1994 World Cup held?

**4** How many hurdles are there in the 400m?

**5** Who broke Marita Koch's nine year record in the 200m at the 1988 Olympic Games?

**6** Who successfully defended his Commonwealth Games 110m hurdles title in 1994?

**7** At which event did Wilson Boit win the World Championship title in 1997?

**8** Who was the 1990 Commonwealth Games men's 800m champion?

**9** Who won her fourth London Marathon in 1988?

**10** Who won the men's 100m at the 1997 World Championships?

**11** What is the weight of the hammer?

**12** At which event did Gary Honey successfully defend his Commonwealth Games title in 1986?

**13** Which Namibian won the men's 200m at the 1994 Commonwealth Games?

**14** Who was the 1998 Commonwealth Games heptathlon champion?

**15** Under what name did Heike Daute win her second long jump World Championship title in 1993?

## *Answers to page 14*

**1** Ivan Pedroso, **2** 1983, **3** Jeff Gutteridge, **4** Roger Black, **5** Fatima Whitbread, **6** Ed Moses, **7** 1990, **8** Michael Johnson, **9** Heptathlon, **10** Pheidippides, **11** Steve Backley, **12** Colin Jackson, **13** Harry Jerome, **14** Hammer, **15** Simon Maina.

# • ATHLETICS - QUIZ 6 •

*Answers on page 15*

**1** In which event did Gail Devers retain her World Championship title in 1995?

**2** Who was the 1990 Commonwealth Games men's 200m champion?

**3** Which Canadian successfully defended his Commonwealth Games 100m hurdles title in 1986?

**4** Who have been the men's winners in the last three World Cups?

**5** At which event did Keith Connor successfully defend his Commonwealth Games title in 1982?

**6** Who won the first two World Championship men's 200m titles?

**7** Who was the first man to run the 5000m in under 13 minutes?

**8** Who set a men's 400m world record in August 1988?

**9** Who won the Commonwealth Games 100yds for Trinidad in 1954?

**10** What nationality is high jumper Javier Sotomayor?

**11** Which Mexican won his third consecutive London Marathon in 1996?

**12** What is the weight of the men's javelin?

**13** At which event did Greg Foster win his third consecutive World Championship title in 1991?

**14** Which Kenyan was the 1998 Commonwealth Games men's 1500m champion?

**15** Who won her third Commonwealth Games javelin title in 1990?

---

*Answers to page 15*

**1** Harold Abrahams, **2** Dinsdale Morgan, **3** Shot, **4** Germany, **5** 1kg, **6** Daley Thompson, **7** 800m, **8** Long Jump, **9** Linford Christie, **10** Larry Myricks, **11** Helsinki **12** David Moorcroft,, **13** High Jump, **14** Derek Ibbotson, **15** Darren Clark.

# • ATHLETICS - QUIZ 7 •

*Answers on page 12*

1. Who won his third consecutive World Indoor Championships long jump title in 1997?
2. Which year saw the first Athletics World Championships?
3. Which pole vaulter was the first to receive a UK life ban for failing a drugs test?
4. Who was the 1986 Commonwealth Games men's 400m champion?
5. Which javelin champion's real surname is Vevad?
6. Who won the men's 400m hurdles in the first three World Cups?
7. In which year was Kriss Akabusi Commonwealth Games 400m hurdles champion?
8. Who won his third consecutive 400m world title in 1997?
9. In which event did Sabine Braun win her second World Championship title in 1997?
10. Whose run to convey news of the Battle of Marathon gave the marathon its name?
11. Who successfully defended his Commonwealth Games javelin title in 1994?
12. Who set a men's 110m hurdles world record in August 1993?
13. Which Canadian won the men's 100yds at the 1966 Commonwealth Games?
14. In which event did Martin Girvan set a UK record?
15. Which Kenyan was the 1998 Commonwealth Games men's 10,000m champion?

***Daley Thompson was only seventeen when he scored a British record best of 7,684 decathlon points in 1976.***

---

## *Answers to page 12*

**1** Steve Backley, **2** Percy Williams, **3** London, **4** 10, **5** Florence Griffith-Joyner, **6** Colin Jackson, **7** 3000m steeplechase, **8** Japhet Kimutai, **9** Ingrid Kristiansen, **10** Maurice Greene, **11** 16lb, **12** Long Jump, **13** Frankie Fredericks, **14** Denise Lewis, **15** Heike Drechsler.

# • ATHLETICS - QUIZ 8 •

*Answers on page 13*

**1** Which Olympic gold medallist was chairman of the British Amateur Athletic Board 1948-75?

**2** Which Jamaican was the 1998 Commonwealth Games men's 400m hurdles champion?

**3** Which event did Udo Beyer win in the first three World Cups?

**4** Which country won the women's 4 x 400m in the 1997 World Championship?

**5** What is the weight of the women's discus?

**6** Who won his third consecutive Commonwealth Games decathlon title in 1986?

**7** At which distance did Wilson Kipketer win successive World Championship titles in 1995 and 1997?

**8** In which event did Beverley Kinch set a UK record?

**9** Who successfully defended his Commonwealth Games 100m title in 1994?

**10** Where were the first World Championships held?

**11** Who won his second consecutive World Indoor Championships long jump title in 1989?

**12** Who was the 1982 Commonwealth Games men's 5000m champion?

**13** At which event is Charles Austin the only American to win the World Championship title?

**14** Who was the first man to run the mile in exactly four minutes?

**15** Which Australian was the 1990 Commonwealth Games men's 400m champion?

---

## *Answers to page 13*

**1** 100m hurdles, **2** Marcus Adam, **3** Mark McKoy, **4** Africa, **5** Triple jump, **6** Calvin Smith, **7** Said Aouita, **8** Butch Reynolds, **9** Mike Agostini, **10** Cuban, **11** Dionicio Ceron, **12** 800g, **13** 110m hurdles, **14** Laban Rotich, **15** Tessa Sanderson.

# • ATHLETICS - QUIZ 9 •

*Answers on page 18*

**1** Which controversial Canadian won the men's 100m in the 1986 Commonwealth Games?

**2** At which event did Sandra Farmer-Patrick win her second consecutive World Cup title in 1992?

**3** Who was the first woman to pass 2m in the high jump?

**4** Who was the 1998 Commonwealth Games women's 200m champion?

**5** Which year saw Abdi Bile win the 1500m World Championship title?

**6** Who won the first three World Championship 100m titles?

**7** What is the shortest distance run at the World Indoor Championships?

**8** For which constituency did Sebastian Coe become Conservative MP?

**9** At what distance was Andrew Lloyd 1990 Commonwealth Games champion?

**10** Who was the overall 1998 Grand Prix men's champion?

**11** In which event was Audrey Abduvaliyev world champion in 1993 and 1995?

**12** Who was unbeaten in the women's high jump 1956-66?

**13** Where were the second Commonwealth Games held in 1934?

**14** Which Australian won both the men's 880yds and the mile at the 1958 Commonwealth Games?

**15** Who won the men's high jump at the 1998 Commonwealth Games?

## *Answers to page 18*

**1** Maria Mutola, **2** 1982, **3** Ludmila Engquist, **4** Edinburgh, **5** Stefka Kostadinova, **6** David Moorcroft, **7** Ben Johnson, **8** Geoff Elliott, **9** Wilson Kipketer, **10** Kenya, **11** Heike Drechsler, **12** Marathon, **13** Debbie Brill, **14** 1981, **15** Goteborg.

# • ATHLETICS - QUIZ 10 •

*Answers on page 19*

**1** In which event did Yordanka Donkova set a world record in August 1988?

**2** Who won both the men's 800m and 1500m at the 1986 Commonwealth Games?

**3** In which year were imperial distances last run at the Commonwealth Games?

**4** What did Catherina McKiernan win in April 1998?

**5** Who was 1987 5000m world champion?

**6** Who, in 1876, was the first man to pass 6ft in the high jump?

**7** From which country is Thabiso Moghali, 1998 Commonwealth Games marathon winner?

**8** Who won his second successive javelin World Championship title in 1995?

**9** Where were the 1991 World Championships held?

**10** Who successfully defended his Commonwealth Games high jump title in 1986?

**11** Who set six world records at Ann Arbor in 1935?

**12** In which year did Wales's Kirsty Wade win at 800m and 1500m at the Commonwealth Games?

**13** Who was the first American men's marathon world champion?

**14** In which city did Roger Bannister first run the mile in under 4 minutes in May 1954?

**15** Where were the 1994 Commonwealth Games held?

---

## *Answers to page 19*

**1** Atlee Mahorn, **2** World Cup, **3** Lynn Davies, **4** Gail Devers, **5** 3ft 6in, **6** Men's 200m, **7** Auckland, **8** Donovan Bailey, **9** 1995, **10** Graeme Fell, **11** Great Britain, **12** Anchorman, **13** Judy Oakes, **14** 800m, **15** Shorter.

# • ATHLETICS - QUIZ 11 •

*Answers on page 16*

**1** Who won her third successive 800m title at the 1997 World Indoor Championships?

**2** Which year saw a tie in the Commonwealth Games men's 200m?

**3** Who was 1997 100m hurdles world champion?

**4** Which was the first city to host the Commonwealth Games twice?

**5** Who won her fourth World Indoor Championships high jump title in 1993?

**6** Who was the 1978 Commonwealth Games 1500m champion?

**7** Which Canadian runner was stripped of titles, world records and an Olympic gold after a positive drugs test?

**8** Who successfully defended his Commonwealth Games pole vault title in 1958?

**9** Which Kenyan-born runner broke Seb Coe's 16-year-old world 800m record in 1997?

**10** Which country has won the 3000m steeplechase in six of the last seven Commonwealth Games?

**11** Who won a record third World Cup long jump title in 1998?

**12** In which men's event was Abel Anton the second Spanish world champion?

**13** Who, in 1970, was the first woman to pass 6ft in the high jump?

**14** In what year was the first London Marathon?

**15** Where were the World Championships held in 1995?

***In 1968 Jim Hines was the first man to run 100 metres in under 10 seconds; his time was 9.9 seconds.***

---

*Answers to page 16*

**1** Ben Johnson, **2** 400m hurdles, **3** Rosie Ackermann, **4** Nova Peris-Kneebone, **5** 1987, **6** Carl Lewis, **7** 60m, **8** Falmouth and Camborne, **9** 5000m, **10** Hicham el Guerrouj, **11** Hammer, **12** Iolanda Balas, **13** London, **14** Herb Elliott, **15** Dalton Grant.

# • ATHLETICS - QUIZ 12 •

*Answers on page 17*

**1** Which Canadian won the men's 200m at the 1986 Commonwealth Games?

**2** Which competition, first held in 1977, has teams representing the five continents?

**3** Which Welshman successfully defended his Commonwealth Games long jump title in 1970?

**4** Who was 1993 world champion in both the women's 100m and 100m hurdles?

**5** What is the height of the hurdles in the men's 110m?

**6** In which event in the 1998 European Championships did British athletes win all three medals?

**7** Where were the 1990 Commonwealth Games held?

**8** Who was 1995 men's 100m world champion?

**9** Which year saw Moses Kiptanui win his third successive 3000m steeplechase world championship title?

**10** Who, in 1970, was the only Canadian to win the Commonwealth Games 3000m steeplechase?

**11** Which country won the 1998 World Cup men's 4 x 400?

**12** What is the last runner in a relay race called?

**13** Which British field athlete won her third Commonwealth Games title in 1998?

**14** What is the longest race in the heptathlon?

**15** When the mile became the 1500m at the 1970 Commonwealth Games, did the race become longer or shorter?

---

## *Answers to page 17*

**1** 100m hurdles, **2** Steve Cram, **3** 1966, **4** London Marathon, **5** Said Aouita, **6** Marshall Jones Brooks, **7** Lesotho, **8** Jan Zelezny, **9** Tokyo, **10** Milt Ottey, **11** Jesse Owens, **12** 1986, **13** Mark Plaatjes, **14** Oxford, **15** Victoria, Canada.

# • ATHLETICS - QUIZ 13 •

*Answers on page 21*

1 Which field event has methods called rotational and O'Brien shift?

2 Which Kenyan successfully defended his 400m title at the 1974 Commonwealth Games?

3 In which year was the women's triple jump added to the World Championships?

4 What event did Judy Simpson win at the 1986 Commonwealth Games?

5 Where was the 1998 World Cup held?

6 Who took the Commonwealth Games 110m hurdles title from Colin Jackson in 1998?

7 In which event was Lia Manoliu the oldest woman Olympic gold medallist?

8 Who was men's 200m world champion in 1991 and 1995?

9 Who won the men's race in the 1998 London Marathon?

10 Having previously represented the USSR, what did Sergey Bubka's country become in 1993?

11 Who won the men's 100m in the 1970 Commonwealth Games?

12 Which women's team won the World Cup in four successive years?

13 Who successfully defended his Commonwealth Games shot title in 1978?

14 Which British triple jumper set a new world record in the European Indoor Athletics Championships in Valencia in 1998?

15 Which New Zealander successfully defended his 3 miles title in the 1962 Commonwealth Games?

---

## *Answers to page 22*

**1** 1974, **2** Javier Sotomayor, **3** Pole Vault, **4** Marathon, **5** Don Quarrie, **6** 7ft, **7** Rome, **8** Mike Smith, **9** Algerian, **10** Evelyn Ashford, **11** 10,000m, **12** Bruny Surin, **13** Jonathan Edwards, **14** Charles Gitonga, **15** Merlene Ottey.

# • ATHLETICS - QUIZ 14 •

*Answers on page 22*

1 Who won the first two World Championship long jump titles?

2 What is the weight of the men's shot?

3 Who won her second consecutive World Indoor Championships 3000m title in 1997?

4 Which Kenyan won the men's 100 yds in the 1962 Commonwealth Games?

5 Which Canadian runner set a world record for the men's 100m in 1996?

6 In which event was Robert Weir 1998 Commonwealth Games champion?

7 Who won her second World Championship heptathlon title in 1993?

8 Who, in 1998, became the first Welshman to win the Commonwealth Games 400m title?

9 Who was unbeaten in the men's 400m hurdles 1977-87?

10 At which distance was Ato Boldon 1997 world champion?

11 Who was the 1986 Commonwealth Games men's 5000m champion?

12 Where was the first World Cup held?

13 In which event did Nick Buckfield set a UK men's record?

14 Which event did Mary Peters win in successive Commonwealth Games?

15 Who is the only Northern Irish Commonwealth Games men's 400m hurdles champion?

## *Answers to page 20*

**1** Shot, **2** Charles Asati, **3** 1993, **4** Heptathlon, **5** Johannesburg, **6** Tony Jarrett, **7** Discus, **8** Michael Johnson, **9** Abel Anton, **10** Ukraine, **11** Don Quarrie, **12** East Germany, **13** Geoff Capes, **14** Ashia Hansen, **15** Murray Halberg.

# • ATHLETICS - QUIZ 15 •

*Answers on page 20*

**1** In which year was Alan Pascoe Commonwealth Games 400m hurdles champion?

**2** Who, in 1989, was the first man to pass 8ft in the high jump?

**3** Which event is the only one to have been won by only one person in the first six World Championships?

**4** Which event's distance was increased by 385 yards in 1908 so that the race would finish in front of the royal box at White City?

**5** Who won his third consecutive Commonwealth Games 100m title in 1978?

**6** What is the diameter of the circle in the shot?

**7** Where were the World Championships held in 1987?

**8** Which Canadian won his second consecutive Commonwealth Games decathlon title in 1994?

**9** What nationality is runner Noureddine Morceli?

**10** Who successfully defended both her 100m and 200m titles at the 1981 World Cup?

**11** At what distance was Eamonn Martin 1990 Commonwealth Games champion?

**12** Who won his second consecutive World Indoor Championships 60m title in 1995?

**13** Which British athlete set a men's triple jump world record in 1995?

**14** Which Kenyan was 1994 Commonwealth Games 400m champion?

**15** Who has won the most world championship medals, with 14?

***Sebastian Coe, who held twelve World records, has acted as a fitness trainer for William Hague.***

---

## *Answers to page 21*

**1** Carl Lewis, **2** 16lb, **3** Gabriela Sjabo, **4** Seraphino Antau, **5** Donovan Bailey, **6** Discus, **7** Jackie Joyner-Kersee, **8** Iwan Thomas, **9** Ed Moses, **10** 200m, **11** Steve Ovett, **12** Dusseldorf, **13** Pole Vault, **14** Pentathlon, **15** Phil Beattie.

# BOXING

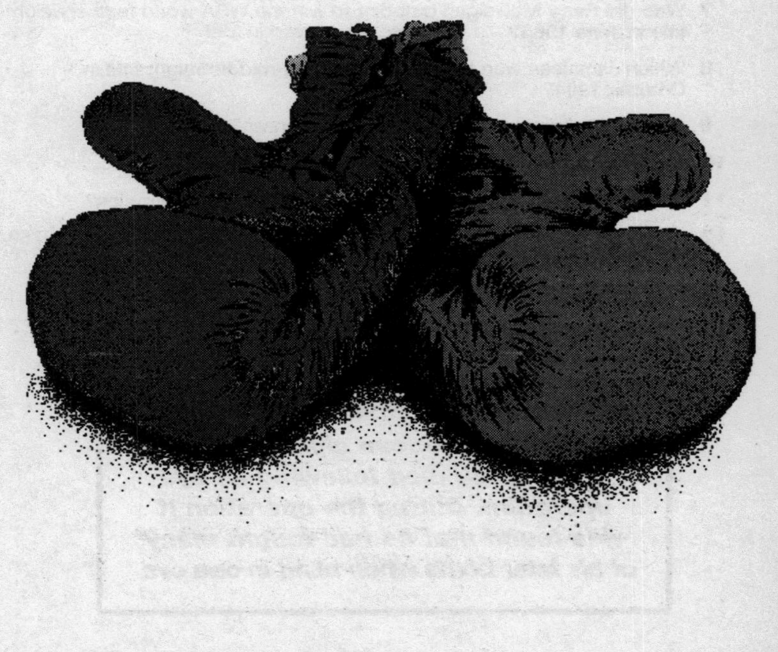

# BOXING - QUIZ 1

*Answers on page 26*

1 Who beat Jack Dempsey in the 'Battle of the Long Count' in 1927?

2 In which year was Mike Tyson born?

3 Which American boxer was known as the 'Hit Man' or 'Motor City Cobra'?

4 Who was the first man to win undisputed world titles at three different weights?

5 Name the first black heavyweight champion?

6 Alexis Arguello won world titles at three different weights. In which country was he born?

7 Who did Barry McGuigan outpoint to win the WBA world featherweight title in June 1985?

8 Which Jamaican won the WBA world light-middleweight title in October 1984?

9 When was Cassius Clay (Muhammad Ali) born?

10 Name the first Argentinian boxer to win a world title?

11 Which American won heavyweight gold at the 1968 Olympics?

12 Which Briton won the WBC world welterweight title in December 1975?

13 Who was his opponent?

14 Which Mexican fighter took Stracey's title in 1976?

15 In which year did Frank Bruno turn professional?

***Legendary American champion boxer Harry Grieg died following an eye operation. During the operation it was found that he had fought many of his later bouts when blind in one eye.***

## *Answers to page 26*

**1** Puerto Rico, **2** True **3** John Conteh, **4** Wilfred Benitez, **5** Scotland **6** False - four times, **7** 1962, **8** Rocky Graziano, **9** England, **10** 1960s, **11** Sheffield, **12** Three, **13** Chris Eubank, **14** Hector Camacho, **15** Boom-Boom.

# BOXING - QUIZ 2

*Answers on page 27*

**1** Who lost to Muhammad Ali in the 'Thrilla in Manila'?

**2** Which American heavyweight was nicknamed the 'Brown Bomber'?

**3** In which year was Joe Louis born -1914 or 1920?

**4** Which former world heavyweight champion announced that he was HIV positive in February 1996?

**5** Name the first man to beat Thomas Hearns professionally?

**6** In which decade was world heavyweight champion George Foreman born?

**7** Name the only man to beat Joe Louis in a world title fight?

**8** Jersey Joe Walcott was 37 years old when he became world heavyweight champion. True or false?

**9** Who lost to Muhammad Ali in the 'Rumble in The Jungle'?

**10** Who was the first man to beat Chris Eubank professionally?

**11** Name the first man to beat Michael Spinks in a professional bout?

**12** Which ring legend beat Donny Lalonde to become WBC world light-heavyweight champion in November 1988?

**13** Where was the Mike Tyson - Frank Bruno world title fight of 1989 staged?

**14** When was Sugar Ray Leonard born?

**15** At which Olympics did Italian Nino Benvenuti win welterweight gold?

---

*Answers to page 27*

**1** Larry Holmes, **2** 1988, Seoul **3** Riddick, Bowe, **4** Trevor Berbick, **5** 1979, **6** Hungary, **7** Cassius Clay (Muhammad Ali), **8** Zaire, **9** 1930s, **10** 1986, **11** Trevor Berbick, **12** American, **13** Jimmy Wilde, **14** Henry Cooper, **15** Riddick Bowe.

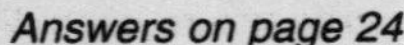

# • BOXING - QUIZ 3 •

*Answers on page 24*

**1** Wilfredo Gomez won world titles at three different weights. In which country was he born?

**2** Lloyd Honeyghan was born in Jamaica. True or false?

**3** Which Briton was stripped of his world light-heavyweight title in 1974 for failing to fight Miguel Cuello?

**4** Who became the youngest ever world champion when he won the WBA light-welterweight title in 1976 - aged 17 years 173 days?

**5** In which country was Ken Buchanan born?

**6** Muhammad Ali defended his world heavyweight crown six times during 1976. True or false?

**7** When was Evander Holyfield born - 1960 or 1962?

**8** Which world middleweight champion was born Rocco Barbella in 1922?

**9** In which country was Lennox Lewis born?

**10** In which decade was Mexican boxing legend Julio Cesar Chavez born?

**11** In which English city was boxer Herol Graham born?

**12** How many successful defences of his WBC world heavyweight title did Larry Holmes make in 1979 - 1, 3 or 5?

**13** Which Briton won the WBO world middleweight title by beating Dan Sherry in February 1991?

**14** Who beat Ray Mancini to win the WBO light-welterweight title in 1989?

**15** What was Ray Mancini's nickname?

## *Answers to page 24*

**1** Gene Tunney, **2** 1966, **3** Thomas Hearns, **4** Bob Fitzsimmons, **5** Jack Johnson, **6** Nicaragua, **7** Eusebio Pedroza, **8** Mike McCallum, **9** 1942, **10** Pascual Perez (1954), **11** George Foreman, **12** John H. Stracey, **13** Jose Napoles, **14** Carlos Palomino, **15** 1982.

# BOXING - QUIZ 4

*Answers on page 25*

1 In 1978, who outpointed Ken Norton to win the WBC heavyweight crown?

2 At which Olympic Games did Lennox Lewis win super-heavyweight gold?

3 Who was his opponent in the final?

4 Name Muhammad Ali's last opponent?

5 In which year did Maurice Hope defeat Rocky Mattioli to become WBC world light-middleweight champion?

6 In which country was Joe Bugner born?

7 Who won the 1960 Olympic Games light-heavyweight gold medal?

8 Name the first African country to host a heavyweight title fight?

9 In which decade was Henry Cooper born?

10 In which year did Mike Tyson win his first world heavyweight title?

11 Who was his opponent?

12 What nationality was world heavyweight champion Max Baer?

13 Which Welsh flyweight was known as the 'Ghost with a Hammer in his Hand'?

14 Which British heavyweight was awarded the OBE in 1969?

15 Which American heavyweight, born in 1967, is nicknamed 'Big Daddy'?

---

*Answers to page 25*

**1** Joe Frazier, **2** Joe Louis, **3** 1914, **4** Tommy Morrison, **5** Sugar Ray Leonard, **6** 1940s, **7** Ezzard Charles, **8** True, **9** George Foreman, **10** Steve Collins, **11** Mike Tyson, **12** Sugar Ray Leonard, **13** Las Vegas Hilton, **14** 1956, **15** 1960 (Rome).

# BOXING - QUIZ 5

*Answers on page 30*

1 What does IBF stand for?

2 In which decade was the IBF formed?

3 Which Irishman stopped Chris Pyatt to win the WBO world middleweight title in May 1994?

4 Which 1930s world heavyweight champion was known as the 'Livermore Larruper'?

5 Which Briton became European heavyweight champion in October 1985?

6 Name the first man to beat Frank Bruno professionally?

7 When was Joe Frazier born - 1944 or 1948?

8 Name the first man to beat Joe Louis professionally?

9 Name the first man to beat Mike Tyson professionally?

10 Who did James 'Buster' Douglas lose to in the first defence of his title?

11 When was the British Boxing Board of Control founded - 1918 or 1928?

12 Which heavyweight champion was nicknamed the 'Manassa Mauler'?

13 Which Swede took the world heavyweight title by defeating Floyd Patterson in 1959?

14 Who was acquitted at the Old Bailey in November 1990 of the attempted murder of Frank Warren?

15 Which boxing legend was known as 'Hands of Stone'?

***The Greatest heavyweight of all time Mohammed Ali was laid out by 'Enry's 'Ammer, Henry Cooper's famed left hook but was saved by the bell and a ripped glove as Ali's camp delayed proceedings.***

## *Answers to page 30*

**1** Liverpool, **2** Guyana, **3** George Foreman, **4** Nicaragua, **5** 1940s, **6** Draw, **7** Muhammad Ali (Cassius Clay), **8** Wilfred Benitez, **9** Two, **10** Jorge Vaca, **11** Mexico, **12** Thirteen, **13** Eight, **14** Teofilo Stevenson, **15** Cuba.

# • BOXING - QUIZ 6 •

*Answers on page 31*

**1** Who, in March 1980, became the first British fighter since Ted 'Kid' Lewis to win a world title in America?

**2** Who did Alan Minter beat in his first defence of the world middleweight title?

**3** In which year did Henry Cooper first fight Muhammad Ali?

**4** Which 1940s world middleweight champion was known as the 'Man of Steel'?

**5** In which decade was ring legend Sugar Ray Robinson born?

**6** Which French boxer, born in 1894, was known as the 'Orchid Man'?

**7** Which American was WBC light-middleweight champion between 1990-93?

**8** Which Briton won light-middleweight bronze at the 1972 Olympics?

**9** The first black African boxer to win an Olympic gold was Robert Wangila in 1988. Which country did he represent?

**10** Who beat Frank Bruno in a WBA world heavyweight title fight in July 1986?

**11** Which Scottish southpaw won the vacant WBC world lightweight title in April 1979?

**12** At which Glasgow venue?

**13** Who won his third world title at different weights by beating Jim Watt in 1981?

**14** How many professional fights did Mike Tyson have in 1985 - 5 ,10 or 15?

**15** Which fellow-Englishman was outpointed by Henry Akinwande in a WBO heavyweight title fight in January 1997?

---

## *Answers to page 31*

**1** 1966, **2** Forty three, **3** 1878, **4** Floyd Patterson, **5** Kentucky, **6** 162 days, **7** 1935, **8** Henry Armstrong, **9** Fifty five, **10** True, **11** Riddick Bowe, **12** Sugar Ray Leonard, **13** Clinton McKenzie, **14** Paul Newman, **15** Flash.

# BOXING - QUIZ 7

*Answers on page 28*

1 In which English city was John Conteh born?

2 In which country was Dennis Andries born?

3 Who won the heavyweight gold medal at the 1968 Olympics?

4 Where was Alexis Arguello born?

5 During which decade was the first heavyweight title fight to be televised?

6 What was the result of the Milton McCrory against Colin Jones WBC world welterweight title fight in March 1983?

7 Who was known as the 'The Louisville Lip'?

8 Who won his third world title by beating Maurice Hope in their WBC light-middleweight bout in 1981?

9 How many world title fights were contested in 1886 - 2, 4 or 6?

10 Who did Lloyd Honeyghan beat to regain the WBC world welterweight title in March 1988?

11 In which country was Jorge Vaca born?

12 How many world heavyweight title fights did Floyd Patterson have - 3, 13 or 23?

13 How many did he win -2, 4 or 8?

14 Which heavyweight struck gold at the 1972, 1976 and 1980 Olympics?

15 Which country did he represent?

## Answers to page 28

**1** International Boxing Federation, **2** 1980s, **3** Steve Collins, **4** Max Baer, **5** Frank Bruno, **6** James 'Bonecrusher' Smith, **7** 1944, **8** Max Schmeling, **9** James 'Buster' Douglas, **10** Evander Holyfield, **11** 1918, **12** Jack Dempsey, **13** Ingemar Johansson, **14** Terry Marsh, **15** Roberto Duran.

# BOXING - QUIZ 8

*Answers on page 29*

**1** In which year did Henry Cooper lose a world title fight to Muhammad Ali?

**2** How many of his 49 professional bouts did Rocky Marciano win inside the distance?

**3** In which year was world heavyweight champion Jack Johnson born - 1878 or 1898?

**4** Which Olympic gold medallist was first to win the world heavyweight crown?

**5** In which American state was Muhammad Ali (Cassius Clay) born?

**6** How long was John Tate's reign as WBA world heavyweight champion?

**7** In which year was Floyd Patterson born - 1935 or 1940?

**8** Which American boxing legend was known as 'Homicide Hank'?

**9** How many professional fights did Henry Cooper have - 35, 55, or 75?

**10** Charlie Magri won the British flyweight title in only his third professional bout. True or false?

**11** Which American beat Herbie Hide to win the WBO world heavyweight title in 1995?

**12** Which American won light-welterweight gold at the 1976 Olympics?

**13** Which Briton did he beat on his way to the final?

**14** Which actor played Rocky Graziano in the film 'Somebody Up There Likes Me'?

**15** Gabriel Elorde was world junior lightweight champion from 1960-67. What was his nickname?

---

*Answers to page 29*

**1** Alan Minter, **2** Vito Antuofermo, **3** 1963, **4** Tony Zale, **5** 1920s, **6** Georges Carpentier, **7** Terry Norris, **8** Alan Minter, **9** Kenya, **10** Tim Witherspoon, **11** Jim Watt, **12** Kelvin Hall, **13** Alexis Arguello, **14** Fifteen, **15** Scott Welch.

# BOXING - QUIZ 9

*Answers on page 34*

1 Which Mexican won 31 of 34 world title fights from 1984-1996?

2 Who did Thomas Hearns beat in March 1987 to win the WBC light-heavyweight title?

3 In which American state was heavyweight champion Jack Johnson born?

4 Which American boxer, nicknamed 'The Hatchet', won the vacant IBF super-middleweight title in June 1997?

5 Who was British heavyweight champion from 1959-69?

6 Who was America's only boxing gold medallist at the 1992 Olympics?

7 Which Jamaican boxer was known as 'The Body Snatcher'?

8 Name the first man to beat Nigel Benn professionally?

9 When was Nigel Benn born - 1962 or 1964?

10 Who beat John Davison to win the vacant WBO featherweight title in 1993?

11 What nationality is Steve Robinson?

12 Who beat Chris Finnegan in May 1973 to win the British light-heavyweight crown?

13 Which Herol became British light-middleweight champion in March 1981?

14 In which year did Maurice Hope win the British light-middlweight title?

15 Which Scotsman beat Charlie Nash to retain his WBC world lightweight title in March 1980?

***Mohammed Ali, who won 55 out of 61 professional bouts, was lost to boxing for three years by refusing to serve in Vietnam for religious reasons.***

## *Answers to page 34*

**1** Oliver McCall, **2** Steve Robinson, **3** False. He was convicted of manslaughter, **4** Jersey Joe Walcott, **5** 1988, **6** Michael Spinks, **7** 1920s, **8** Oscar De La Hoya, **9** Glenn McCrory, **10** Tunisia, **11** 1950s, **12** True, **13** John L. Gardner, **14** Robin Reid, **15** 1952, Helsinki.

# BOXING - QUIZ 10

*Answers on page 35*

**1** Which Briton beat Jorge Ahumada to win the vacant WBC light-heavyweight title in October 1974?

**2** How many times did light-heavyweight champion Archie Moore fight for the world heavyweight crown?

**3** Which Australian drew with Azumah Nelson in a WBC super-featherweight title fight in June 1991?

**4** Who did Muhammad Ali (Cassius Clay) defeat in 1964 to win his first world heavyweight title?

**5** The first boxer from a communist country to win a world title was Mate Parlov. What nationality was he?

**6** What do the initials WBA stand for?

**7** Which Guyanan boxer held the WBC world featherweight title from 1984-88?

**8** Which flashy fighter beat Don Curry to land the undisputed world welterweight title in September 1986?

**9** Which Mexican legend was unbeaten in his first 90 professional bouts from 1980-94?

**10** Who won super-heavyweight gold at the 1986 Commonwealth Games?

**11** At which Olympics did Pernell Whitaker win lightweight gold?

**12** Which Swede beat Henry Cooper to retain the European heavyweight title in May 1957?

**13** How many world title fights were contested in 1936 - 4, 8 or 16?

**14** Name the only man to hold three world titles simultaneously?

**15** At which Olympics did Britain's Anthony Willis win light-welterweight bronze?

---

## *Answers to page 35*

**1** True, **2** Montreal, **3** Scotland, **4** Sugar Ray Robinson, **5** English **6** 1950s, **7** Watson, **8** Michael Moorer, **9** 1970, **10** Freddie Mills, **11** Sibson, **12** 1978, **13** Frankie Randall, **14** Joe Louis, **15** Tommy Farr.

# BOXING - QUIZ 11

*Answers on page 32*

1 Who did Frank Bruno outpoint to win the WBC world heavyweight title in 1995?

2 Who did Prince Naseem Hamed stop to win the WBO world featherweight title in September 1995?

3 Promoter Don King was once convicted for murder. True or false?

4 Which world heavyweight champion was born Arnold Raymond Cream in 1914 at Merchantville, New Jersey?

5 At which Olympic Games did Ray Mercer win heavyweight gold?

6 Larry Holmes won his first 48 professional fights. Who did he lose to in the 49th?

7 In which decade was the Ring Magazine first published?

8 Name the only American boxer to win gold at the 1992 Olympics?

9 Which County Durham-born boxer won the vacant IBF world cruiserweight title on 3 June, 1989?

10 In which North African country was Charlie Magri born?

11 In which decade was Charlie Magri born?

12 Terry Marsh, the former IBF world light-welterweight champion, lost his first nine amateur fights. True or false?

13 Who was British heavyweight champion from 1978-1981?

14 Who did Joe Calzaghe outpoint in a world title bout at Newcastle in February 1999?

15 At which Olympics did Floyd Patterson win middleweight gold?

## *Answers to page 32*

**1** Julio Cesar Chavez, **2** Dennis Andries, **3** Texas, **4** Charles Brewer, **5** Henry Cooper, **6** Oscar De La Hoya, **7** Mike McCallum, **8** Michael Watson, **9** 1964, **10** Steve Robinson, **11** Welsh, **12** John Conteh, **13** Graham, **14** 1974, **15** Jim Watt.

# BOXING - QUIZ 12

*Answers on page 33*

1 Chris Eubank was unbeaten in his first 43 professional fights. True or false?

2 Which Canadian city staged the first Sugar Ray Leonard - Roberto Duran fight?

3 In which country was world lightweight champion Jim Watt born?

4 Who did Randolph Turpin beat to take the world middleweight title in 1951?

5 What nationality was Randolph Turpin?

6 In which decade did Ingemar Johansson beat Joe Erskine to retain the European heavyweight title?

7 Which Michael won the Commonwealth middleweight title in 1989?

8 Who beat Evander Holyfield to win the WBA and IBF world heavyweight titles in 1994?

9 At which Commonwealth Games did John Conteh win middleweight gold?

10 Which Briton was undisputed world light-heavyweight champion from July 1948-January 1950?

11 Which Tony lost to Dennis Andries in a WBC light-heavyweight title fight in September 1986?

12 At which Commonwealth Games did Jamaica's Mike McCallum win welterweight gold?

13 Name the first man to beat Julio Cesar Chavez in a professional bout?

14 Who beat James J. Braddock to win the world heavyweight title in June 1937?

15 Against which Welshman did Joe Louis make his first title defence?

---

### *Answers to page 33*

**1** John Conteh, **2** Two, **3** Jeff Fenech, **4** Sonny Liston, **5** Yugoslavian, **6** World Boxing Association, **7** Azumah Nelson, **8** Lloyd Honeyghan, **9** Julio Cesar Chavez, **10** Lennox Lewis, **11** 1984, **12** Ingemar Johansson, **13** Sixteen, **14** Henry Armstrong, **15** 1980.

# BOXING - QUIZ 13

*Answers on page 38*

1 In which country was Lennox Lewis born?

2 Which nation did he represent in the 1988 Olympic Games?

3 Who was stripped of his world heavyweight title for refusing to be drafted during the Vietnam War?

4 Who was WBA heavyweight champion from 1965-1967?

5 Which American lightweight won gold at the 1984 Olympics?

6 Which Welshman beat Kirkland Laing to win the British welterweight title in 1980?

7 In which year was Nigel Benn born?

8 During which decade was the first WBA title fight?

9 What was Herol Graham's nickname?

10 Which American boxer is nicknamed 'Lights Out'?

11 Name the first man to beat James Toney professionally?

12 In which country was former world middleweight champion Carlos Monzon born?

13 In which decade was heavyweight champion Tim Witherspoon born?

14 Who won the WBC world welterweight title by beating Wilfred Benitez at Las Vegas in November 1979?

15 Which Swede regained the European heavyweight title in 1962?

***Hungarian born, Joe Bugner has held the British, European, Commonwealth and Australian titles, twice went the distance with Ali and held the great Joe Frazier to a points decision.***

## *Answers to page 38*

**1** Iran Barkley, **2** Michael Dokes, **3** Sixty four, **4** 1987, **5** Thomas Hearns, **6** 1981, **7** Henry Cooper, **8** Brian London, **9** Miguel Angel Gonzalez, **10** Henry Cooper, **11** Michael Bentt, **12** Jeff Lampkin, **13** Dan Sherry, **14** Joe Frazier, **15** 1971.

# BOXING - QUIZ 14

*Answers on page 39*

**1** Who beat Frank Bruno in a world heavyweight title fight in February 1989?

**2** In which round did the referee stop the fight?

**3** At which Olympics did Britain's Richard McTaggart win lightweight gold?

**4** Who was 'Smokin' Joe'?

**5** Who beat Barry McGuigan to win the WBA world featherweight title in June 1986?

**6** Name the second man to beat Nigel Benn professionally?

**7** How many boxing gold medals did England win at the 1974 Commonwealth Games?

**8** How many times did Muhammad Ali defend his world heavyweight crown in 1977 - 2, 4 or 6?

**9** Which Briton lost his WBC super-middleweight crown to South African Thulane Malinga in December 1997?

**10** In which weight division did Britain's Harry Mallin win gold medals at the 1920 and 1924 Olympics?

**11** How many world heavyweight title fights did Joe Frazier contest - 4, 8 or 12?

**12** At which Olympics did America's Roy Jones win light-middleweight silver?

**13** In which decade was Larry Holmes born?

**14** At which Olympic Games did America's Mark Breland win welterweight gold?

**15** During which decade was the first world title fight to be broadcast in colour?

---

## *Answers to page 39*

**1** Four, **2** 1920s, **3** 1971, **4** 284 days, **5** James 'Bonecrusher' Smith, **6** Thirty, **7** Floyd Patterson, **8** 1950s, **9** Richard Dunn, **10** Clinton McKenzie, **11** John L Gardner, **12** Johnny Owen, **13** Roberto Duran, **14** Sugar Ray Robinson, **15** Fourteen.

# BOXING - QUIZ 15

*Answers on page 36*

1 Who did James Toney beat to win the IBF super-middleweight crown in 1993?

2 Who beat Mike Weaver in 63 seconds of their WBA heavyweight title bout in 1982?

3 How many days was Randolph Turpin world middleweight champion - 64, 164 or 264?

4 In which year did Tony Sibson win his Lonsdale Belt?

5 Who, by winning the WBC middleweight crown in October 1986, became the first man to win world titles at four weights?

6 In which year did Joe Louis die?

7 Which British boxer won the European heavyweight title in 1964?

8 Which fellow-Briton was his opponent?

9 Which Mexican beat Wilfredo Rocha to win the vacant WBC world lightweight title in August 1992?

10 Which Briton regained the European heavyweight title in 1968?

11 Who did Herbie Hide beat to become WBO world heavyweight champion in 1994?

12 Who defeated Glenn McCrory to win the IBF cruiserweight title on 22 March, 1990?

13 Which Canadian won light-middleweight gold at the 1986 Commonwealth Games.?

14 Name the first man to defeat Muhammad Ali professionally?

15 ...in which year?

## *Answers to page 36*

**1** England, **2** Canada, **3** Muhammad Ali, **4** Ernie Terrell, **5** Pernell Whitaker, **6** Colin Jones, **7** 1964, **8** 1960's, **9** 'Bomber', **10** James Toney, **11** Roy Jones, **12** Argentina, **13** 1950s, **14** Sugar Ray Leonard, **15** Ingemar Johansson.

# • BOXING - QUIZ 16 •

*Answers on page 37*

1 How many of his 54 professional fights did Sonny Liston lose - 0, 4 or 8?

2 In which decade was the NBA (forerunner of the WBA) formed?

3 When did Henry Cooper retire?

4 How many days did Muhammad Ali's third reign as a world heavyweight champion last - 84, 184 or 284?

5 Who did Mike Tyson beat to take the WBA heavyweight title in March 1987?

6 How many world title fights were contested in 1966 - 30, 60 or 90?

7 Name the first Olympic gold medallist to become heavyweight champion of the world?

8 In which decade did Brian London win the Commonwealth heavyweight title?

9 Which Briton won the European heavyweight title in April 1976?

10 Which lightweight won Lonsdale Belts in 1981 and 1983?

11 Which Briton won the European heavyweight title in 1980?

12 Which Welsh bantamweight was known as the 'Merthyr Matchstick'?

13 Which Panama boxing legend made his professional debut in 1967?

14 Which American legend won the vacant world welterwight title by outpointing Tommy Bell in 1946?

15 How many world heavyweight title fights did Arthur Donovan referee between 1933 and 1946 - 8, 14 or 20?

---

## *Answers to page 37*

**1** Mike Tyson, **2** Five, **3** 1956, **4** Joe Frazier, **5** Steve Cruz, **6** Chris Eubank, **7** Three, **8** Two, **9** Robin Reid, **10** Middleweight, **11** Twelve, **12** 1988, **13** 1940s, **14** 1984, **15** 1960s.

# • BOXING - QUIZ 17 •

*Answers on page 42*

1 Which Briton lost to Muhammad Ali in a world title fight in May 1976?

2 At which Olympics did Britain's William Fisher win light-middleweight bronze?

3 In which decade was Pat Cowdell born?

4 Who beat Joe Frazier to win the world heavyweight title in January 1973?

5 When was Barry McGuigan born -1959 or 1961?

6 Which Michael beat Victor Cordoba to become WBA super-middleweight champion on 12 September, 1992?

7 Who stopped William 'Caveman' Lee in 67 seconds of their world middleweight title fight in March 1982?

8 Which light-heavyweight took just 259 days to win a Lonsdale Belt in 1984?

9 In which country was former world featherweight champ Eusebio Pedroza born?

10 When was Marvin Hagler born - 1952 or 1958?

11 Terry Marsh became the first British professional to win a world title and retire undefeated. True or false?

12 Which Scottish lightweight won a Lonsdale Belt in 1973?

13 Which American beat John Mugabi to win the vacant WBO middleweight title on 20 November, 1991?

14 Which Briton lost his WBC super-middleweight title to Sugar Boy Malinga in March 1996?

15 At which Commonwealth Games did England's Chris Pyatt win welterweight gold?

---

## *Answers to page 42*

**1** Thomas Hearns, **2** 1948, **3** 1940s, **4** Terry Lawless, **5** Herol Graham, **6** Virgin Islands, **7** Jersey Joe Walcott, **8** Carlos Monzon, **9** 1966, **10** 1978, **11** Maurice Hope, **12** Marvin Hagler, **13** Missouri, **14** 1940s, **15** 1980.

# BOXING - QUIZ 18

*Answers on page 43*

1 Who did Henry Cooper beat to win the British heavyweight title in January 1959?

2 Who beat Gary Mason to win the British heavyweight title in March 1991?

3 Which English light-heavyweight won a Lonsdale Belt in 1975?

4 Who is known as the 'Celtic Warrior'?

5 In which city was Steve Collins born?

6 Which Kirkland won the British welterweight title in 1979?

7 In which decade was the first all-European world heavyweight title fight?

8 In which English county was Richard Dunn born?

9 Who beat Billy Hardy to retain the IBF and WBO featherweight titles in May 1997?

10 Who beat Wilfred Benitez to take the WBC light-middleweight title in 1982?

11 Which Briton beat Mauro Galvano to become WBC super-middleweight champion in October 1992?

12 Name the second man to beat Thomas Hearns in a professional fight?

13 In which English city was Tony Sibson born?

14 Which world heavyweight champion was known as the 'Brockton Blockbuster'?

15 Which American was world light-heavyweight champion from 1968-74?

***Eastender Lennox Lewis boxed for the Canadian national team in the 1988 Seoul Olympic Games.***

*Answers to page 43*

**1** Cruiserweight, **2** Sheffield, **3** True, **4** Max Schmeling, **5** Herbie Hide, **6** Evander Holyfield, **7** Prince Naseem Hamed, **8** 1970s, **9** Evander Holyfield, **10** Dave 'Boy' Green, **11** 1960s, **12** John H. Stracey, **13** Robin Reid, **14** McKenzie, **15** 1920s.

# • BOXING - QUIZ 19 •

*Answers on page 40*

1 Name the first professional to kayo Roberto Duran?

2 At which Olympics did Britain's John Wright win middleweight silver?

3 In which decade were Chris and Kevin Finnegan born

4 Who managed Jim Watt, Maurice Hope and Charlie Magri to world titles?

5 Which Briton lost to Julian Jackson in a WBC middleweight title fight in November 1990?

6 Where was Julian Jackson born?

7 Who refereed the 1965 title fight between Muhammmad Ali and Sonny Liston?

8 Which Argentinian defended his world middleweight crown fourteen t times before retiring as undefeated champion?

9 In which year was Chris Eubank born?

10 At which Commonwealth Games did Nelson Azumah (later known as Azumah Nelson) win featherweight gold?

11 Which light-middleweight won a Lonsdale Belt in 1976?

12 Who stopped Thomas Hearns in round three of their world middleweight title bout in April 1985?

13 In which American state were Leon and Michael Spinks born?

14 In which decade was Jim Watt born?

15 In which year did Frank Warren promote his first contest licensed by the British Board of Control?

## *Answers to page 40*

**1** Richard Dunn, **2** 1960, Rome, **3** 1950s, **4** George Foreman, **5** 1961, **6** Nunn **7** Marvin Hagler, **8** Dennis Andries, **9** Panama, **10** 1952, **11** True, **12** Ken Buchanan, **13** Gerald McClellan, **14** Nigel Benn, **15** 1982.

# • BOXING - QUIZ 20 •

*Answers on page 41*

**1** Which weight division is between heavyweight and light-heavyweight?

**2** In which English city was Prince Naseem Hamed born?

**3** Henry Cooper's twin brother also fought professionally, under the name of Jim Cooper. True or false?

**4** Which heavyweight champion was nicknamed the 'Black Uhlan'?

**5** Who retained his WBO heavyweight crown with a second round win over Germany's Willie Fischer in September 1998?

**6** Which American won the WBA cruiserweight title in July 1986?

**7** Who retained his WBO featherweight crown against Belfast's Wayne McCullogh in October 1998?

**8** During which decade was the first world title fight to be held in a communist country?

**9** Who successfully defended his IBF world heavyweight title against Vaughn Bean in September 1998?

**10** Against which Briton, in March 1980, did Sugar Ray Leonard win the first defence of his WBC welterweight title?

**11** In which decade did Ken Buchanan become British lightweight champion?

**12** Who beat Bobby Arthur to win the British welterweight title in June 1973?

**13** Which former bookie's clerk beat Vincenzo Nardiello to become WBC super-middleweight champion in October 1996?

**14** Which Clinton won the British light-welterweight title in 1978?

**15** In which decade was Sugar Ray Robinson born?

---

*Answers to page 41*

**1** Brian London, **2** Lennox Lewis, **3** Chris Finnegan, **4** Steve Collins, **5** Dublin, **6** Laing, **7** 1930's, **8** Yorkshire, **9** Prince Naseem Hamed, **10** Thomas Hearns, **11** Nigel Benn, **12** Marvin Hagler, **13** Leicester, **14** Rocky Marciano, **15** Bob Foster.

# BOXING - QUIZ 21

*Answers on page 46*

**1** In which English city was Ryan Rhodes born?

**2** When was Lennox Lewis born?

**3** Which Irishman was outpointed by Mike McCallum in a WBA middleweight title fight in February 1990?

**4** Which heavyweight champion was known as the 'Black Cloud'?

**5** Who did Henry Cooper beat to regain the British heavyweight title in March 1970?

**6** What was the result of the Vito Antuofermo versus Marvin Hagler world title fight in November 1979?

**7** Who stopped Vito Antuofermo to win the European light-middleweight title in October 1976?

**8** Which Cornelius won the WBC world junior-lightweight title in 1981?

**9** In which African country was Cornelius Boza-Edwards born?

**10** Which English middleweight won a Lonsdale Belt in 1976?

**11** At which Commonwealth Games did England's Rod Douglas win middleweight gold?

**12** Which Scottish lightweight won a Lonsdale Belt in 1977?

**13** In which city was Jim Watt born?

**14** Which Briton won the European light-welterweight title in 1976?

**15** How many of his three world heavyweight title fights did Ken Norton lose?

***In 1995 Steve Collins was the first man to beat Chris Eubank. Only to do it again the next time they met.***

---

*Answers to page 46*

**1** Jake La Motta, **2** Atlantic City, **3** Roberto Duran, **4** Three, **5** Robert Dickie, **6** Massachusetts, **7** Seventy, **8** Joe Bugner, **9** 1972, **10** Leon Spinks, **11** Kevin Lueshing, **12** Twenty five, **13** Light-middleweight, **14** 1950s, **15** Raging Bull.

# BOXING - QUIZ 22

*Answers on page 47*

1. Who beat Julio Cesar Chavez in 1996 to win the WBC world welterweight title?
2. Which Leeds-born boxer lost to Nigel Benn in their WBC super-middleweight title bout in February 1994?
3. Who beat Frank Grant to become British super-middleweight champion in November 1993?
4. Which veteran beat Michael Moorer in a WBA/ IBF heavyweight title fight in 1994?
5. Which fellow-Englishman lost to Chris Eubank in a WBO super-middleweight title fight in December 1994?
6. When was Oscar De La Hoya born - 1967 or 1973?
7. How many first round victories did Joe Louis record in world title fights?
8. Which Sunderland-born boxer beat Steve Robinson in February 1997 to become European featherweight champ?
9. Who beat Archie Moore for the vacant world heavyweight title in November 1956?
10. In winning the title, Patterson became the youngest world heavyweight champion. True or false?
11. Who was acquitted at the Old Bailey in 1988 of the attempted murder of Frank Warren?
12. During which decade was the first IBF title fight?
13. Name the two brothers who won gold medals at the 1976 Olympics?
14. How many world heavyweight title fights did Ezzard Charles have - 3, 13 or 23?
15. In which decade was Joe Frazier born?

---

***Answers to page 47***

**1** Johnny Owen, **2** 1960s, **3** Barney Eastwood, **4** 1960, **5** Pernell Whitaker, **6** Herbie Hide, **7** Nigeria, **8** Evander Holyfield, **9** True, **10** Thomas, **11** Lennox Lewis, **12** Dave 'Boy' Green, **13** Tennessee, **14** True, **15** Welsh.

# BOXING - QUIZ 23

*Answers on page 44*

**1** Name the first man to defeat Sugar Ray Robinson in a professional contest?

**2** In which American city did Lloyd Honeyghan defeat Don Curry?

**3** Which boxing legend was known as 'Hands of Stone'?

**4** How many of his 66 professional fights did Joe Louis lose?

**5** Which boxer won a Lonsdale Belt in 203 days during 1986?

**6** In which American state was Rocky Marciano born?

**7** How many world title fights were staged in 1976 - 50, 70 or 90?

**8** Who regained the Commonwealth heavyweight title by beating Richard Dunn on 12 October, 1976?

**9** When did Jim Watt win his first British lightweight title -1972 or 1977?

**10** Who beat Muhammad Ali in a world heavyweight title fight in February 1978?

**11** Which Briton won the vacant IBO weltwerweight title by beating Cirilo Nino in July 1996?

**12** How many world heavyweight title fights did Muhammad Ali contest?

**13** In which weight division did Roberto Duran win his third world title?

**14** During which decade was the first live televising of a world title weigh-in?

**15** Which Martin Scorsese film stars Robert De Niro as Jake La Motta?

---

## *Answers to page 44*

**1** Sheffield, **2** 1965, **3** Steve Collins, **4** Larry Holmes, **5** Jack Bodel,l **6** A draw **7** Maurice Hope, **8** Boza-Edwards, **9** Uganda, **10** Alan Minter, **11** 1986, **12** Jim Watt, **13** Glasgow, **14** Dave 'Boy' Green, **15** Three.

# BOXING - QUIZ 24

*Answers on page 45*

**1** Which Welsh bantamweight won a Lonsdale Belt in 1979?

**2** In which decade did Las Vegas stage its first world title fight?

**3** Name Barry McGuigan's former manager who was awarded £450,000 damages in a libel action in 1992?

**4** When was Lloyd Honeyghan born - 1960 or 1964?

**5** Who did Oscar De La Hoya outpoint to win the WBC world welterweight crown in April 1997?

**6** Which Norwich-based boxer beat Michael Murray to win the vacant British heavyweight title in February 1993?

**7** In which African country was Herbie Hide born?

**8** Which heavyweight boxer is nicknamed 'The Real Deal'?

**9** Evander Holyfield won light-heavyweight bronze at the 1984 Olympics. True or false?

**10** Which Pinklon won the WBC world heavyweight title in August 1984?

**11** Which Briton beat Tommy Morrison in a non-title fight in October 1995?

**12** Which Briton lost to Carlos Palomino in a WBC welterweight title fight in 1977?

**13** In which American state was Thomas Hearns born?

**14** Muhammad Ali only fought one world title fight under the name of Cassius Clay. True or false?

**15** What nationality is Nicky Piper?

---

## *Answers to page 45*

**1** Oscar De La Hoya, **2** Henry Wharton, **3** Neville Brown, **4** George Foreman, **5** Henry Wharton, **6** 1973, **7** Five, **8** Billy Hardy, **9** Floyd Patterson, **10** True, **11** Terry Marsh, **12** 1980s, **13** Leon and Michael Spinks, **14** Thirteen, **15** 1940s.

# BOXING - QUIZ 25

*Answers on page 50*

1 Who beat Kevin Lueshing to retain the IBF welterweight title in January 1997?

2 In which year was Steve Collins born?

3 Which Mike won the WBA world heavyweight title on 31 March, 1980?

4 Which American lost his IBF featherweight title to Prince Naseem Hamed in February 1997?

5 Which English boxer lost to Keith Holmes in a WBC middleweight title fight in October 1996?

6 At which Olympics did Richie Woodhall win light-middleweight bronze?

7 In which weight division did Michael Spinks win his first world title?

8 Which French boxer was known as the 'Orchid Man?

9 When was the first world title bout under Queensberry Rules - 1884 or 1904?

10 In which decade was the first world title fight held in Brazil?

11 Who did Rocky Marciano beat to win the world heavyweight title in 1952?

12 In which decade was a woman judge first used in a world heavyweight title fight?

13 Who did Larry Holmes outpoint to win the WBC world heavyweight title in 1978?

14 In which American state was Larry Holmes born?

15 Which New York venue staged the Ali-Frazier fight in March 1971?

---

## *Answers to page 50*

**1** Marvin Hagler, **2** Kevin Finnegan, **3** Jersey Joe Walcott, **4** James Toney, **5** Gerry Cooney, **6** Ryan Rhodes, **7** Two, **8** Hector Camacho, **9** Colin Jones, **10** Chris Eubank, **11** True, **12** 1940s, **13** Tony Sibson, **14** True, **15** Seven.

# BOXING - QUIZ 26

*Answers on page 51*

1. When was Chris Eubank born?
2. Which ring legend added 'Marvelous' to his name?
3. In which year did Sugar Ray Leonard turn professsional?
4. Which fellow-Scot lost to Ken Buchanan in a British lightweight title fight in January 1973?
5. Which Welshman lost to Nigel Benn in a WBC super-middleweight title fight in December 1992?
6. Name the first boxer to beat Sugar Ray Leonard professionally?
7. Which Englishman won the European middleweight title in 1986?
8. In which decade was Roberto Duran born?
9. In which country was Roberto Duran born?
10. How many of his 234 professional bouts did Archie Moore lose - 13, 26 or 39?
11. At which Olympics did Henry Tillman win heavyweight gold?
12. Who beat Henry Cooper to win the British, European and Commonwealth heavyweight titles on 16 March, 1971?
13. In which year was Joe Calzaghe born -1972 or 1975?
14. What do the initials WBC stand for?
15. Which American boxer was nicknamed 'Second To'?

***Popular as ever in the USA, Prince Naseem Hamed biggest fan has to be Bill Clinton who said, "He's pretty cool. When's he back in the States."***

---

*Answers to page 51*

**1** Floyd Patterson, **2** Brian London, **3** Antigua, **4** 1984, **5** Chris Pyatt, **6** Lloyd Honeyghan, **7** Frank Bruno, **8** Eigh, **9** 1995, **10** Robert Dickie, **11** Pat Cowdell, **12** 1953, **13** Joe Louis, **14** Dennis Andries, **15** Frank Bruno.

# BOXING - QUIZ 27

*Answers on page 48*

1 Who stopped Alan Minter at Wembley in 1980 to win the world middleweight title?

2 Which middleweight won a Lonsdale Belt in 1979?

3 Who was the first man to floor Rocky Marciano in a professional fight?

4 Michael 'Second To' Nunn won his first 36 pro fights. Who beat him in the 37th?

5 Name the 'white hope' beaten by Larry Holmes in a world title fight in June 1982?

6 Which light-middleweight set a new record by winning a Lonsdale Belt in ninety days?

7 How many times was Floyd Patterson stopped in the first round of world title fights?

8 Which fighter is known as 'Macho' or 'Macho Man'?

9 Which Welsh welterweight won a Lonsdale Belt in 1981?

10 Which Brighton-based fighter entered boxing arenas to the sound of Tina Turner's 'Simply the Best'?

11 Henry Cooper lost the first three title fights he contested. True or false?

12 In which decade was the last scheduled twenty-round world title fight?

13 Which English boxer won the European middleweight title in 1980?

14 Leon Spinks won the world heavyweight title in 1978 in only his eighth professional fight. True or false?

15 How many world heavyweight title fights did Rocky Marciano have?

## *Answers to page 48*

**1** Felix Trinidad, **2** 1964, **3** Weaver, **4** Tom Johnson, **5** Richie Woodhall, **6** 1988, **7** Light-heavyweight, **8** Georges Carpentiers, **9** 1884 **10** 1960s, **11** Jersey Joe Walcott, **12** 1970s, **13** Ken Norton, **14** Georgia, **15** Madison Square Garden.

# BOXING - QUIZ 28

*Answers on page 49*

1 Name the first boxer to regain the world heavyweight title?

2 Who did Henry Cooper beat to win the Commonwealth heavyweight title in Januray 1959?

3 Where was Maurice Hope born?

4 At which Olympic Games did Tyrell Biggs win super-heavyweight gold?

5 Which Briton won the European light-middleweight title in 1986?

6 Which welterweight won a Lonsdale Belt in 1985?

7 Who did Mike Tyson beat in March 1996 to regain the WBC heavyweight crown?

8 How many successful defences of the British heavyweight title did Henry Cooper make?

9 In which year did Chris Eubank lose two world title fights to Steve Collins?

10 Which featherweight won a Lonsdale Belt in 1986?

11 Which British featherweight lost to WBC champion Salvador Sanchez in 1981?

12 When was Leon Spinks born - 1950 or 1953?

13 Who was undisputed world heavyweight champion for 11 years 252 days?

14 Which light-heavyweight won a Lonsdale Belt in 1984?

15 Who did Lennox Lewis beat in his second defence of his WBC world heavyweight crown at Cardiff in 1993?

## *Answers to page 49*

**1** 1966, **2** Marvin Hagler, **3** 1977, **4** Jim Watt, **5** Nicky Piper, **6** Roberto Duran, **7** Herol Graham, **8** 1950s, **9** Panama, **10** Twenty six, **11** 1984, **12** Joe Bugner, **13** 1972, **14** World Boxing Council, **15** Michael Nunn.

# BOXING - QUIZ 29

*Answers on page 54*

**1** At which Olympic Games did Britain's Terry Spinks win flyweight gold?

**2** In which decade was Ingemar Johansson born?

**3** Which English fighter won the European welterweight title in 1979?

**4** In which year did Sugar Ray Leonard beat Ayub Kalule of Uganda to take the WBA light-middleweight title?

**5** In which decade was Henry Cooper born?

**6** In which American state was Joe Louis born?

**7** Which Charlie won the WBC flyweight title in 1983?

**8** Who beat Joe Bugner to win the British heavyweight title in September 1971?

**9** Which IBF heavyweight champion was beaten by Mike Tyson in August 1987?

**10** What does IBF stand for?

**11** Which English fighter won the European light-weltwerweight title in 1985?

**12** Which English fighter was known as the 'Dark Destroyer'?

**13** In which year did Kevin Finnegan win his first British middleweight title -1972 or 1974?

**14** Who did Muhammed Ali beat to win the WBA world heavyweight title in September 1978?

**15** Which Jim won the European featherweight title in 1985?

***Before the days of Mike Tyson, the youngest holder of the Heavyweight Championship was Floyd Patterson, who was only 21.***

---

## *Answers to page 54*

**1** Evander Holyfield, **2** Colin Power, **3** 1948, **4** 1950s, **5** Two, **6** Henry Cooper, **7** Highbury, **8** Ten, **9** 1984, **10** Fourteen, **11** 1980, **12** Loftus Road, **13** Three, **14** Bob Foster, **15** Sonny Liston.

# BOXING - QUIZ 30

*Answers on page 55*

**1** During which decade was a four-roped ring first used in a world title fight?

**2** In which year did Johnny Owen become European bantamweight champion - 1975 or 1980?

**3** Which Briton was world flyweight champion in 1966?

**4** Who did Don Curry beat to win the undisputed world welterweight title in December 1995?

**5** Who was WBC world light-middleweight champion from 1977-79?

**6** Who beat Nigel Benn in two world title fights in 1996?

**7** In 1992, who dumped his WBC world heavyweight belt in a dustbin after refusing to fight Lennox Lewis?

**8** What nationality is heavyweight boxer Riddick Bowe?

**9** Which Leeds-born fighter lost to Robin Reid in a WBC super-middleweight title fight in May 1997?

**10** In which English city was Chris Eubank born?

**11** In which year did Randolph Turpin first become British light-heavyweight champion -1952 or 1957?

**12** Who won the vacant world heavyweight title in 1930 after his opponent, Jack Sharkey, was disqualified?

**13** What nationality was Max Schmeling?

**14** Who did Danny McAlinden beat to win the British heavyweight title in June 1972?

**15** Which undisputed world welterweight champion was nicknamed the 'Cobra?

---

## *Answers to page 55*

**1** Jake La Motta, **2** Henry Cooper, Brian London, Joe Bugner and Richard Dunn, **3** James Toney, **4** False. He was 24, **5** Jose Luis Ramirez, **6** Michael Spinks, **7** Tony Sibson, **8** Two, **9** Five, **10** Freddie Mills, **11** 1974, **12** 1950s, **13** Tony Sibson, **14** Evander Holyfield, **15** A para-glider landed in the ring!

# BOXING - QUIZ 31

*Answers on page 52*

**1** Who beat Mike Tyson in November 1996 to win the WBA world heavyweight title?

**2** Which British fighter won the European light-welterweight title in 1978?

**3** Britain's Donald Scott won light-heavyweight silver at the Olympic Games. In which year?

**4** In which decade did Henry Cooper make his professional debut?

**5** How many boxing gold medals did England win at the 1982 Commonwealth Games?

**6** Which British heavyweight lost a world title fight to Muhammad Ali in May 1966?

**7** At which football stadium was the fight held?

**8** How many times did Henry Cooper successfully defend his Commonwealth heavyweight title 5, 10 or 15?

**9** At which Olympics did America's Mark Breland win welterweight gold?

**10** How many professional fights did Henry Cooper lose - 2, 8 or 14?

**11** In which year did John Conteh retire - 1976 or 1980?

**12** At which football stadium did Barry McGuigan win his world title fight with Eusebio Pedroza?

**13** How many Lonsdale Belts did Henry Cooper win?

**14** Which world champion refereed the Joe Frazier versus Jimmy Ellis fight in 1974?

**15** Who beat Floyd Patterson in the first round of their world heavyweight title bout in September 1962?

## *Answers to page 52*

**1** 1956, **2** 1930s, **3** Dave 'Boy' Green, **4** 1981, **5** 1930s, **6** Alabama, **7** Magri, **8** Jack Bodell, **9** Tony Tucker, **10** International Boxing Federation, **11** Terry Marsh, **12** Nigel Benn, **13** 1974, **14** Leon Spinks, **15** McDonnell.

# BOXING - QUIZ 32

*Answers on page 53*

**1** Who was nicknamed the 'Bronx Bull'?

**2** Name the four British boxers who fought Muhammad Ali professionally?

**3** Which American beat Iran Barkley to win the IBF super-middleweight t title in February 1993?

**4** Rocky Marciano made his professional debut at the age of 21. True or false?

**5** Name the first man to beat Pernell Whitaker in a professional fight?

**6** In September 1985, who became IBF heavyweight champion with a controversial points victory over Larry Holmes?

**7** Which Briton won the Commonwealth middleweight title on 4 March, 1980?

**8** How many times did Sonny Liston win world title fights in the first round?

**9** In which round did Muhammad Ali beat Henry Cooper in 1963?

**10** Which Briton was undisputed world light-heavyweight champ from 1948-50?

**11** At which Commonwealth Games did England's Neville Meade win heavyweight gold -1974 or 1986?

**12** In which decade was Joe Bugner born?

**13** Which fellow-Englishman was Alan Minter's last opponent?

**14** In 1993, who beat Riddick Bowe to regain the WBA world heavyweight title?

**15** How was the fight bizarrely interrupted?

---

## *Answers to page 53*

**1** 1960s, **2** 1980, **3** Walter McGowan, **4** Milton McCrory, **5** Rocky Mattioli, **6** Steve Collins, **7** Riddick Bowe, **8** American, **9** Henry Wharton, **10** London, **11** 1952, **12** Max Schmeling, **13** German, **14** Jack Bodell, **15** Don Curry.

# • BOXING - QUIZ 33 •

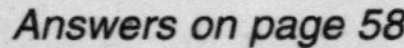
*Answers on page 58*

1 Which Italian world heavyweight champ was nicknamed the 'Ambling Alp'?

2 What was Ray Mancini's nickname?

3 Which Briton controversially lost his WBO world featherweight title to Colombia's Ruben Palacio in 1992?

4 Maurice Hope was beaten by Bunny Johnson in a British middleweight title bout in 1972. True or false?

5 Who beat Gerald McClellan in the 10th round of their super-middleweight title bout in February 1995?

6 Who beat Lennox Lewis to win the WBC heavyweight title in September 1994?

7 Which Briton lost to Floyd Patterson in a world heavyweight title bout in May 1959?

8 Who won heavyweight gold at the 1964 Olympic Games?

9 Which boxing legend outpointed Iran Barkley to take the WBC world middleweight title in February 1989?

10 In which decade was 'Honest Jack' Bodell born?

11 Which Maurice won the Commonwealth light-middleweight title in 1976?

12 Which Chris won the vacant WBO middleweight title by outpointing Sumbu Kalambay in May 1993?

13 Which Italian won the European light-middleweight crown in 1976?

## *Answers to page 58*

**1** George Foreman and Muhammad Ali (Both twice), **2** Bruno, **3** Henry Cooper, **4** Ken Norton, **5** Jones, **6** Three, **7** 1990, **8** 1972, **9** Italy, **10** Tony Tucker, **11** 1920s, **12** Pernell Whitaker, **13** Salvador Sanchez, **14** James Toney, **15** Dunn.

# • BOXING - QUIZ 34 •

*Answers on page 59*

**1** Which American legend won the WBA world welterweight title by beating Jose Cuevas in August 1980?

**2** In which year did Barry McGuigan win the European featherweight title?

**3** In which American city is Madison Square Garden?

**4** Which British boxer lost to Muhammad Ali in a world title fight in August 1966?

**5** Which former heavyweight champion lost a world title fight to Evander Holyfield at the age of 42?

**6** In which decade was Iran 'The Blade' Barkley born?

**7** Which English boxer won bantamweight gold at the 1974 Commonwealth Games?

**8** Which Briton won middleweight gold at the 1968 Olympics?

**9** For how many days did Frank Bruno hold the WBC world heavyweight crown - 97, 197 or 297?

**10** Who was known as the 'Clones Cyclone'?

**11** Name the first man to kayo Roberto Duran in a professional bout?

**12** Which Neville won the British heavyweight title in 1981?

**13** Which South London-born boxer floored Tommy Morrison in the 1st round to become WBO heavyweight champion in 1993?

**14** Who was WBC world light-heavyweight champion from 1979 to 1981?

**15** How many world title fights were fought in 1986 - 75, 95 or 115?

***Henry Cooper is the only boxer to have held three Lonsdale Belts outright.***

---

*Answers to page 59*

**1** Bob Fitzsimmons, **2** False. He never fought in England, **3** 1940s, 4 None, **5** Kirkland Laing, **6** Kevin Finnegan, **7** Ryan Rhodes, **8** 1993, **9** True, **10** 1981, **11** Larry Holmes (in 1984), **12** 145, **13** 1978, **14** Twenty six, **15** Jack Dempsey.

# • BOXING - QUIZ 35 •

*Answers on page 56*

1 Name the two boxers to beat Joe Frazier professionally?

2 Which Frank was ABA heavyweight champion in 1980?

3 Which heavyweight won his first Lonsdale Belt in 1964?

4 Who beat Muhammad Ali in 1973?

5 Which Colin won the Commonwealth welterweight title in 1981?

6 How many of his 102 professional fights did Carlos Monzon lose - 3, 6, or 9?

7 In which year did James 'Buster' Douglas defeat Mike Tyson?

8 At which Olympics did Britain's George Turpin win bantamweight bronze?

9 In which country was Vito Antuofermo born?

10 Which American did Lennox Lewis beat in his first defence of the WBC world heavyweight crown, in 1993?

11 In which decade was former world featherweight champin Willie Pep born?

12 Which American won his fourth world title at different weights by beating Julio Cesar Vasquez for the WBA light-middleweight title in March 1995?

13 Which Mexican was WBC world featherweight champion from 1980-1982?

14 Which American beat Iran Barkley to win the IBF super-middleweight title on 13 February, 1993?

15 Which Richard defeated Bunny Johnson to win the British heavyweight title in September 1975?

## *Answers to page 56*

**1** Primo Carnera, **2** Boom-Boom, **3** Colin McMillan, **4** False. It was 1975, **5** Nigel Benn, **6** Oliver McCall, **7** Brian London, **8** Joe Frazier, **9** Roberto Duran, **10** 1940s, **11** Hope, **12** Pyatt, **13** Vito Antuofermo, **14** 1914, **15** Julian Jackson.

# BOXING - QUIZ 36

*Answers on page 57*

**1** Name the first English world heavyweight champion?

**2** Bob Fitzsimmons only fought in England once. True or false?

**3** In which decade was Ken Buchanan born?

**4** How many losses did Rocky Marciano suffer in 49 professional fights?

**5** Which Nottingham-based boxer beat Roberto Duran in September 1982?

**6** Who did Alan Minter beat to win his first British middleweight title in November 1975?

**7** Which Sheffield-born boxer won the vacant British light-middleweight title by beating Paul Jones in December 1996?

**8** In which year did Eamonn Loughran win the vacant WBO welterweight title by outpointing Lorenzo Smith in Belfast -1991 or 1993?

**9** Jack Dempsey refereed the first world title fight in the Philippines. True or false?

**10** When did Azumah Nelson win his first Commonwealth featherweight title?

**11** Who was the IBF's first world heavyweight champion?

**12** How many of his 234 opponents did Archie Moore kayo - 45, 95 or 145?

**13** At which Commonwealth Games did Finbar (Barry) McGuigan win bantamweight gold?

**14** How many world title fights did Henry Armstrong have - 16, 26 or 36?

**15** Who floored Luis 'Angel' Firpo seven times in the first round of their heavyweight world title fight in September 1923?

---

## *Answers to page 57*

**1** Thomas Hearns, **2** 1983, **3** New York, **4** Brian London, **5** George Foreman, **6** 1960s, **7** Pat Cowdell, **8** Chris Finnegan, **9** 197 days, **10** Barry McGuigan, **11** Thomas Hearns, **12** Meade, **13** Michael Bentt, **14** Matthew Saad Muhammad, **15** Ninety five.

# BOXING - QUIZ 37

*Answers on page 62*

1 During which decade was the first WBC world title fight?

2 Who beat Muhammad Ali in a world title fight in October 1980?

3 In which decade was Larry Holmes born?

4 Which Greg became WBA world heavyweight champion in December 1984?

5 ...who was his South African opponent?

6 Who beat WBA lightweight champion Ken Buchanan in 1972?

7 Who beat Gene 'Mad Dog' Hatcher in the first minute of their WBC/IBF welterweight title fight in August 1987?

8 Name the first man in history to win world titles at five officially r recognised weights?

9 In which decade was the last scheduled 20-round contest?

10 Who became the first Briton to win world titles at two different weights when he won the WBO bantamweight title in July 1991?

11 How many world heavyweight title fights did Jack Dempsey have?

12 How many did he lose?

13 At which Olympic Games did Jerry Page win light-welterweight gold?

14 What nationality was Primo Carnera?

15 Which American was world heavyweight champion from April 1915 to July 1919?

***The first ever heavyweight champion was recorded in 1719 - the mighty James Figg.***

## *Answers to page 62*

**1** 1984, **2** Dennis Andries, **3** Colin Jones, **4** John L Gardner, **5** 1976, **6** 1978, **7** 1969, **8** Mexican, **9** Sixty two, **10** 1976, **11** Oscar De La Hoya, **12** 1970s, **13** Uganda, **14** Gene Tunney, **15** Jersey Joe Walcott.

# BOXING - QUIZ 38

*Answers on page 63*

**1** Who did Sugar Ray Leonard beat in 1981 to win the undisputed welterweight title?

**2** When was Michael Spinks born -1950 or 1956?

**3** Who was world heavyweight champion from March 1968 to January 1973?

**4** Who beat Richard Dunn to regain the British heavyweight title in October 1976?

**5** In which decade did Terry Downes win his first British middleweight title?

**6** How many world title fights did Rocky Marciano have?

**7** In which decade was the last scheduled 25-round contest?

**8** How many times was Floyd Patterson floored in world heavyweight title fights -7, 17 or 27?

**9** Which Paul was ABA featherweight champion in 1986?

**10** How many world heavyweight title fights did Joe Louis contest - 19, 23 or 27?

**11** Who was world heavyweight champion from Jan 1973 to Oct 1974?

**12** Who did Chris Eubank beat to win the vacant WBO world super-middleweight title on 21 September, 1991?

**13** At which football ground?

**14** How many successful world title defences did Marvin Hagler make - 8, 12 or 16?

**15** The referee of the Bob Fitzsimmons versus Tom Sharkey non-title bout in 1896 was Wyatt Earp. True or false?

---

## *Answers to page 63*

**1** 1985, **2** Notice, **3** 1950s, **4** Four, **5** 1967, **6** 1984, **7** 1940s, **8** Honeyghan, **9** 1961, **10** True, **11** Archie Moore, **12** Nigel Benn, **13** Sugar Ray Robinson, **14** Jeff Harding, **15** Sugar Ray Leonard.

# • BOXING - QUIZ 39 •

*Answers on page 60*

**1** At which Olympic Games was the super-heavyweight division introduced?

**2** Who won the WBC light-heavyweight title for the third time with a seventh round kayo of Jeff Harding in July 1990?

**3** Which Welsh welterweight was outpointed by Milton McCrory in a WBC world title fight in August 1983?

**4** Who beat Billy Aird in October 1978 to become British heavyweight champ?

**5** In which year did Alan Minter win his first Lonsdale Belt?

**6** In which year did Johnny Owen win the Commonwealth bantamweight title?

**7** In which year did Henry Cooper receive the OBE?

**8** What nationality was Lupe Pintor?

**9** How many of his 78 professional contests did Jack Dempsey win - 62, 68 or 74?

**10** At which Olympic Games did Pat Cowdell win bantamweight bronze?

**11** Who outpointed Ike Quartey to retain his WBC welterweight world at Las Vegas in February 1999?

**12** In which decade did Tony Sibson win his first British middleweight title?

**13** In which country was Cornelius Boza-Edwards born?

**14** In September 1926, approximately 120 000 spectators watched the Gene Tunney versus Jack Dempsey world title bout. Who won the fight?

**15** Who refereed the 1961 world heavyweight title fight between Floyd Patterson and Tom McNeeley?

---

## *Answers to page 60*

**1** 1960s. **2** Larry Holmes. **3** 1940s. **4** Page. **5** Gerrie Coetzee. **6** Roberto Duran. **7** Lloyd Honeyghan, **8** Sugar Ray Leonard, **9** 1970s, **10** Duke McKenzie, **11** Eight, **12** Two, **13** 1984, **14** Italian, **15** Jess Willard.

# • BOXING - QUIZ 40 •

*Answers on page 61*

1 When did Lloyd Honeyghan win the European welterweight title - 1983 or 1985?

2 Which Horace was ABA heavyweight champion in 1983?

3 In which decade was Dave 'Boy' Green born?

4 How many of his 37 professional fights did Joe Frazier lose - 2, 4 or 6?

5 When was England's Henry Wharton born - 1967 or 1972?

6 In which year was Sugar Ray Leonard floored for the first time in his professional career?

7 In which decade was heavyweight boxer Ken Norton born?

8 Which Lloyd won the vacant British welterweight title in April 1983?

9 When was Frank Bruno born?

10 Roberto Duran won the first ten defences of his WBA lightweight crown by kayo. True or false?

11 Against who did Rocky Marciano make his sixth and final world title defence?

12 Which English fighter was ABA middleweight champion in 1986?

13 Which ring legend went undefeated in 91 pro fights from 1943 to 1951?

14 Who did Dennis Andries lose his WBC light-heavyweight title to in September 1991?

15 Who beat Marvin Hagler in their WBC world middleweight title fight in April 1987?

## *Answers to page 61*

**1** Thomas Hearns, **2** 1956, **3** Joe Frazier, **4** Joe Bugner, **5** 1950s, **6** Seven, **7** 1941, **8** Seventeen, **9** Hodgkinson, **10** Twenty seven, **11** George Foreman, **12** Michael Watson, **13** White Hart Lane, **14** Twelve, **15** True.

# CRICKET

# • CRICKET - QUIZ 1 •

*Answers on page 68*

1 In which year was the last Gentlemen v Players match held?

2 Who were the 1994 Sunday League champions?

3 What is Birmingham's Test ground called?

4 Whose 204 is the highest individual innings in women's Test cricket?

5 Who made their first County Championship appearance in 1905?

6 What is inscribed 'JC 1729'?

7 Whose record Test partnership in 1960 occupied 9 hours 39 minutes?

8 How many counties compete in the County Championship?

9 After which season did John Arlott retire from the commentary box?

10 How is an over-watered pitch described?

11 Which city has employed four Test cricket grounds?

12 Who holds the Durham record for the highest score?

13 Who scored 708 against England at the Oval in 1987?

14 Which New Zealand cricketer broke the record for the longest scoreless Test innings in March 1999?

15 Who was Essex captain 1967-73?

---

## *Answers to page 68*

**1** Mike Gatting, **2** Australia, **3** Lancashire, **4** Four and a quarter inches, **5** Old Trafford, **6** Northamptonshire, **7** 1975, **8** Hampshire, **9** Nottinghamshire, **10** University Match, **11** Lord's, **12** Surrey, **13** Groundsman, **14** 1864, **15** Allan Border.

# CRICKET - QUIZ 2

*Answers on page 69*

**1** At which ground were the first three World Cup finals held?

**2** Who was Kent captain 1977 and 1981-82?

**3** Who were the 1993 Sunday League champions?

**4** What is the average weight of a modern bat?

**5** For whom did E H Hendren score 40,302 runs?

**6** Where was the first Test match venue?

**7** Which Australian captain scored centuries in his first and last Tests?

**8** Who successfully defended their County Championship title in 1963?

**9** What is a player who can both bowl and bat called?

**10** Whom did Douglas Jardine succeed as captain of Surrey?

**11** Who won their third consecutive Gillette Cup in 1972?

**12** Which Surrey and England fast bowler played saxophone in a jazz band at the Savoy in 1927?

**13** When was the 'Golden Year' when Compton and Edrich each scored over 3,000 runs?

**14** Who beat Lancashire to win the 1991 Benson & Hedges Cup?

**15** Who has held the Derbyshire record for the highest score since 1896?

---

*Answers to page 69*

**1** Ray Lindwall, **2** Foster, **3** Lancashire, **4** Xenophon Balaskas, **5** 1775, **6** Brian Close, **7** Ground Staff, **8** Derbyshire, **9** Ten, **10** Lord's, **11** New Zealand, **12** Worcestershire, **13** Donald Bradman, **14** West Indies, **15** None.

# CRICKET - QUIZ 3

*Answers on page 66*

1. Who famously swore at umpire Shakoor Rana?
2. In which country is the Sheffield Shield contested?
3. Who successfully defended their Sunday League title in 1970?
4. What is a bat's maximum width?
5. What is Manchester's Test ground called?
6. For whom did Dennis Brookes score 28,980 runs?
7. In which year was the first World Cup held?
8. Of which county was George Stephenson captain in 1979?
9. Who were the 1981 County champions?
10. What, having started in 1827, is the oldest surviving 'great' fixture?
11. In which ground's Memorial Gallery are the Ashes kept?
12. Who won the 1997 Benson & Hedges Cup?
13. Who do Australians call a curator?
14. Which year saw the first appearance of John Wisden's The Cricketer's Almanack?
15. Who has made the highest individual aggregate of runs in Test cricket with 11,174?

***'The Great Cricketer' as the Grace Gate at Lords reads, describes the one and only W.G.Grace. Altogether he scored 54,904 runs, took 2,876 wickets, caught 877 and played his last test for England at the age of 50.***

## *Answers to page 66*

**1** 1962, **2** Warwickshire, **3** Edgbaston, **4** Kirsty Flavel, **5** Northamptonshire, **6** Oldest surviving cricket bat, **7** Gary Sobers and Frank Worrell, **8** Seventeen, **9** 1980, **10** Greasy, **11** Colombo, **12** John Morris, **13** Pakistan, **14** Geoff Allott, **15** Brian Taylor.

# • CRICKET - QUIZ 4 •

*Answers on page 67*

**1** Which fast bowler played 61 Tests for Australia from 1946 to 1960?

**2** What is the surname of the seven brothers who all played for Worcestershire?

**3** Who were the 1998 Sunday League champions?

**4** Which South African cricketer was known as 'Bally'?

**5** In which year was the first six-seamed ball made?

**6** Who was Yorkshire captain 1963-1970?

**7** What are the junior members of the playing staff of a county called?

**8** Who beat Northamptonshire in 1981 to become the first NatWest Trophy champions?

**9** In how many ways can a batsman lose his wicket?

**10** Where did the first University Match take place in 1827?

**11** Who scored 671-4 against Sri Lanka in 1990-91?

**12** Who successfully defended their County Championship title in 1965?

**13** Who was known as 'The Don'?

**14** Who were the 1979 World Cup champions?

**15** How many times have Northamptonshire won the County Championship?

---

## *Answers to page 67*

**1** Lord's, **2** Asif Iqbal, **3** Glamorgan, **4** 2lb 5oz, **5** Middlesex, **6** Melbourne, **7** Greg Chappell, **8** Yorkshire, **9** All-rounder, **10** Percy Fender, **11** Lancashire, **12** Maurice Allom, **13** 1947, **14** Worcestershire, **15** George Davidson.

# CRICKET - QUIZ 5

*Answers on page 72*

**1** Which county had 25 points deducted in the 1998 County Championships for an unfit pitch?

**2** Which year's University Match was abandoned without a ball being bowled?

**3** Who captained England to women's World Cup victory in 1993?

**4** Which country beat England at the Oval in August 1998 thanks to the 16 wickets taken by off-spinner Muttiah Muralitharan?

**5** What is a cricket ball's maximum circumference?

**6** Where was the 1987-88 World Cup final held?

**7** Of which county was D J Brown captain 1975-77?

**8** Who has held the Yorkshire record for the highest score since 1905?

**9** Who beat Sussex to win the 1968 Gillette Cup?

**10** What is the fielding position Backward Point now usually called?

**11** Who captained Northamptonshire to NatWest Trophy victory in 1992?

**12** Which city's Test ground is Trent Bridge?

**13** What is a defensive stroke that is neither forward nor back called?

**14** Which way of getting out, introduced in 1980, has yet to claim its first victim at first-class level?

**15** When did Derbyshire last win the County Championship?

## *Answers to page 72*

**1** Glamorgan, **2** Harrow bat, **3** Leicestershire, **4** West Indies, **5** Khalid Ibadulla, **6** Essex, **7** Anil Kumble, **8** A blue, **9** Kepler Wessels, **10** Hampshire, **11** Len Hutton, **12** Leeds, **13**Four and three-eighths inches , **14** Pakistan, **15** Majid Khan.

# CRICKET - QUIZ 6

*Answers on page 73*

1 For whom did Fred Titmus appear a record 642 times?

2 Who in 1993 was the last England batsman to be dismissed for having handled the ball?

3 Whose 1820 innings of 278 was the highest at Lord's until 1925?

4 Who beat Worcestershire to win the 1994 Benson & Hedges Cup?

5 What is South Africa's main domestic first-class competition called?

6 Who were the 1996 County champions?

7 How is a fast, head-high full pitch better known?

8 Who scored 380 for Australia against New Zealand in 1973-74?

9 Which football World Cup-winner played a county cricket match?

10 Who beat Lancashire to win the NatWest Trophy in 1986?

11 Who captained Gloucestershire 1959-60 and Worcestershire 1968-70?

12 Who won the first World Cup in 1975?

13 What is a ball struck an instant after it has bounced called?

14 Who were the 1986 Sunday League champions?

15 Which Warwickshire and England captain made three University Match centuries?

## *Answers to page 73*

**1** Lancashire, **2** Prince Ranjitsinhji, **3** Betty Snowball, **4** Derbyshire, **5** John Edrich, **6** Twenty-two yards, **7** None, **8** Seymour Nurse, **9** Sri Lanka, **10** Middlesex, **11** Hitting the ball twice, **12** R G Pollock, **13** Gloucestershire, **14** Hat-trick, **15** Mark, by four minutes.

# • CRICKET - QUIZ 7 •

*Answers on page 70*

1 Who set a record of 20 County Championship defeats in 1925?

2 What is the name for a small bat suitable for a teenager?

3 For whom did wicket-keeper R W Tolchard make 903 dismissals?

4 Which country's domestic first-class competition is the Red Stripe Cup?

5 Which Warwickshire player in 1963 was the last person to be dismissed for obstructing the field?

6 Who beat Nottinghamshire to win the 1985 NatWest Trophy?

7 Which Indian leg spinner has become only the second player in history to take all ten wickets in a Test innings?

8 What is awarded for appearing for Cambridge or Oxford in a University Match?

9 Who played for Australia in the 1980s and South Africa in the 1990s?

10 Who were the 1973 County champions?

11 Whose 364 against Australia in 1938 is England's highest Test innings?

12 Which city's Test ground is Headingley?

13 How long are today's bails?

14 Who were the 1991-92 World Cup champions?

15 Who was Glamorgan captain 1973-76?

## *Answers to page 70*

**1** Northamptonshire, **2** 1988, **3** Karen Smithies, **4** Sri Lanka, **5** Nine inches, **6** Calcutta, **7** Warwickshire, **8** George Hirst, **9** Warwickshire, **10** Gully, **11** Allan Lamb, **12** Nottingham, **13**Half-cock , **14** Timed out, **15** 1936.

# CRICKET - QUIZ 8

*Answers on page 71*

**1** Who beat Kent to win the 1995 Benson & Hedges Cup?

**2** Which member of Indian royalty played for Sussex?

**3** Whose 189 is the highest innings for England in women's Test cricket?

**4** Who were the 1990 Sunday League champions?

**5** Who was Surrey captain 1973-77?

**6** What is the length of a cricket pitch?

**7** How many times have Durham won the County Championship?

**8** Which West Indian was caught off a ball that bounced off the head of a fielder in 1968?

**9** Which country scored 547-8d against Australia in 1992-93?

**10** Who were the 1980 County champions?

**11** How was J H King the last person to be dismissed in 1906?

**12** Whose 274 against Australia in 1969-70 is South Africa's highest Test innings?

**13** Who beat Sussex to win the 1973 Gillette Cup?

**14** What is the taking of three wickets with consecutive balls called?

**15** Who is the younger of the Australian Waugh brothers?

***According to the experts the 'bat' originates from around 3,400BC, nobody knows when the first game was played. It is suggested that it may have had prehistoric beginnings.***

---

*Answers to page 71*

**1** Middlesex, **2** Graham Gooch, **3** William Ward, **4** Warwickshire, **5** The Castle Cup, **6** Leicestershire, **7** Beamer, **8** Greg Chappell, **9** Geoff Hurst, **10** Sussex, **11** Tom Graveney, **12** West Indies, **13** Half volley, **14**Hampshire , **15** Mike Smith.

# CRICKET - QUIZ 9

*Answers on page 76*

**1** What is the term for a ball which moves in flight from off to leg?

**2** Who won the 1997 NatWest Trophy?

**3** Which country's domestic first-class competition is The Shell Trophy?

**4** Which Nottinghamshire wicket-keeper has taken six dismissals in an innings four times?

**5** What is the umpire signalling by extending both arms horizontally?

**6** Which New Zealander got 6-10 in the 1982 women's World Cup?

**7** Of which county was J R Boxton captain 1970-72?

**8** In which year was the first hundred partnership recorded?

**9** Who were the 1974 County champions?

**10** Whose record of 10,122 Test runs did Allan Border break in 1993?

**11** What is a fast, short-pitched ball aimed to reach the batsman at shoulder height called?

**12** What is the name of Cape Town's Test ground?

**13** For which county did Wilfred Rhodes appear a record 881 times?

**14** Which batsman holds the record for the most England runs in an Ashes series?

**15** Which Sussex captain became the Anglican Bishop of Liverpool?

## *Answers to page 76*

**1** Middlesex, **2** Sussex, **3** Sir Pelham Warner, **4** England, **5** Nottinghamshire, **6** 1793, **7** Sunil Gavaskar, **8** Gloucestershire, **9** New Zealand, **10** Ian Botham, **11** Yorkshire, **12** The Ranji Trophy, **13** Mushtaq Mohammad, **14** Law 36, **15** Hobart.

# • CRICKET - QUIZ 10 •

*Answers on page 77*

**1** Whose 299 against Sri Lanka in 1990-91 is New Zealand's highest Test innings?

**2** What is the term for a batsman getting a golden duck in both innings?

**3** Who were the 1992 Sunday League champions?

**4** At which ground were the Hobbs Gates built in 1934?

**5** Who won the 1996 Benson & Hedges Cup?

**6** What is the maximum distance the boundary may be from the centre of the pitch?

**7** Who were the 1983 World Cup champions?

**8** Who has held the Surrey record for the highest score since 1899?

**9** Who won a record seven successive County Championship titles in the 1950s?

**10** In which year did Graham Gooch become captain of Essex?

**11** Who devised the first radial scoring chart in 1905?

**12** Who beat Somerset to win the Gillette Cup in 1967?

**13** Which county cricket-playing brothers were also first division footballers?

**14** Who made a record 573 appearances for Lancashire?

**15** Whose badge features a dragon?

---

## *Answers to page 77*

**1** Jack Hobbs, **2** Northamptonshire, **3** Gajanand Pathmanathan, **4** Nottinghamshire, **5** 8ft 8in, **6** Hampshire, **7** Mohammed, **8** John Willes, **9** Ray Illingworth, **10** Yorkshire, **11** Middlesex, **12** Hanif Mohammad, **13** Melbourne, **14** None, **15** Worcestershire.

# CRICKET - QUIZ 11

*Answers on page 74*

**1** Who were the 1990 County champions?

**2** Who successfully defended their Gillette Cup title in 1964?

**3** Which Middlesex and England captain was known as 'Plum'?

**4** Which country won the first women's World Cup?

**5** For whom did George Gunn appear a record 583 times?

**6** When were seasonal batting averages first published?

**7** Whose 236 against West Indies in 1983-84 is India's highest Test innings?

**8** Which county has been captained by T W, J K and D A Graveney?

**9** Whose 26 against England in 1954-55 is a Test record low?

**10** Who resigned from Somerset over the sacking of Viv Richards and Joel Garner?

**11** Who won a record 25 out of 32 County Championship matches in 1923?

**12** What has been India's premier championship since 1946?

**13** Who, at 17, was the youngest player to score a Test hundred?

**14** Which Law defines the lbw rule?

**15** Which city's Test ground is the Bellerive Oval?

---

## *Answers to page 74*

**1** Inswinger, **2** Essex, **3** New Zealand, **4** Bruce French, **5** A wide, **6** Jackie Lord, **7** Derbyshire, **8** 1769, **9**Worcestershire , **10** Sunil Gavaskar, **11** Bouncer, **12** Newlands, **13** Yorkshire, **14** David Gower, **15** David Sheppard.

# • CRICKET - QUIZ 12 •

*Answers on page 75*

**1** Which cricketing legend's first names were John Berry?

**2** Who beat Essex to win the 1980 Benson & Hedges Cup?

**3** Who gained blues for Oxford 1975-78 and Cambridge 1983?

**4** Who were the 1987 County champions?

**5** How long is the bowling crease?

**6** Who beat Surrey to win the NatWest Trophy in 1991?

**7** What is the surname of brothers Hanif, Mushtaq, Sadiq and Wasir who all played for Pakistan?

**8** Who, in 1822, was the first player to be no-balled for throwing?

**9** Who was Yorkshire captain 1982-83?

**10** Who have remained unbeaten during a County Championship season five times?

**11** Which county's home ground is Lord's?

**12** Whose 337 against West Indies in 1957-58 is Pakistan's highest Test innings?

**13** Where was the 1991-92 World Cup final held?

**14** How many runs are scored in a maiden over?

**15** Who were the 1971 Sunday League champions?

***The opening ceremony for the 1996 Cricket World Cup was so badly handled that the Indian Government contemplated arresting the organiser on a charge of wasting public money.***

---

*Answers to page 75*

**1** Martin Crowe, **2** King pair, **3** Middlesex, **4** The Oval, **5** Lancashire, **6** Ninety yards, **7** India, **8** Robert Abel, **9** Surrey, **10** 1986, **11** Bill Paterson, **12** Kent, **13** Leslie and Dennis Compton, **14** George Tyldesley, **15** Somerset.

# CRICKET - QUIZ 13

*Answers on page 80*

1 Who were the 1985 County champions?

2 Whose 398-5 in 1996 is a World Cup record?

3 Of which county was Glenn Turner captain in 1981?

4 Who hit the first six in women's Test cricket?

5 For what is the castle a colloquial term?

6 What is the name of Jamaica's Test ground?

7 Whose badge is a gold running fox on green ground?

8 Which cricketer was also the first president of the English Bowls Association?

9 In which year was overarm bowling legalised?

10 Who were unbeaten in the 1969 County Championship?

11 What was New Zealand's Shell Trophy originally called?

12 Which Sussex wicket-keeper was the first to dispense with a long-stop?

13 Who beat Middlesex to win the 1989 NatWest Trophy?

14 Whose 267 against New Zealand in 1990-91 is Sri Lanka's highest Test innings?

15 As what was the Oval used in WWII?

## *Answers to page 80*

**1** Warwickshire, **2** Light, weather and the state of the pitch, **3** Glenys Page, **4** The Nursery, **5** Allan Border, **6** Pakistan, **7** Jack Hobbs, **8** Hampshire, **9** Carried his bat, **10** Calcutta, **11** Lancashire, **12** Lord's, **13** Australia, **14** None, **15** Glamorgan.

# • CRICKET - QUIZ 14 •

*Answers on page 81*

**1** Who was Hampshire captain 1985-87?

**2** Who successfully defended their Sunday League title in 1973?

**3** What is India's domestic knock-out competition called?

**4** For whom did Harold Gimblett score 21,142 runs?

**5** Which club's ground is on Broadhalfpenny Down?

**6** Whose 266 against Sri Lanka in 1994-95 is Zimbabwe's highest Test innings?

**7** Who successfully defended their County Championship title in 1960?

**8** Who only scored 62 against Australia in 1981-82?

**9** Who were the first Benson & Hedges Cup winners?

**10** Which England captain's 7 for 6 is the best innings analysis in women's Test cricket?

**11** Which cricket and football international was also the World long jump record-holder?

**12** Who won the 1998 NatWest Trophy?

**13** What is the area in front of the bowler's end sightscreen called?

**14** In which year did the original Lord's pavilion burn down during a Harrow v Winchester match?

**15** Who were unbeaten in the 1972 County Championship?

---

*Answers to page 81*

**1** Ray Illingworth, **2** Warwickshire, **3** Sri Lanka, **4** 1898, **5** Surrey, **6** Seven, **7** Bob Willis, **8** Leicestershire, **9** Chinaman, **10** Harold Larwood, **11** Learie Constantine, **12** One, **13** Leg break, **14** Hampshire, **15** 999mins (16hrs 29mins).

# • CRICKET - QUIZ 15 •

*Answers on page 78*

**1** Who were the 1972 County champions?

**2** What are the three constantly varying factors affecting play?

**3** Which New Zealander got 6-20 in the 1973 women's World Cup?

**4** What is the name of the Lord's practice ground?

**5** Who holds the record for most Test appearances with 156?

**6** Which country's premier national championship is called The Qaid-e-Azam Trophy?

**7** Who was the first professional sportsman to be knighted?

**8** Who were the 1975 Sunday League champions?

**9** What is an opening batsman said to have done if he's still in at the fall of the tenth wicket?

**10** In which city is the Eden Gardens ground?

**11** Who were unbeaten in the 1974 County Championship?

**12** At which ground did American Indians camp in 1844, giving dancing and archery displays?

**13** Who were the 1987-88 World Cup champions?

**14** How many times have Somerset won the County Championship?

**15** Of which county was Rodney Ontong captain 1984-86?

***Whenever Curtly Ambrose takes yet another test wicket, his mother marches into the street in his hometown in Antigua, and rings a bell.***

---

## *Answers to page 78*

**1** Middlesex, **2** Sri Lanka, **3** Worcestershire, **4** Rachael Heyhoe Flint, **5** Wicket, **6** Sabina Park, **7** Leicestershire, **8** W G Grace, **9** 1864, **10** Glamorgan, **11** The Plunket Shield, **12** Harry Phillips, **13** Warwickshire, **14** Aravinda de Silva, **15** Prisoner-of-war camp.

# • CRICKET - QUIZ 16 •

*Answers on page 79*

**1** Who was England captain when they regained the Ashes in 1971?

**2** Who were the 1997 Sunday League champions?

**3** Which country's domestic first-class competition is called The Lakspray Trophy?

**4** In which year did the MCC establish the Board of Control?

**5** Whose home ground is the Oval?

**6** How many counties participated in the first Minor Counties Championship?

**7** Who left Surrey and captained Warwickshire 1980-84?

**8** Who beat Middlesex to win the 1975 Benson & Hedges Cup?

**9** What is a left-arm bowler's off-break to a right-handed batsman called?

**10** Which former Nottinghamshire and England fast bowler was at the centre of the bodyline controversy in the 1932-33 Ashes series?

**11** Which former West Indian cricketer was created a life peer in 1969?

**12** By how many runs did Essex beat Nottinghamshire to win the 1985 NatWest Trophy?

**13** What is a ball that turns from leg to off called?

**14** Who were unbeaten in the 1973 County Championship?

**15** How long was Hanif Mohammad's record first-class individual innings?

---

## *Answers to page 79*

**1** Mark Nicholas, **2** Kent, **3** The Duleep Trophy, **4** Somerset, **5** Hambledon, **6** D L Houghton, **7** Yorkshire, **8** Pakistan, **9** Leicestershire, **10** Mary Duggan, **11** Charles Fry, **12** Lancashire, **13** Long field, **14** 1825, **15** Warwickshire.

# CRICKET - QUIZ 17

*Answers on page 84*

1 Of which club was Geoff Howarth captain 1984-85?

2 Who captained Surrey to County Championship victory in 1955?

3 What does lbw stand for?

4 In which year was Pakistan elected a full member of the ICC?

5 For whom did L G Berry score 30,143 runs?

6 Which England cricket captain was also an Olympic boxing champion?

7 What sort of catching is practised using a cradle?

8 Who holds the record for World Cup dismissals with 22?

9 Which country won the 1978 women's cricket World Cup?

10 After whom was the new Lord's stand named in 1958?

11 Who beat Derbyshire to win the 1969 Gillette Cup?

12 How many hundreds have Wally Hammond, Colin Cowdrey and Geoff Boycott all scored for England?

13 What is the surname of the three Sri Lankan brothers who have all opened the innings for their country?

14 Where is the Kensington Oval?

15 Who scored 2165 runs for Derbyshire in 1959?

## *Answers to page 84*

**1** Yorkshire, **2** 1895, **3** Sri Lanka, **4** Frank Woolley, **5** Wellington, **6** Middlesex, **7** Zimbabwe, **8** D C Morgan, **9** Matting, **10** Adelaide, **11** 1981, **12** Denis Compton, **13** Australia, **14** Glamorgan, **15** Weekes, Worrell, Walcott.

# CRICKET - QUIZ 18

*Answers on page 85*

1 Who left Lancashire to captain Derbyshire 1981-83?

2 Who won the 1998 Benson & Hedges Cup?

3 Which Test cricketer also won an FA Cup medal?

4 Which Law determines when a ball is dead?

5 Who finished the 1967 County Championship season without a single victory?

6 In which year was the first overseas cricket tour?

7 To how many overs are innings limited in the B & H Cup?

8 Who captained Derbyshire to their 1993 Benson & Hedges win?

9 For whom did Bill Alley score 2,761 runs in 1961?

10 Who beat Middlesex to win the 1975 Gillette Cup?

11 What is the umpire signalling by raising the index finger above the head?

12 Who scored a record five 100s in one Test series?

13 Which country instituted the inter-provincial Singer Trophy in 1989?

14 Who were the 1996 Sunday League champions?

15 Who gained blues for Cambridge 1975-76 and Oxford 1978?

---

*Answers to page 85*

**1** Edward IV, **2** Leicestershire, **3** 1969, **4** Kent, **5** Australia, **6** Derbyshire, **7** None, **8** Warwickshire, **9** Nottinghamshire, **10** England, **11** Javed Miandad, **12** Johannesburg, **13** Somerset, **14** Meat, **15** Jack Hobbs.

# • CRICKET - QUIZ 19 •

*Answers on page 82*

**1** Of which county was John Hampshire captain 1979-80 before joining Derbyshire?

**2** In which year was the first Minor Counties Championship held?

**3** Who only scored 72 against Pakistan in 1994-95?

**4** Who made a record 764 appearances for Kent?

**5** Which city's Test ground is Basin Reserve?

**6** Who beat Kent to win the 1984 NatWest Trophy?

**7** Which country's domestic first-class championship is called The Logan Cup?

**8** Who made 540 appearances for Derbyshire?

**9** What can be made of jute or coir?

**10** Which Australian city has an Oval ground?

**11** In which year was Sri Lanka elected a full member of the ICC?

**12** Who, at 20, was the youngest player to score a century for England?

**13** Who were the 1997 women's cricket World Cup champions?

**14** Who finished the 1979 County Championship season without a single victory?

**15** Who were West Indies's 'Three Ws'?

## *Answers to page 82*

**1** Surrey, **2** Stuart Surridge, **3** Leg before wicket, **4** 1952, **5** Leicestershire, **6** J W H T Douglas, **7** Slip catching, **8** Wasim Bari, **9** Australia, **10** Sir Pelham Warner, **11** Yorkshire, **12** Twenty-two, **13** Wettimuny, **14** Barbados, **15** Donald Carr.

# • CRICKET - QUIZ 20 •

*Answers on page 83*

**1** Which king's 1477 decree made cricket illegal until 1748?

**2** Who beat Essex to win the 1985 Benson & Hedges Cup?

**3** Which year saw the first Sunday League championship?

**4** Of which county was Chris Tavere captain 1983-84?

**5** Which country sent the first overseas team to England?

**6** For which county did D Smith score 20,516 runs?

**7** How many runs are scored in a duck?

**8** Who finished the 1982 County Championship season without a single victory?

**9** For which county did Gary Sobers play?

**10** Which country won the 1993 women's cricket World Cup?

**11** Who, at 19, was the youngest Test player to score a double century?

**12** In which city is the New Wanderers ground?

**13** Who beat Northamptonshire to win the 1979 Gillette Cup?

**14** What is the middle of a bat's blade at its thickest part called?

**15** Who was known as 'The Master', scoring 1000 runs in a season 24 times?

***Cricketer Micheal Atherton has a lady admirer who sends cakes to him and calls herself 'Your No 1 Suffolk Fan and Crazy Cake Lady'.***

---

*Answers to page 83*

**1** Barry Wood, **2** Essex, **3** Dennis Compton, **4** Law 23, **5** Nottinghamshire, **6** 1859, **7** Fifty-five, **8** Kim Barnett, **9** Somerset, **10** Lancashire, **11** Out, **12** Clyde Walcott, **13** Sri Lanka, **14** Surrey, **15** Stephen Wookey.

# CRICKET - QUIZ 21

*Answers on page 88*

1 Who played for both West Indies and New Zealand in the 1950s?

2 What is the opposite of square?

3 Whose badge features the Prince of Wales' Feathers?

4 In which country was the first Test match held?

5 For which county did West Indian off-spinner Lance Gibbs play?

6 For whom did Ken Suttle appear a record 423 consecutive times?

7 What is the qualifying requirement for first-class batting averages?

8 Of which county was A C D Ingleby-Mackenzie captain 1958-65?

9 Who captained the winning England team in the first women's World Cup?

10 Who were 1981 Sunday League champions?

11 Which city has a National and a Defence Stadium?

12 What is the term for a batsman sent in to play out time shortly before close of play?

13 Who, at 46, was the oldest man to score a century at Test level?

14 Who joined Durham from Northamptonshire to become its highest scorer?

15 For which county did England captain Mike Denness play?

## Answers to page 88

**1** Athanasios Traicos, **2** Out-cricket, **3** Belinda Clark, **4** Brian Close, **5** Lancashire, **6** Worcestershire, **7** James Lillywhite, **8** Sussex, **9** Keith Fletcher, **10** Fly slip, **11** Bob Taylor, **12** Brisbane, **13** A no-ball, **14** Allan Border, **15** Surrey.

# CRICKET - QUIZ 22

*Answers on page 89*

1. Of which county was John Mortimore captain 1965-67?
2. What is the highest grade of match apart from Test cricket?
3. Which county did Allan Border join in 1986?
4. Who were the 1974 Sunday League champions?
5. What is a ball that turns from off to leg on pitching called?
6. Who, at 21, was Test cricket's youngest triple century-maker?
7. For which county did England captain Ted Dexter play?
8. Who beat Essex to win the 1989 Benson & Hedges Cup?
9. Where was the 1978 women's cricket World Cup held?
10. For whom did Jack Hobbs score 43,554 runs?
11. Who has made the most appearances for Durham?
12. By how many runs did Australia win the first ever Test?
13. Who beat Sussex to win the 1993 NatWest Trophy?
14. In which city is Kingsmead ground?
15. Who were Yorkshire's 'great twin brethren', the two most successful County Championship all-rounders?

---

### *Answers to page 89*

**1** Derbyshire, **2** Essex, **3** Outswinger, **4** Sachin Tendulkar, **5** Somerset, **6** Alfred Shaw, **7** Kent, **8** Dunedin, **9** 200, **10** Roy Booth, **11** Worcestershire, **12** Staffordshire, **13** Tom Dollery, **14** Gilbert Jessop, **15** Chelmsford.

# CRICKET - QUIZ 23

*Answers on page 86*

1 Who played for South Africa 1969-70 and Zimbabwe 1993-94?

2 What is the collective effort of the fielding team called?

3 Who scored a women's World Cup record 229 in 1997?

4 Which Yorkshire captain later played for Somerset?

5 Who beat Northamptonshire to win the 1990 NatWest Trophy?

6 For which county did New Zealanders John Parker and Glenn Turner play?

7 Who captained England in the first ever Test match?

8 Whose badge is the County Arms of Six Martlets?

9 Who made 575 appearances for Essex?

10 Which unusual fielding position lies halfway between the slips and the boundary?

11 Which record-breaking wicket-keeper started his career with Derbyshire in 1961?

12 In which city is the Woolloongabba ground?

13 What is the umpire signalling by extending one arm horizontally?

14 Who holds the record for the most Test innings with 265?

15 Of which county was Roger Knight captain 1978-83?

---

## *Answers to page 86*

**1** Simpson Guillen, **2** Fine, **3** Surrey, **4** Australia, **5** Warwickshire, **6** Sussex, **7** 6 completed innings, **8** Hampshire, **9** Rachael Heyhoe Flint, **10** Essex, **11** Karachi, **12** Night-watchman, **13** Jack Hobbs, **14** Wayne Larkins, **15** Kent.

# • CRICKET - QUIZ 24 •

*Answers on page 87*

1 Of which county was J B Bolus captain 1973-75?

2 Who successfully defended their Sunday League title in 1985?

3 What term is used for a ball which moves in flight from leg to off?

4 Who, at 16, was the yougest player to reach a Test fifty?

5 For whom did Brian Langford appear a record 504 times?

6 Who got eight wickets for England in the first Test match?

7 Who beat Derbyshire to win the 1978 Benson & Hedges Cup?

8 In which city is Carisbrook ground?

9 By how many runs in a five-day match must a side be leading to force a Follow-on?

10 Who took a County Championship record 88 catches for Worcestershire in 1964?

11 For which county did Basil d'Oliveira play?

12 Who were Minor Counties champions 1991-93?

13 Who captained Warwickshire to their 1951 County Championship win?

14 Which batsman, who scored England's fastest Test century, was nicknamed 'The Croucher'?

15 In which market town is Essex County Ground?

***England used four different captains against the West Indies in 1988- Mike Gatting, John Embury, Chris Cowdrey and Graham Gooch - and lost the series 4-0.***

---

*Answers to page 87*

**1** Gloucestershire, **2** First-class, **3** Essex, **4** Leicestershire, **5** Off-break, **6** Gary Sobers, **7** Sussex, **8** Nottinghamshire, **9** India, **10** Surrey, **11** Simon Brown, **12** 45, **13** Warwickshire, **14** Durham, **15** George Hirst and Wilfred Rhodes.

# • CRICKET - QUIZ 25 •

*Answers on page 92*

1 Which spin-bowler has scored Test cricket's highest number of pairs of ducks as a batsman?

2 Which England and Yorkshire captain later played for Leicestershire?

3 Who won the 1996 NatWest Trophy?

4 What is an off-break bowled with a leg-break action called?

5 Who won blues for Oxford 1975 and Cambridge 1976?

6 Where was the 1982 women's cricket World Cup held?

7 Who were the 1970 County champions?

8 For which county did Graham Gooch score 2559 runs in 1984?

9 Which city's Test ground is Bramall Lane?

10 Which line across the pitch marks the forward limit of the batsman's safe ground?

11 Who bowled Clyde Walcott his only Test duck?

12 Who became Surrey captain in 1992?

13 Who scored 758-8d against West Indies in 1954-55?

14 Who made a record 492 appearances for Northamptonshire?

15 Which county did Mike Gatting join in 1975?

## *Answers to page 92*

**1** Chris Cowdrey, **2** Hampshire, **3** Richard Hadlee, **4** ndia, **5** Sabina Park, **6** The Sunday League, **7** Mike Brearley, **8** Robert Turner, **9** Middlesex, **10** Alec Stewart, **11** Delhi, **12** Kent, **13** Sunil Gavaskar, **14** Essex, **15** Gul Mohamed.

# • CRICKET - QUIZ 26 •

*Answers on page 93*

**1** For which county did South African Ken McEwan play?

**2** Which bowler has taken the most Test wickets with 434?

**3** Of which county was Javed Miandad captain in 1982?

**4** What is the space between a batsman's feet and his bat called?

**5** Who beat Glamorgan to win the 1977 Gillette Cup?

**6** Who resigned the captaincy of the England cricket team following the Test series defeat against the West Indies in 1998?

**7** Who scored 29,434 runs for Essex?

**8** To how many overs is each individual bowler limited in the Benson & Hedges Cup?

**9** How many times have Sussex won the County Championship?

**10** Who finally took the County Championship title away from Surrey in 1959?

**11** What separated Gentlemen from Players?

**12** In which year was the only Benson & Hedges Cup tie?

**13** Who was the first wicket-keeper to make 100 Test dismissals?

**14** Which fielding position is square with the wicket on the offside?

**15** Which Yorkshire cricketer was the first professional to captain England?

---

## *Answers to page 93*

**1** Rodney Marsh, **2** Yorkshire, **3** Australia, **4** Thomas White, **5** Glamorgan, **6** Hove, **7** Freddie Brown, **8** Essex, **9** Adam Hollioake, **10** Worcestershire, **11** Gloucestershire, **12** Ian Botham, **13** Green-top, **14** Hamilton, **15** England had to catch the boat home.

# • CRICKET - QUIZ 27 •

*Answers on page 90*

1. Who was Kent captain 1985-87?
2. For which county did David Gower leave Leicestershire?
3. Which bowler took 431 wickets for New Zealand?
4. Who scored 676-7 against Sri Lanka in 1986-87?
5. Which ground in Jamaica made cricket history in 1998 when a Test was abandoned because of a dangerous pitch?
6. Which is the only one-day county competition which cannot be extended due to bad weather?
7. Who became Middlesex captain in 1971?
8. Which Somerset wicket-keeper equalled the county record for dismissals in an innings in 1995?
9. Who were the 1993 County Champions?
10. Who replaced Michael Atherton as England captain?
11. Which city's Test ground is Feroz Shah Kotla?
12. Who beat Worcestershire to win the 1973 Benson & Hedges Cup?
13. Who holds the record for Test hundreds with 34?
14. Which is the only county to have its name on its badge?
15. Who played for India 1946-53 and Pakistan 1956-57?

***England wicket-keeper Jack Russell wore the same cap, gloves and wicket-keeping pads for 15 years.***

## *Answers to page 90*

**1** Bhagwar Chandrasekhar, **2** Ray Illingworth, **3** Lancashire, **4** Googly, **5** David Jarrett, **6** New Zealand, **7** Kent, **8** Essex, **9** Sheffield, **10** Popping crease, **11** Ray Lindwall, **12** Alex Stewart, **13** Australia, **14** Dennis Brookes, **15** Middlesex.

# • CRICKET - QUIZ 28 •

*Answers on page 91*

**1** Which wicket-keeper made 355 dismissals for Australia?

**2** Of which county was Chris Old captain 1981-82?

**3** Which country won the 1988 women's cricket World Cup?

**4** Whose 1771 use of a bat wider than the wicket led to width restrictions on bats?

**5** Which county has a gold daffodil on its badge?

**6** In which resort is Sussex's HQ?

**7** Which England player left Surrey to captain Northamptonshire?

**8** Who successfully defended their County Championship title in 1992?

**9** Who captained the England cricket team that won the Champions Trophy in Sharjah in 1997?

**10** Who beat Warwickshire to win the 1994 NatWest Trophy?

**11** Which county did Chris Broad leave for Nottinghamshire?

**12** Which bowler took 383 wickets for England?

**13** What is a well-grassed pitch called?

**14** In which city is Trust Bank (Seddon) Park?

**15** Why was England's 'Timeless Test' in South Africa abandonned as a draw after 10 days?

---

## *Answers to page 91*

**1** Essex, **2** Kapil Dev, **3** Glamorgan, **4** Gate, **5** Middlesex, **6** Michael Atherton, **7** Keith Fletcher, **8** Eleven, **9** None, **10** Yorkshire, **11**Amateur status , **12** 1987, **13** Bert Oldfield, **14** Point, **15** Len Hutton.

# CRICKET - QUIZ 29

*Answers on page 96*

1 For which county did Richard Hadlee play?

2 In which country was the first women's cricket World Cup held?

3 To whom were the original Ashes presented in 1882-83?

4 Who beat Warwickshire to win the 1984 Benson & Hedges Cup?

5 Which Somerset captain was also a rugby international?

6 How is a grub bowled?

7 Who played for India 1946 and Pakistan 1952-58?

8 Who were the 1977 Sunday League champions?

9 What is the surname of the Sussex brothers who hold eight individual county records between them?

10 For which county did Hugh Morris score 2276 runs in 1990?

11 Which bowler took 376 wickets for West Indies?

12 Where is the Queen's Park Oval?

13 What is a bat's maximum length?

14 Who were the 1961 County champions?

15 Of which county was Doug Insole captain 1951-60?

## *Answers to page 96*

**1** Scunthorpe United, **2** Warwickshire, **3** Jeffrey Dujon, **4** 28ins, **5** Clive Lloyd, **6** Sussex, **7** Hampshire, **8** Lucknow, **9** Alan Jones, **10**Essex , **11** Played on, **12** Dennis Lillee, **13** Northamptonshire, **14** South Africa, **15** A leg-bye

# CRICKET - QUIZ 30

*Answers on page 97*

**1** For which county did Steve Waugh play?

**2** Who was the first batsman to score 1000 runs in Test cricket?

**3** What is a cricket ball's maximum weight?

**4** Who beat Surrey to win the 1965 Gillette Cup?

**5** Who was the bespectacled Warwickshire captain 1957-67?

**6** On which side does the gully stand?

**7** For whom did Thomas Hayward score 3,246 runs in 1906?

**8** Which Australian woman cricketer scored 193 against England in 1987?

**9** Who were the 1976 County champions?

**10** In which 1882 publication did the mock obituary appear that gave rise to the Ashes?

**11** Who has made the most appearances for Glamorgan with 647?

**12** In which year was the Gillette Cup first held?

**13** Where in the West Indies is the Recreation Ground?

**14** Who beat Derbyshire to win the 1988 Benson & Hedges Cup?

**15** For which county did Clive Lloyd play?

---

*Answers to page 97*

**1** Harry Pilling, **2** Derbyshire, **3** D Kenyon, **4** Australia, **5** Nine inches, **6** 1981, **7** Alan Knott, **8** Surrey, **9** David Gower, **10** Yes, **11** Cardiff, **12** Kumar Duleepsinhji, **13** Warwickshire, **14** Two scores of zero in the same match, **15** Worcestershire.

# CRICKET - QUIZ 31

*Answers on page 94*

1 For which football team did Ian Botham play?

2 Whose badge is the Bear and Ragged Staff?

3 Which wicket-keeper made 272 dismissals for West Indies?

4 What is the height of today's wickets?

5 Under whose captaincy did West Indies achieve 26 successive Test Victories?

6 Who were the first Gillette Cup champions?

7 Of which county was Nick Pocock captain 1980-84?

8 In which city is K D 'Babu' Singh Stadium?

9 Who is Glamorgan's highest scorer with 34,056 runs?

10 Who came last in the County Championship in 1988 and 1989?

11 What is the ball said to be when deflected into the stumps with the bat?

12 Who took 355 wickets for Australia?

13 Who beat Lancashire to win the 1976 Gillette Cup?

14 Who scored 622-9d against Australia in 1969-70?

15 What is the umpire signalling by touching a raised knee with the hand?

***The Lords cricket ground has moved site twice since it was first laid out, but each time the turf was dug up and moved to the new site.***

## Answers to page 94

**1** Nottinghamshire, **2** England, **3** The Hon Ivo Bligh, **4** Lancashire, **5** Sammy Woods, **6** Under-arm, **7** Abdul Kardar, **8** Leicestershire, **9** Langridge, **10** Glamorgan, **11** Malcolm Marshall, **12** Trinidad, **13** 38ins, **14** Hampshire, **15** Essex.

# CRICKET - QUIZ 32

*Answers on page 95*

1 Which Lancashire player was the first to score 1,000 runs in the Sunday League?

2 Who beat Lancashire to win the 1993 Benson & Hedges Cup?

3 Who was Worcestershire captain 1959-67?

4 Which country won the 1982 women's cricket World Cup?

5 What is the width of today's wickets?

6 In which year was the only NatWest Trophy tie?

7 Which wicket-keeper made 269 dismissals for England?

8 Who were the 1971 County champions?

9 Which England captain made his Leicestershire debut in 1975?

10 Are wides and no-balls included when working out bowling averages?

11 In which city is Glamorgan's Sophia Gardens Ground?

12 Who holds the Sussex record for the highest score?

13 Who were the 1980 Sunday League champions?

14 What is a 'pair of spectacles'?

15 Whose badge is Shield Argent a Fess between three Pears Sable?

## *Answers to page 95*

**1** Somerset, **2** Arthur Shrewsbury, **3** Five and three quarter ounces, **4** Yorkshire, **5** Mike Smith, **6** Offside, **7** Surrey, **8** Denise Annetts, **9** Middlesex, **10** The Sporting Times, **11** Donald Shepherd, **12** 1963, **13** St John's, Antigua, **14** Hampshire, **15** Lancashire.

# • CRICKET - QUIZ 33 •

*Answers on page 100*

1 Who beat Northamptonshire to win the 1995 NatWest Trophy?

2 Who first played for Kent aged 17 and took 101 wickets in both his first two seasons?

3 In which year was the first women's cricket World Cup held?

4 Under which Law are beamers forbidden?

5 Who holds the copyright of the Laws of Cricket?

6 Who won their third consecutive County Championship title in 1968?

7 Which bowler took 325 wickets for England?

8 For which county did England captains Fry, Gilligan, Dexter and Greig play?

9 Who play at the Phoenix County Ground?

10 Who was the first to score 2000 and 3000 runs in Test cricket?

11 Law 22 allows for overs of which two numbers of deliveries?

12 Of which county did Hugh Morris become captain in 1986?

13 Who were the 1989 Sunday League champions?

14 In which city is McLean Park ground?

15 For whom did Harold Gibbons score 2,654 in 1934?

---

*Answers to page 100*

**1** John Crawley, **2** Worcestershire, **3** Georgetown, Guyana, **4** Fifty yards, **5** Sussex, **6** Bob Taylor, **7** 1791, **8** Kent, **9** Allan Border, **10** Bobby Parks, **11** Gloucestershire, **12** Peter Marner, **13** Essex, **14** A hat-trick, **15** Malcolm Nash.

# CRICKET - QUIZ 34

*Answers on page 101*

**1** Which Yorkshire and England left-hand spinner died in battle in Sicily?

**2** Who captained England in the infamous Bodyline series against Australia?

**3** Which England cricketer made his maiden Test century in the 5th Test against the West Indies in 1998?

**4** For what is a bosie the Australian term?

**5** Who were NatWest Trophy runners-up in 1983 and 1984?

**6** For whom did Wally Hammond score 2860 runs in 1933?

**7** Which New Zealand fast bowler's father was New Zealand captain?

**8** When was the last code of the Laws of Cricket issued?

**9** For whom did John Langridge score 2,850 runs in 1949?

**10** Where is Warwickshire's home ground?

**11** Who holds the record for the most World Cup runs with 1,083?

**12** Who were the 1975 County champions?

**13** What is the bowler's approach to his delivery stride called?

**14** In which year did the Gillette Cup become the NatWest Trophy?

**15** Who was the first bowler to take all 10 wickets in a Test innings?

## *Answers to page 101*

**1** Gloucestershire, **2** Port Elizabeth, **3** Clive Lloyd, **4** Zimbabwe, **5** Kent, **6** Jimmy Matthews, **7** Yorkshire, **8** Charlotte Edwards, **9** Under-arm, **10** Surrey, **11** Hampshire, **12** Alan Knott, **13** Seam, **14** Sixty, **15** Mike Smith.

# • CRICKET - QUIZ 35 •

*Answers on page 98*

1. Which England cricketer was mugged in Cairns during their 1998-99 Ashes tour?
2. For whom did Donald Kenyon score 33,490 runs?
3. Where in the West Indies is the Bourda ground?
4. What is the minimum distance the boundary may be from the centre of the pitch?
5. Who were the 1982 Sunday League champions?
6. Who gave up his short captaincy of Derbyshire because he thought it was affecting his wicket-keeping?
7. In which year did Samuel Britcher publish the first cricket annual?
8. Who beat Worcestershire to win the 1973 Benson & Hedges Cup?
9. Who uncharacteristically dropped an easy catch that would have given Jeff Thomson his 200th Test wicket?
10. Which wicket-keeper made a record 700 dismissals for Hampshire?
11. Of which county was C T M Pugh captain 1961-62?
12. Who was the Gillette Cup's first Man of the Match?
13. Who were County Championship runners-up in 1989 and 1990?
14. What was 'The Demon' Spofforth the first to make in a Test in 1879?
15. Against which Glamorgan bowler did Gary Sobers hit six sixes in an over?

---

## *Answers to page 98*

**1** Warwickshire, **2** Derek Underwood, **3** 1973, **4** Law 42, **5** MCC, **6** Yorkshire, **7** Bob Willis, **8** Sussex, **9** Gloucestershire, **10** Clem Hill, **11** Six and eight, **12** Glamorgan, **13** Lancashire, **14** Napier, **15** Worcestershire.

# CRICKET - QUIZ 36

*Answers on page 99*

**1** Who beat Kent to win the 1977 Benson & Hedges Cup?

**2** Where in South Africa is St George's Park ground?

**3** From whom did Viv Richards take over the West Indies captaincy?

**4** Who scored 544-9d against Pakistan in 1994-95?

**5** Who were the 1978 County champions?

**6** Who is the only bowler to have made two hat-tricks in the same Test?

**7** Of which county was David Bairstow captain 1984-86?

**8** Which England player was 173 not out in the 1997 women's World Cup?

**9** What was the original form of bowling?

**10** Who beat Warwickshire by 9 wickets to win the 1982 NatWest Trophy?

**11** For which club did Charles Mead make 48,892 runs?

**12** Which Kent player was the first Test wicket-keeper to take 250 wickets?

**13** What is the stitching around the circumference of a ball called?

**14** To how many overs are innings limited in the NatWest Trophy?

**15** Who made 2,417 runs for Warwickshire in 1959?

***The first five match series of Tests in England was played against Australia in 1899. Four games were drawn, Australia won at Lord's by 10 wickets.***

---

*Answers to page 99*

**1** Hedley Verity, **2** Douglas Jardine, **3** Mark Ramprakash, **4** Googly, **5** Kent, **6** Gloucestershire, **7** Richard Hadlee, **8** 1980, **9** Sussex, **10** Edgbaston, **11** Javed Miandad, **12** Leicestershire, **13** Run-up, **14** 1981, **15** Jim Laker.

# CRICKET - QUIZ 37

*Answers on page 104*

1 Which country's most successful Test bowler is H J Tayfield?

2 Whose badge is a red rose?

3 What does TCCB stand for?

4 Who became, in 1935, the first woman to score a Test century?

5 What was South Africa's Castle Cup originally called?

6 Who beat Lancashire to win the 1974 Gillette Cup?

7 What is the highest Test match aggregate, England v South Africa 1939?

8 Of which county was Eddie Barlow captain 1976-78?

9 Who was the first to reach 4000 and 5000 runs in Test cricket?

10 What is the term for a ball's deviation from the straight on pitching?

11 Which former England captain was appointed Chairman of the England Selectors in 1982?

12 Who, in 1862, was the first to be no-balled for bowling overarm?

13 Who were the 1986 County champions?

14 Who holds Warwickshire's highest score record with 501 not out?

15 Who took over the Australian captaincy from his brother Ian?

## *Answers to page 104*

**1** Warwickshire, **2** Brian Statham, **3** Marylebone, **4** Kent, **5** Tom Graveney, **6** William Keeton, **7** 100, **8** W G Grace, **9** James Langridge, **10** Geoff Miller, **11** Hampshire, **12** Sticky wicket, **13** Lancashire, **14** Australia, **15** Wally Hammond.

# • CRICKET - QUIZ 38 •

*Answers on page 105*

**1** Who were the 1995 Sunday League champions?

**2** What is another name for forward short leg?

**3** Which wicket-keeper has made 228 dismissals for Pakistan?

**4** Who were the 1982 County champions?

**5** Who introduced the googly at Lord's in 1900?

**6** Who was given the initials MCC by his cricket-mad father?

**7** For whom did Charles Parker appear 602 times?

**8** What is the umpire signalling by crossing and recrossing the wrists below the waist?

**9** Who was Yorkshire captain 1971-78?

**10** Who beat Surrey to win the 1979 Benson & Hedges Cup?

**11** What is the term for a fast off-break, usually produced by the bowler cutting his fingers across the seam?

**12** Who is known as The Lion of Pakistan?

**13** For whom has Dennis Amiss scored 35,146 runs?

**14** Which South African has played for Natal, Hampshire and South Australia?

**15** Who holds the Somerset record for the highest score?

---

*Answers to page 105*

**1** Fred Trueman, **2** The League Cup, **3** Norman Gifford, **4** Shane Warne, **5** Kent, **6** S M H Kirmani, **7** Change bowler, **8** Jack Hobbs, **9** Worcestershire, **10** Alan Davidson, **11** 1977, **12** 12, **13** Wally Hammond, **14** Shooter, **15** South Africa.

# CRICKET - QUIZ 39

*Answers on page 102*

1 Who came last in the County Championship in 1981 and 1982?

2 Which Lancashire and England player was known as 'The Greyhound'?

3 Which club was formed as an offshoot of the Star and Garter club?

4 Who beat Worcestershire to win the 1976 Benson & Hedges Cup?

5 Who broke his little finger as substitute wicket-keeper in the 1955 Test against South Africa?

6 Who holds the Nottinghamshire record for the highest score?

7 How many runs are scored in a century?

8 Who is believed to be the only player to make a Test dismissal off his first ball as wicket-keeper?

9 Who appeared for Sussex a record 622 times?

10 Which off-spinner was Derbyshire captain 1979-81?

11 Who beat Surrey to win the 1991 NatWest Trophy?

12 What is another name for a glue pot?

13 For whom did George Tyldesley score 34,222 runs?

14 In which country was the 1988 women's cricket World Cup held?

15 Who was the first fielder to hold 100 Test catches?

***The first reference to cricket in the West Indies occurred in 1806 - the St Anne's club of Barbados met on May 12th.***

## *Answers to page 102*

**1** South Africa, **2** Lancashire, **3** Test and County Cricket Board, **4** Myrtle Maclagan, **5** The Currie Cup, **6** Kent, **7** 1,981, **8** Derbyshire, **9** Jack Hobbs, **10** Break, **11** Peter May, **12** Edgar Willsher, **13** Essex, **14** Brian Lara, **15** Greg Chappell.

# CRICKET - QUIZ 40

*Answers on page 103*

**1** Which Yorkshire player was the first Test bowler to reach 300 wickets?

**2** What was the Benson & Hedges Cup originally called?

**3** Who was Worcestershire captain 1971-80 and Warwickshire captain 1985-1987?

**4** Which spin bowler has become only the second Australian to take 300 Test wickets?

**5** Who play at the St Lawrence Ground?

**6** Which wicket-keeper made 198 dismissals for India?

**7** What is the bowler brought on after the opening pair called?

**8** Who made a record 598 appearances for Surrey?

**9** Who successfully defended their Sunday League title in 1988?

**10** Which Australian all-rounder was known as 'Davo'?

**11** In which year were Kent and Middlesex joint County champions?

**12** To how many overs is each bowler limited in the NatWest Trophy?

**13** Who was the first to score 6000 and 7000 runs in Test cricket?

**14** What is the term for a ball that does not rise off the ground after pitching?

**15** Which cricket team gave the West Indies their first ever 5-0 Test series defeat in 1998-99?

---

## *Answers to page 103*

**1** Kent, **2** Silly mid-on, **3** Wasim Bari, **4** Middlesex, **5** Bernard Bosanquet, **6** Colin Cowdrey, **7** Gloucestershire, **8** A dead ball, **9** Geoffrey Boycott, **10** Essex, **11** Break-back, **12** Imran Khan, **13** Warwickshire, **14** Barry Richards, **15** Viv Richards.

# CRICKET - QUIZ 41

*Answers on page 108*

**1** Who was the first professional to be appointed captain of England in England?

**2** Who beat Somerset to win the 1978 Gillette Cup?

**3** Who captained Australia 28 times in 6 series 1958-63?

**4** Who holds the record for World Cup wickets with 34?

**5** In which year did the International Cricket Conference become the International Cricket Council?

**6** Of which county was R N S Hobbs captain in 1979?

**7** Who were the 1998 County champions?

**8** Who holds the Northamptonshire record for the highest score?

**9** For whom has William Quaife appeared a record 665 times?

**10** Which wicket-keeper made 176 dismissals for New Zealand?

**11** Who only scored 53 against Pakistan in 1986-87?

**12** Which wood is normally used for stumps?

**13** Who successfully defended their Benson & Hedges Title by nine wickets in 1982?

**14** In which year was the first women's Test match played?

**15** For whom did Wally Hammond score 33,664 runs?

---

## *Answers to page 108*

**1** Neil Harvey, **2** George Giffen, **3** 1957, **4** Glamorgan, **5** Frank Worrell, **6** Warren Hegg, **7** Yorkshire, **8** England, **9** John Langridge, **10** Middlesex, **11** Slip, **12** 1992, **13** Samuel Coe, **14** Two, **15** Mansur Ali Khan.

# CRICKET - QUIZ 42

*Answers on page 109*

**1** What is the umpire signalling by raising an open hand above the head?

**2** Who beat Leicestershire to win the 1992 NatWest Trophy?

**3** Which Australian wicket-keeper took 74 against England in 1959?

**4** What is a bowler called who infringes Law 24 by throwing instead of bowling?

**5** Who was the first to reach 8000 runs in Test cricket?

**6** Whose badge is a white rose?

**7** Which royal position was cricket and football international Charles Fry offered?

**8** Who successfully defended their County Championship title in 1984?

**9** In which year were India, New Zealand and West Indies elected full members of the ICC?

**10** What is an extremely defensive batsman called?

**11** Which county's captaincy went from M J K Smith to A C Smith in 1968?

**12** Who holds the Middlesex record for the highest score?

**13** Who were the 1991 Sunday League champions?

**14** What is the scoring of 1000 Test runs allied to the taking of 100 wickets called?

**15** Which Test ground is Lancashire's HQ?

---

*Answers to page 109*

**1** Godfrey Evans, **2** Mark Taylor, **3** Lancashire, **4** Peter May, **5** USA and Canada, **6** Donald Kenyon, **7** Donkey drop, **8** Lancaster Park, **9** Essex, **10** 1992, **11** Richie Benaud, **12** Yorkshire, **13** Tail, **14** ,W G Grace **15** South Africa.

# CRICKET - QUIZ 43

*Answers on page 106*

**1** Who took over the Australian captaincy when Richie Benaud injured his shoulder in 1961?

**2** Who was the first player to complete a Test double, 1000 runs and 100 wickets?

**3** In which year were first-day declarations incorporated into the Laws?

**4** Who were the 1969 County champions?

**5** Who was West Indies captain 1960-63?

**6** Which Lancashire wicket-keeper made a record 7 catches in an innings in 1989?

**7** Of which county was J V Wilson captain in 1960-62?

**8** In which country was the 1993 women's cricket World Cup held?

**9** Who scored 34,152 runs for Sussex?

**10** Who beat Worcestershire to win the 1988 NatWest Trophy?

**11** Which fielding position is on the offside and adjacent to the wicket-keeper?

**12** In which year was Zimbabwe elected a full member of the ICC?

**13** Who holds the Leicestershire record for the highest score?

**14** By how many runs did Middlesex beat Kent in the 1986 Benson & Hedges Cup?

**15** Who, at 21, was the youngest Test captain?

## *Answers to page 106*

**1** Len Hutton, **2** Sussex, **3** Richie Benaud, **4** Imran Khan, **5** 1969, **6** Glamorgan, **7** Essex, **8** Raman Subba Row CBE, **9** Warwickshire, **10** I D S Smith, **11** West Indies, **12** Ash, **13** Somerset, **14** 1934, **15** Gloucestershire.

# • CRICKET - QUIZ 44 •

*Answers on page 107*

1 Whose 219 dismissals was a wicket-keeping Test record for 17 years until 1976?

2 Who is the only batsman to have scored 1000 runs in the year of his Test debut?

3 Who beat Worcestershire to win the 1990 Benson & Hedges Cup?

4 Which Surrey player captained England 41 times?

5 Which two countries played the first international match in 1844?

6 Who made a record 589 appearances for Worcestershire?

7 What is a ball bowled high into the air by a slow bowler called?

8 What is Christchurch's ground called?

9 Of which county was Trevor Bailey captain 1961-66?

10 In which year did Durham first appear in the County Championship?

11 Who was the first player to complete a Test double double, 2000 runs and 200 wickets?

12 Who were the 1983 Sunday League champions?

13 What is the lower places in the batting order called?

14 Who still holds Gloucestershire's highest score record of 318 not out?

15 Which country's 'second division' competition is called the UCB Bowl?

***In 1994, in a little known pub in Northampton, due to overwhelming pressure, changed its sign from WG Grace to Brian Lara.***

*Answers to page 107*

**1** A bye, **2** Northamptonshire, **3** Wally Grout, **4** Chucker, **5** Gary Sobers, **6** Yorkshire, **7**King of Albania , **8** ,Essex **9** 1926, **10** Stone-waller, **11** Warwickshire, **12** John Robertson, **13** Nottinghamshire, **14** The double, **15** Old Trafford.

# CRICKET - QUIZ 45

*Answers on page 112*

1 Whose badge is a white horse on a red ground?

2 Who, at 23, was the youngest England captain?

3 Who took 19 wickets in the fourth Test against Australia in 1956?

4 Who beat Leicestershire to win the 1974 Benson & Hedges Cup?

5 Which type of spin causes the ball to gain pace after bouncing?

6 What is the term for a stroke aimed with a perpendicular arc of the bat?

7 In which capital city is the Sinhalese Sports Club Ground?

8 Who came last in the County Championship in 1965 and 1966?

9 Who holds the Lancashire record for the highest score?

10 Which Yorkshire and England player's right arm was shorter that his left after a war injury?

11 Who beat Kent to win the 1983 NatWest Trophy?

12 To how many overs are innings limited in the Sunday League?

13 Who was Gloucestershire captain 1977-81?

14 In which year was South Africa elected a full member of the ICC?

15 For whom did Herbert Sutcliffe score 2,883 in 1932?

## *Answers to page 112*

**1** Worcestershire, **2** Herbert Sutcliffe, **3** A boundary, **4** Eden Park, **5** Hampshire, **6** William Ashdown, **7** Don Bradman, **8** Graham Gooch, **9** Surrey, **10** Ian Chappell, **11** Godfrey Evans, **12** Leicestershire, **13** 1877, **14** Kent, **15** W G Grace.

# • CRICKET - QUIZ 46 •

*Answers on page 113*

1 Which England bowler took six second innings wickets to give England a surprise victory in the 4th Test against Australia in 1998?

2 In which city is the Wankhede Stadium?

3 When was the first Test match held in England?

4 Who was the first player to complete a Test treble double, 3000 runs and 300 wickets?

5 What are extras called in Australia?

6 Who were the 1997 County champions?

7 Which Surrey and England player was nicknamed 'big fella'?

8 Who made 700 appearances for Hampshire?

9 What was the NatWest Trophy originally called?

10 Of which county was D C Morgan captain 1965-69?

11 What is the emergency substitute fielder called?

12 Who beat Sussex to win the 1968 Gillette Cup?

13 Which Australian was 143 not out in the 1988 women's World Cup?

14 What was West Indies's Red Stripe Cup originally called?

15 Who holds the Worcestershire record for the highest score with 405 not out?

---

## *Answers to page 113*

**1** Richard Moore, **2** Kent, **3** Flipper, **4** 1926, **5** Zimbabwe, **6** Allan Border, **7** Phil Neale, **8** Essex, **9** Ian Botham, **10** D W Gregory, **11** A broken arm, **12** Middlesex, **13** Headingley, **14** 1939, **15** Brian Lara.

# • CRICKET - QUIZ 47 •

*Answers on page 110*

**1** Who successfully defended their County Championship title in 1989?

**2** Who scored 38,558 runs for Yorkshire?

**3** What is the umpire signalling by waving the arm from side to side?

**4** What is Auckland's ground called?

**5** Who beat Kent to win the 1992 Benson & Hedges Cup?

**6** Who holds the Kent record for the highest score?

**7** Who, had he not been bowled out for 0 in his last Test, would have had a Test average of 100?

**8** Who scored the highest individual aggregate in a Test match with 456?

**9** Of which county was Micky Stewart captain 1963-72?

**10** Who was Australia's captain when England regained the Ashes in 1971?

**11** Whose Test record of the longest innings without scoring did Geoff Allott beat?

**12** For whom did W E Astill make a record 628 appearances?

**13** In which year was the first Test match held?

**14** Who were the 1976 Sunday League champions?

**15** Who, at 50, was the oldest Test captain?

***Since 1896 no team has lost the Old Trafford Test and finished the summer holding the Ashes.***

---

## *Answers to page 110*

**1**Kent , **2** Monty Bowden, **3** Jim Laker, **4** Surrey, **5** Top-spin, **6** Drive, **7** Colombo, **8** Nottinghamshire, **9** Archibald MacLaren, **10** Len Hutton, **11** Somerset, **12** 40, **13** Mike Procter, **14** 1991, **15** Yorkshire.

# CRICKET - QUIZ 48

*Answers on page 111*

**1** Who holds the Hampshire record for the highest score?

**2** For whom did Frank Woolley score 47,868 runs?

**3** What is delivered using only the tips of the first and third fingers of the right hand?

**4** In which year was the Women's Cricket Association formed?

**5** In which country is the Bulawayo Athletic Club?

**6** Who made the most consecutive Test appearances with 153?

**7** Who was Worcestershire captain 1982-88?

**8** Who were the 1979 County champions?

**9** Who resigned as England captain after the second Test against Australia in 1981 after making a 'pair'?

**10** Who captained Australia in the first ever Test match?

**11** What prevented Geoffrey Boycott playing for the England side that regained the Ashes in 1971?

**12** Who beat Surrey to win the 1980 Gillette Cup?

**13** Where is Yorkshire's home ground?

**14** Which year saw the England's 'Timeless Test' against South Africa?

**15** Who holds the highest individual Test innings with 375?

---

## *Answers to page 111*

**1** Dean Headley, **2** Bombay, **3** 1880, **4** Ian Botham, **5** Sundries, **6** Surrey, **7** Alec Bedser, **8** Charles Mead, **9** The Knock-Out Cup, **10** Derbyshire, **11** Twelfth man, **12** Warwickshire, **13** Lindsay Reeler, **14** The Shell Shield, **15** Graeme Hick.

# CRICKET - QUIZ 49

*Answers on page 115*

1 Who was Kent captain 1957-71?

2 Who scored 903-7d against Australia in 1938?

3 For which Australian side did Ian Botham play?

4 By how many runs in a three- or four-day match must a side be leading to force a Follow-on?

5 Which Gillette Cup forerunner was only held once, in 1962?

6 Which South African-born player's inclusion in the England side led to the cancellation of a South African tour?

7 Who beat Essex to win the 1983 Benson & Hedges Cup?

8 What connects the year of the Queen's birth, her Coronation year and her Silver Jubilee?

9 For whom did George Gunn score 31,592 runs?

10 Who holds the Glamorgan record for the highest score?

11 Who were the 1979 Sunday League champions?

12 Who have won the County Championship most times with 29?

13 Who, at 18, was the youngest Englishman to play Test cricket?

14 What is the umpire signalling by raising both arms above the head?

15 Who successfully defended their County Championship title in 1995?

---

## *Answers to page 115*

**1** E H Hendren, **2** Nottinghamshire, **3** Dickie Bird, **4** 1972, **5** West Indies, **6** Mike Brearley, **7** Full toss, **8** Essex, **9** Percival Perrin, **10** 1949 and 1950, **11** Alvin Kallicharran, **12** The Ashes Song, **13** Hampshire, **14** Redoubtables WCC, **15** Gary Sobers.

# CRICKET - QUIZ 50

*Answers on page 114*

**1** Which Middlesex player also played football for Coventry City, Man City and QPR?

**2** Who beat Northamptonshire to win the 1987 NatWest Trophy?

**3** Who holds the record number of Test appearances as an umpire?

**4** In which year was the first Benson & Hedges Cup held?

**5** Whose score was 790-3d against Pakistan in 1957-58?

**6** Who was the new England captain when they regained the Ashes in 1977?

**7** What is a ball that reaches the batsman without bouncing called?

**8** Of which county was Keith Fletcher captain 1974-85?

**9** Who holds the Essex record for the highest score?

**10** Which two consecutive years saw County Championship ties?

**11** Whose 206 for Warwickshire is the highest score in any limited-overs match in Britain?

**12** What was the name of the song the MCC recorded in 1971, sung to the tune of 'Show me your winkle tonight'?

**13** Who were the 1973 County champions?

**14** What is the oldest surviving women's cricket club?

**15** Who, at 21, was the youngest to score a triple century in Test cricket?

## *Answers to page 114*

**1** Colin Cowdrey, **2** England, **3** Queensland, **4** 150, **5** Midlands Knock-Out Cup, **6** Basil d'Oliveira, **7** Middlesex, **8** England regained the Ashes, **9** Nottinghamshire, **10** David Davies, **11** Somerset, **12** Yorkshire, **13** Brian Close, **14** A six, **15** Warwickshire.

# FOOTBALL

# • FOOTBALL - QUIZ 1 •

*Answers on page 120*

1 Which English team plays at Gay Meadow?
2 Who was manager of England from 1982-1990?
3 Which club won the European Cup in 1974?
4 What nationality is Peter Schmeichel?
5 Which Leeds and England striker was nicknamed 'Sniffer'?
6 Which Italian was voted World Footballer of the Year in 1982?
7 Of which club side is Tony Blair a keen supporter?
8 Which club won the FA Cup in 1976?
9 Who won the European Cup in 1991?
10 When was the Football Association formed?
11 Who succeeded Don Revie as England manager?
12 Who scored most goals at the 1966 World Cup?
13 Oakwell is the home of which English club?
14 Who kept goal for Arsenal in the 1972 FA Cup final?
15 Which English club is known as the 'Blades'?

## *Answers to page 120*

**1** Darlington, **2** Uwe Seeler, **3** 1972, **4** 1985, **5** Coventry City, **6** Watford, **7** Leicester City, **8** Nolberto Solano, **9** Fédération Internationale de Football Association, **10** ,Underhill **11** 1972, **12** Gary McAllister, **13** Southampton, **14** 1888, **15** Aston VIlla.

# FOOTBALL - QUIZ 2

*Answers on page 121*

1 How many FA Cups did Newcastle United win during the 1950s?

2 Which team plays at Ibrox?

3 What nationality is Tomas Brolin?

4 Which Second Division side lost in the final of the 1992 FA Cup?

5 Which club sold Dennis Bergkamp to Inter Milan in 1993?

6 Which English team plays at Griffin Park?

7 Who was the leading goalscorer at the 1978 World Cup?

8 Which club won the League Championship in the 1990-91 season?

9 From which club did Rangers sign Colin Hendry?

10 In which country was Ivor Allchurch born?

11 Who succeeded Brian Clough as manager of Nottingham Forest?

12 Which club sold Kevin Keegan to Newcastle United in 1982?

13 Which English team is known as the 'Bantams'?

14 How many FA Cup finals did Manchester United reach during the 1970's?

15 Which country won the 1990 World Cup?

---

*Answers to page 121*

**1** Bury, **2** Alan Curbishley, **3** Roberto Di Matteo, **4** Preston North End, **5** Enzo Bearzot, **6** Blackpool, **7** Bulgarian, **8** Barnsley, **9** Costa Rican, **10** Ray Wilkins, **11** The Shay, **12** Viorel Moldovan, **13** Allan Clarke, **14** Northampton, **15** Sheffield Wednesday.

# • FOOTBALL - QUIZ 3 •

*Answers on page 118*

**1** Which team plays at Feethams?

**2** Who captained West Germany in the 1966 World Cup final?

**3** In which year did Leeds United first win the FA Cup?

**4** In which year did UEFA ban all English club sides from European competitions?

**5** From which club did Dion Dublin join Aston Villa in 1998?

**6** Which team plays its home matches at Vicarage Road?

**7** From which club did Gordon Banks join Stoke City in 1967?

**8** Name the first Peruvian to score in the English Premier League?

**9** What does FIFA stand for?

**10** Where do Barnet play?

**11** In which year was Steve McManaman born?

**12** Which Scottish player missed a penalty against England in the 1996 European Championships?

**13** From which club did Blackburn Rovers sign Kevin Davies?

**14** When was the Football League formed?

**15** From which club did Dwight Yorke join Manchester United in 1988?

---

## *Answers to page 118*

**1** Shrewsbury Town, **2** Bobby Robson, **3** Bayern Munich, **4** Danish, **5** Allan Clarke, **6** Paulo Rossi, **7** Newcastle United, **8** Southampton, **9** Red Star Belgrade, **10** 1863, **11** Ron Greenwood, **12** Eusebio, **13** Barnsley, **14** Bob Wilson, **15** Sheffield United.

# FOOTBALL - QUIZ 4

*Answers on page 119*

**1** Gigg Lane is the home of which club?

**2** Which manager started the 1998-99 season as manager of Charlton Atheltic?

**3** Which Chelsea player scored in the first minute of the 1997 FA Cup final?

**4** Which team plays at Deepdale?

**5** Who managed Italy at the 1982 World Cup?

**6** Which team plays at Bloomfield Road?

**7** What nationality is Hristo Stoichkov?

**8** Which English club is known as the 'Tykes'?

**9** What nationality is Paolo Wanchope?

**10** Which England player was sent off during the 1986 World Cup?

**11** Where do Halifax Town play?

**12** Who scored Romania's first goal in their 2-1 win over England in the 1998 World Cup?

**13** Who scored Leeds United's winning goal in the 1972 FA Cup final?

**14** Which English club is known as the 'Cobblers'?

**15** Which team plays its home matches at Hillsborough?

***A yellow and green flag half the size of a football pitch and signed by supporters wishing their side good luck was received by the Brazilian World Cup side.***

---

*Answers to page119*

**1** 3, **2** Rangers, **3** Sweden, **4** Sunderland, **5** AJAX, **6** Brentford, **7** Mario Kempes, **8** Arsenal, **9** Blackburn Rovers, **10** Wales, **11** Frank Clark, **12** Southampton, **13** Bradford City, **14** 3, **15** West Germany.

# • FOOTBALL - QUIZ 5 •

*Answers on page 124*

1 How many goals did Kevin Keegan score for England?

2 How many senior caps did he win?

3 Which country won the European Championships in 1960?

4 Which Scottish club is known as 'Killie'?

5 What nationality is ex-Everton striker Daniel Amokachi?

6 Who scored the only goal of the 1990 World Cup final?

7 Which team beat Everton 10-4 in the 1958-59 season?

8 In which country was Billy Bremner born?

9 Who scored Northern Ireland's winner v Spain at the 1982 World Cup?

10 Which team plays at the Reebok Stadium?

11 How many goals did Pele score in the final of the 1958 World Cup?

12 Which Englishman refereed the 1974 World Cup final?

13 Which Russian did Euesbio once describe as 'the peerless goalkeeper of the century'?

14 Which team won the first Scottish Cup in 1874?

15 In which year was Stanley Matthews born ?

## *Answers to page 124*

**1** Walter Smith, **2** 1971, **3** Aston Villa, **4** Tottenham Hotspur, **5** Des Walker, **6** Dutch, **7** Wolverhampton Wanderers, **8** Newcastle United, **9** 1991, **10** Spurs and Arsenal, **11** Birmingham, **12** 1964, **13** Newcastle United, **14** Johan Cruyff, **15** Dermot Gallacher.

# • FOOTBALL - QUIZ 6 •

*Answers on page 125*

1. Which nation thrashed El Salvador 10-1 in the 1982 World Cup finals?
2. Elland Road is the home of which club?
3. England met Paraguay in the 2nd round of the 1986 World Cup What was the score?
4. In which year was the FA Charity Shield first played at Wembley?
5. Which Scottish team plays at Tannadice Park?
6. Which club did Kevin Keegan manage before Fulham?
7. Who signed for Newcastle United shortly after appearing in the 1998 World Cup Final?
8. Who won the FA Cup in 1949?
9. In which year did Brian Clough's reign as manager of Nottingham Forest end?
10. Which Spanish club won the 1956 European Cup?
11. Which Scottish club is known as the 'Accies'?
12. Which English team is known as the 'Shakers'?
13. Who succeeded George Graham as manager of Leeds United?
14. Who won the 1962 World Cup?
15. Who was England manager prior to Alf Ramsey?

---

*Answers to page 125*

**1** Bolton, Barnsley and Crystal Palace, **2** None, **3** Morocco, **4** Rangers, **5** Denmark, **6** 7, **7** Bournemouth, **8** Emile Heskey, **9** Manchester City, **10** Sunderland, **11** Trevor Brooking, **12** Nat Lofthouse, **13** Glenn Hoddle, **14** Carlisle United, **15** Wales.

# FOOTBALL - QUIZ 7

*Answers on page 122*

**1** Who began the 1998-99 season as manager of Everton?

**2** In which year was Stan Collymore born?

**3** John Gregory started the 1998-99 season as manager of which club?

**4** Which club won the FA Cup in 1967?

**5** Which Nottingham Forest player scored an own goal in the 1991 FA Cup final?

**6** What nationality is Marc Overmars?

**7** Which team plays its home matches at Molineux?

**8** From which club did Manchester United sign Andy Cole?

**9** In which year did Wembley first stage an FA Cup semi-final?

**10** Name the teams involved?

**11** In which English city is Villa Park?

**12** In which year did Pat Jennings join Tottenham Hotspur?

**13** Which club won the 1955 FA Cup?

**14** Name Holland's captain in the 1974 World Cup final?

**15** Who refereed the 1996 FA Cup final?

***During the England v Romania World Cup match, British telecom said there were 16 million fewer calls than usual. After the match there was a surge of electricity as 450,000 kettles were turned on.***

---

*Answers to page 122*

**1** 20, **2** 63, **3** USSR, **4** Kilmarnock, **5** Nigerian, **6** Andreas Brehme, **7** Tottenham Hotspur, **8** Scotland, **9** Gerry Armstrong, **10** Bolton Wanderers, **11** 2, **12** Jack Taylor, **13** Lev Yashin, **14** Queen's Park, **15** 1915.

# • FOOTBALL - QUIZ 8 •

*Answers on page 123*

**1** Name the three clubs relegated from the English Premier League in 1998?

**2** How many of their five games did England lose in the 1982 World Cup finals?

**3** Which country beat Scotland 3-0 in the 1998 World Cup?

**4** Who won the Scottish Cup in 1978 and 1979?

**5** Which nation won the 1992 European Championships?

**6** How many goals did England score in the 1986 World Cup finals?

**7** Which English team plays at Dean Court?

**8** Which English striker is nicknamed 'Brunoí?

**9** Which club won the League Cup in 1976?

**10** Which club signed Lee Clark from Newcastle United?

**11** Who scored the only goal of the 1980 FA Cup final?

**12** Which player scored in every round of the 1953 FA Cup?

**13** Who succeeded Terry Venables as England manager?

**14** Brunton Park is the home of which English club?

**15** In which country was Neville Southall born?

---

*Answers to page123*

**1** Hungary, **2** Leeds United, **3** England 3, Paraguay 0, **4** 1974, **5** Dundee United, **6** Newcastle United, **7** Stephane Guivarc'h, **8** Wolverhampton Wanderers, **9** 1993, **10** Real Madrid, **11** Hamilton Academicals, **12** Bury, **13** David O'Leary, **14** Brazil, **15** Walter Winterbottom.

# FOOTBALL - QUIZ 9

*Answers on page 128*

**1** Who succeeded Ron Greenwood as England manager?

**2** From which club did Liverpool sign Paul Ince?

**3** Which West German converted a penalty in the 1974 World Cup final?

**4** In which country do Independiente play?

**5** Who was leading goalscorer at the 1986 World Cup?

**6** How many goals did he score?

**7** At which ground do Gillingham play?

**8** From which club did Manchester United sign Roy Keane?

**9** Which country beat England 1-0 at the 1986 World Cup finals?

**10** Which Welsh international joined Juventus for £32 million in 1987?

**11** What nationality is Manchester United defender Jaap Stam?

**12** How many FA Cup finals did Everton reach during the 1980s?

**13** How many did they win?

**14** Who won the European Cup in 1961 and 1962?

**15** Who scored the only goal of the 1968 FA Cup final?

---

## *Answers to page 128*

**1** Brondby, **2** Motherwell, **3** Italy, **4** West Ham United, **5** Poland and Brazil, **6** Holland, **7** Nayim, **8** West Bromich Albion, **9** Bradford City, **10** 1986, **11** West Germany, **12** 1908, **13** Antonio Rattin, **14** Feyenoord, **15** 1962.

# • FOOTBALL - QUIZ 10 •

*Answers on page 129*

**1** Which club plays at Craven Cottage?

**2** Which two nations defeated Scotland in Italia '90?

**3** Which country won the European Championships in 1988?

**4** Which country hosted the 1992 European Championships?

**5** Who succeeded Dave Sexton as mananager of Manchester United?

**6** Who scored the only goal in the 1978 FA Cup final?

**7** In which year did Brian Clough win his first full England cap?

**8** Which English team plays at the Stadium of Light?

**9** Which country won the 1976 European Championships?

**10** Which Italian was voted World Footballer of the Year in 1994?

**11** By what nickname are Crystal Palace known?

**12** Who scored the only goal of the 1995 FA Cup final?

**13** Name the referee involved in the Paolo Di Canio incident at Hillsborough in 1998?

**14** Which African nation beat West Germany 2-1 in the 1982 World Cup finals?

**15** Which team beat Newcastle United 9-1 in 1908?

## *Answers to page 129*

**1** John Robertson, **2** Blackburn Rovers, **3** Newcastle United, **4** 1897, **5** AC Milan, **6** Brazil, **7** Twice, **8** Ipswich Town, **9** Barcelona, **10** Roma, **11** Barcelona, **12** Terry Venables, **13** Sunderland, **14** Grimsby Town, **15** Jaap Stam.

# • FOOTBALL - QUIZ 11 •

*Answers on page 126*

1 From which Danish club did Manchester United sign Peter Schmeichel?

2 Which Scottish team plays at Fir Park?

3 Who won the 1938 World Cup?

4 Which team plays its home matches at Upton Park?

5 Which countries lost in the semi-finals of the 1974 World Cup?

6 Which country lost in successive World Cup finals during the 1970s?

7 Which former Spurs player scored for Real Zaragoza v Arsenal in the 1995 Cup Winners' Cup final?

8 From which club did Manchester United sign Bryan Robson in 1981?

9 Which club plays at the Pulse Stadium?

10 In which year was the first all-Merseyside FA Cup final?

11 Who lost 3-1 in the final of the 1982 World Cup?

12 In which year was the FA Charity Shield introduced?

13 Name the Argentinian captain sent off against England in the 1966 World Cup?

14 Name the first Dutch club to win the European Cup?

15 In which year was Ruud Gullit born?

## *Answers to page 126*

**1** Bobby Robson, **2** Inter Milan, **3** Paul Breitner, **4** Argentina, **5** Gary Lineker, **6** 6, **7** Priestfield, **8** Nottingham Forest, **9** Portugal, **10** Ian Rush, **11** Dutch, **12** 4, **13** 1, **14** Benfica, **15** Jeff Astle.

# • FOOTBALL - QUIZ 12 •

*Answers on page 127*

1 Which Nottingham Forest player scored the only goal of the 1980 European Cup final?

2 Which team plays at Ewood Park?

3 Which team lost 2-0 in the final of the 1998 FA Cup?

4 In which year was Juventus formed?

5 Which Italian club won the European Cup in 1963?

6 In which country do Botafogo play?

7 How many times did Manchester United win the FA Cup during the 1980s?

8 Which English club won the UEFA Cup in 1981?

9 From which club did Ronaldo join Inter Milan?

10 Which Italian team lost to Liverpool in the 1984 European Cup final?

11 From which club did Napoli sign Diego Maradona in 1984?

12 Which manager led Barcelona to the 1986 European Cup final?

13 Which English club signed Ally McCoist for £400,000 in 1981?

14 Which English club is known as the 'Mariners'?

15 Which Dutch defender joined Manchester United for £10 million in 1998?

***England's biggest hiccup of all was the 1950 World Cup defeat by USA at Belo Horizonte in Brazil. Some papers thought 0-1 was a misprint and turned it into a 10-1 slaughter!***

---

*Answers to page 127*

**1** Fulham, **2** Costa Rica and Brazil, **3** Holland, **4** Sweden, **5** Ron Atkinson, **6** Roger Osborne, **7** 1959, **8** Sunderland, **9** Czechoslovakia, **10** Paolo Maldini, **11** The 'Eagles', **12** Paul Rideout, **13** Paul Alcock, **14** Algeria, **15** Sunderland.

# • FOOTBALL - QUIZ 13 •

*Answers on page 132*

1 Who succeeded Bob Paisley as manager of Liverpool?

2 From which club did Manchester United sign Eric Cantona?

3 Who captained Hungary in the 1954 World Cup final?

4 Who scored England's winner against Belgium in the 1990 World Cup?

5 Who scored England's winner against Egypt in the same tournament?

6 Who won the FA Cup in 1992?

7 England did not qualify for the 1978 World Cup finals True or false?

8 Who was England manager from 1946-1963?

9 Which club lost 2-0 in the 1975 FA Cup final?

10 Which club signed Roberto Baggio from Fiorentina in 1990?

11 Which club won the League Cup in four successive seasons during the 1980s?

12 Which player suffered a broken neck in the 1956 FA Cup final?

13 What position was he playing?

14 From which club did Arsenal sign Dennis Bergkamp in 1995?

15 Who kept goal for Spurs in the 1987 FA Cup final?

## *Answers to page 132*

**1** France, **2** Daniel Passarella, **3** Liverpool, **4** Kevin Keegan, **5** Holland, **6** Jairzinho, **7** Romanian, **8** The Valley, **9** Crewe Alexandra, **10** England, **11** Marseille, **12** Ajax, 1971-73, **13** Bobby Kerr, **14** Kevin Keegan and Trevor Brooking, **15** Tottenham Hotspur.

# • FOOTBALL - QUIZ 14 •

*Answers on page 133*

**1** From which club did Dennis Wise join Chelsea?

**2** Which club won the FA Cup in 1973?

**3** Which English team lost in the final of the 1973 Cup Winners' Cup?

**4** Which club won the Scottish Cup in 1991?

**5** Which Newcastle player scored a hat trick against Barcelona in 1997?

**6** In which year was the FA Cup first held?

**7** Which English team plays at the Abbey Stadium?

**8** What was the score in the England v Switzerland match during the 1996 European Championships?

**9** Who was World Footballer of the Year in 1984 and 1985?

**10** Which English team is known as the 'Rams'?

**11** In which year was Glenn Hoddle born?

**12** Who captained the winning side in the 1978 FA Cup final?

**13** Which two nations lost in the semi-finals of the 1970 World Cup?

**14** Which club became the first to win the League and FA Cup double?

**15** From which Italian club did Manchester United sign Denis Law in 1962?

## *Answers to page 133*

**1** FC Bruges, **2** Wembley (FA Cup final, 1991), **3** Ipswich Town, **4** Morton, **5** Brian Kidd, **6** Chelsea, **7** Trevor Cherry, **8** True, **9** Napoli, **10** Hereford United, **11** Steve McManaman, **12** Argentina, **13** Newcastle United, **14** Wembley, **15** West Germany.

# • FOOTBALL - QUIZ 15 •

*Answers on page 130*

1 In which country were the 1984 European Championships staged?

2 Name Argentina's manager at the 1998 World Cup?

3 Who won the FA Cup in 1974?

4 Who was voted European Footballer of the Year in 1978 and 1979?

5 In which country do Feyenoord play?

6 Who scored in all six of Brazil's games at the 1970 World Cup?

7 What nationality is Gheorghe Hagi?

8 Name Charlton Athletic's home ground?

9 Which English club is known as the 'Railwaymen'?

10 Which country hosted Euro '96?

11 Which French club suffered a penalty shoot-out defeat by Red Star Belgrade in the 1991 European Cup final?

12 Which Dutch team won the European Cup in three successive seaons?

13 Name the captain of the winning side in the 1973 FA Cup final?

14 Who scored England's goals in the 2-0 defeat of Italy at Wembley in 1977?

15 Name the first British club to win a European trophy?

## *Answers to page 130*

**1** Joe Fagan, **2** Leeds United, **3** Ferenc Puskas, **4** David Platt, **5** Mark Wright, **6** Liverpool, **7** True, **8** Walter Winterbottom, **9** Fulham, **10** Juventus, **11** Liverpool, **12** Bert Trautmann, **13** Goalkeeper, **14** Inter Milan, **15** Ray Clemence.

# • FOOTBALL - QUIZ 16 •

*Answers on page 131*

**1** Who lost in the final of the 1978 European Cup?

**2** At which ground did Paul Gascoigne play his last game for Spurs?

**3** Name the winners of the 1978 FA Cup?

**4** From which Scottish club did Joe Jordan join Leeds United?

**5** Which Manchester United player celebrated his 19th birthday by scoring in the 1968 European Cup final?

**6** From which club did Blackburn Rovers sign Graeme Le Saux?

**7** Name the England player sent off against Argentina on June 15, 1977?

**8** 'Match of the Day' was originally screened on BBC2 True or false?

**9** Which Italian club side plays at the San Paolo Stadium?

**10** Which non-league team beat Newcastle United in the 1972 FA Cup?

**11** Which Liverpool player scored two goals in the 1995 League Cup final?

**12** Which country won the World Cup in 1986?

**13** From which club did Blackburn Rovers sign winger Keith Gillespie in 1998?

**14** Which stadium hosted the 1978 European Cup final?

**15** Who lost to Czechoslovakia in the final of the 1976 European Championships?

***Preston North End were the first ever team to win the Football League in 1888-89.***

---

*Answers to page 131*

**1** Wimbledon, **2** Sunderland, **3** Leeds United, **4** Motherwell, **5** Faustino Asprilla, **6** 1871, **7** Cambridge United, **8** 1-1, **9** Michel Platini, **10** Derby County, **11** 1957, **12** Mick Mills, **13** West Germany and Uruguay, **14** Preston North End (1889), **15** Torino.

# FOOTBALL - QUIZ 17

*Answers on page 136*

1 Which club did Kenny Dalglish manage before Newcastle United?

2 Who captained Leicester City in the 1969 FA Cup final?

3 What nationality is Eric Cantona?

4 In which year was Neville Southall born - 1958 or 1960?

5 What nationality is goalkeeper Andoni Zubizarreta?

6 Which team plays at Turf Moor?

7 Who won the 1990 European Cup?

8 Where do Derby County play?

9 Which English club is nicknamed the 'Saints'?

10 For which club did Glenn Hoddle make his professional debut?

11 Name the two players to have scored in four World Cups?

12 Which English team plays at Layer Road?

13 In which country do Atletico Madrid play?

14 From which club did Newcastle United sign Warren Barton?

15 Who captained England in the 1966 World Cup final?

## *Answers to page 136*

**1** Bobby Robson, **2** It found the missing World Cup trophy, **3** 1975, **4** Coventry City, **5** Stanley Matthews, **6** Socrates, **7** Uruguay, **8** Terry Venables, **9** Herbert Chapman, **10** Leeds United, **11** Juventus, **12** 44 days, **13** Lazio, **14** Chesterfield, **15** Argentina and Uruguay.

# • FOOTBALL - QUIZ 18 •

*Answers on page 137*

**1** Which team plays at Blundell Park?

**2** Which club won the 1961 Scottish Cup?

**3** Which two Charlton players were sent off for fighting with each other in an FA Cup tie in 1979?

**4** Who coached Juventus to the UEFA Cup in 1990?

**5** Which team plays at Loftus Road?

**6** Who won the first FA Cup of the 1960s?

**7** Name the first English club to win the European Cup?

**8** What nationality is Ally McCoist?

**9** Who scored Argentina's goals in the 2-1 win over England at the 1986 World Cup?

**10** How many times was Scottish international Willie Johnston sent off during his career?

**11** Which stadium hosted the 1998 World Cup final?

**12** Which Liverpool player scored the only goal of the 1978 European Cup final?

**13** Who won the 1970 FA Cup?

**14** From which club did Blackburn Rovers sign Chris Sutton?

**15** What nationality is Paolo Wanchope?

---

## *Answers to page 137*

**1** Spain, **2** St James's Park, **3** 11, **4** Fabien Barthez, **5** Chester, **6** Frankie Bunn, **7** Scarborough, **8** West Bromich Albion, **9** West Ham United, **10** Dutch, **11** Dave Bassett, **12** Arsenal, **13** Geoff Hurst, **14** Sutton United, **15** The 'Magpies'.

# • FOOTBALL - QUIZ 19 •

*Answers on page 134*

1 Name the manager of the winning side in the 1978 FA Cup final?

2 Why did a dog named Pickles hit the headlines in 1966?

3 When did Brian Clough become manager of Nottingham Forest?

4 Which team plays at Highfield Road?

5 Which Englishman was voted European Footballer of the Year in 1956?

6 Who captained Brazil at the 1982 World Cup?

7 Which nation won the 1930 World Cup?

8 Who was England's manager at the 1996 European Championships?

9 Name the manager who led both Huddersfield Town and Arsenal to League Championship titles?

10 At which club did David Batty make his professional debut?

11 Which Italian club won the 1996 European Cup?

12 How long was Brian Clough manager of Leeds United?

13 From which club did Chelsea sign Roberto Di Matteo?

14 Which English team plays at the Recreation Ground?

15 Which nations competed in the first international match between South American countries?

---

## *Answers to page 134*

**1** Blackburn Rovers, **2** David Nish, **3** French, **4** 1958, **5** Spanish, **6** Burnley, **7** AC Milan, **8** Pride Park, **9** Southampton, **10** Spurs, **11** Pele and Uwe Seeler, **12** Colchester , **13** Spain, **14** Wimbledon, **15** Bobby Moore.

# • FOOTBALL - QUIZ 20 •

*Answers on page 135*

1 Which country won the 1964 European Championships?

2 At which ground do Newcastle United play?

3 How many goals did England score in the 1966 World Cup finals - 10, 11 or 12?

4 Who kept goal for France in the 1998 World Cup final?

5 From which club did Liverpool sign Ian Rush in 1980?

6 Which Oldham Athletic player scored six goals in a League Cup tie in 1989?

7 Against which team?

8 Which club is known as the 'Baggies'?

9 Who won the FA Cup in 1975?

10 What is the nationality of Arsenal striker Dennis Bergkamp?

11 Who started the 1998-99 season as manager of Nottingham Forest?

12 Which club won the 1936 FA Cup?

13 Who scored a hat trick in the 1966 World Cup final?

14 Which non-league team knocked Coventry City out of the 1989 FA Cup?

15 What is the nickname of Newcastle United?

***On April 27th, 1974 the Manchester derby between United and City was abandoned due to a pitch invasion. The result 0-1 meant that United went down to Division Two, but only for one season.***

---

*Answers to page 135*

**1** Grimsby Town, **2** Dunfermline Athletic, **3** Mike Flanagan and Derek Hales, **4** Dino Zoff, **5** Queen's Park Rangers, **6** Wolverhampton Wanderers, **7** Manchester United, **8** Scottish, **9** Diego Maradona, **10** 21, **11** Stade de France, **12** Kenny Dalglish, **13** Chelsea, **14** Norwich City, **15** Costa Rican.

# • FOOTBALL - QUIZ 21 •

*Answers on page 140*

1 Which club plays its home matches at Meadow Lane?

2 In which year was Kenny Dalglish born - 1951 or 1952?

3 Which player scored sixty League goals in the 1927-28 season?

4 Which team plays at Maine Road?

5 What nationality is Patrick Vieira?

6 Who was Arsenal's captain in the 1998 FA Cup final?

7 Which country knocked Argentina out of the 1994 World Cup?

8 Who succeeded Bill Shankly as Liverpool manager?

9 Who was Scotland's manager at the 1978 World Cup?

10 How many FA Cup final goals did Ian Rush score during the 1980s?

11 Who captained Aberdeen in the final of the 1983 Cup Winners' Cup?

12 Which Portuguese city is home to Benfica?

13 Against which country was David Beckham sent off during the 1998 World Cup?

14 What nationality is Arsene Wenger?

15 Stanley Rous became President of FIFA in 1962 - in which English county was he born?

---

## *Answers to page 140*

**1** French, **2** Jim Smith, **3** Preston North End, **4** Fabrizio Ravanelli, **5** Stoke City, **6** West Bromich Albion, **7** Leeds United, **8** False. It was 1990, **9** Liverpool, **10** Sunderland, **11** 2, **12** Bobby Charlton, **13** Alf Ramsey and Bobby Robson, **14** Newcastle United, **15** Lothar Matthaus .

# • FOOTBALL - QUIZ 22 •

*Answers on page 141*

1 Which Scottish team plays at Easter Road?
2 In which year was Gary Lineker born?
3 Where do Chester City play?
4 Which country knocked England out of the 1958 World Cup?
5 Which club won their first Scottish Cup in 1947?
6 When did the Football League celebrate its centenary?
7 Which Russian goalkeeper was known as the 'Black Panther'?
8 England did not qualify for the 1994 World Cup finals True or false?
9 From which club did Wimbledon sign John Fashanu?
10 Which English team plays at Millmoor?
11 How many times did Billy Wright captain England -70, 80 or 90?
12 Which country defeated West Germany 8-3 in the 1954 World Cup?
13 Who captained Brazil in the 1970 World Cup final?
14 Which Scottish team plays at Pittodrie?
15 Who scored the winning goal in the 1979 FA Cup final?

*Answers to page 141*

**1** Tottenham Hotspur, **2** Everton, **3** Arsenal, **4** 7, **5** Gary Lineker, **6** Phil and Gary Neville, **7** Leeds United, **8** Huddersfield Town, **9** 5, **10** True, **11** Johnny Haynes , **12** Mozambique, **13** Don Revie, **14** 1978, **15** Spain.

# • FOOTBALL - QUIZ 23 •

*Answers on page 138*

**1** What nationality is Nicolas Anelka?

**2** Which manager is known as the 'Bald Eagle'?

**3** Which team lost 3-2 to West Ham United in the 1964 FA Cup final?

**4** Which Italian striker is nicknamed the 'White Feather'?

**5** Which club won the 1972 League Cup?

**6** From which club did Steve Bull join Wolverhampton Wanderers?

**7** Name the winners of the 1968 Football League Cup?

**8** Gary Lineker first captained England in 1988 True or false?

**9** In which city is Goodison Park?

**10** Which club is known as the 'Rokerites'?

**11** How many World Cup finals did Brazil reach during the 1960s?

**12** Who scored 247 goals in 754 games for Manchester United?

**13** Name the two Ipswich Town managers who went on to manage England?

**14** Which English club won the Fairs Cup in 1969?

**15** Who was World Footballer of the Year in 1990?

***Jimmy Greaves played 57 times for England scoring a massive 44 goals. Some will never forgive his exclusion in the 1966 World Cup.***

## *Answers to page 138*

**1** Notts County, **2** 1951, **3** ,Dixie Dean **4** Manchester City, **5** French, **6** Tony Adams, **7** Romania, **8** Bob Paisley, **9** Ally McLeod, **10** 4, **11** Willie Miller, **12** Lisbon, **13** Argentina, **14** French, **15** Norfolk.

# • FOOTBALL - QUIZ 24 •

*Answers on page 139*

**1** From which club did Manchester United sign Teddy Sheringham?

**2** Which team won the League Championship in the 1986-87 season?

**3** Which team plays at Highbury?

**4** How many matches did England lose under Don Revie - 5, 7 or 9?

**5** Which England player scored four goals at the 1990 World Cup?

**6** Which two brothers played in the 1996 FA Cup final?

**7** Which club did George Graham manage before Spurs?

**8** Which English club plays at the McAlpine Stadium?

**9** How many FA Cup final goals has Ian Rush scored?

**10** Sunderland did not field an international player in the 1973 FA Cup final True or false?

**11** Who, in 1961, became Britain's first £100-a-week footballer?

**12** Where was Eusebio born?

**13** Who resigned as England manager in 1977?

**14** In which year did Gary Lineker turn professional with Leicester City?

**15** In which country do Valencia play?

---

## *Answers to page 139*

**1** Hibernian, **2** 1960, **3** Deva Stadium, **4** Soviet Union, **5** Aberdeen, **6** 1988, **7** Lev Yashin, **8** True, **9** Millwall, **10** Rotherham United, **11** 90, **12** Hungary, **13** Carlos Alberto, **14** Aberdeen, **15** Alan Sunderland.

# • FOOTBALL - QUIZ 25 •

*Answers on page 144*

1 From which club did Middlesbrough sign Paul Gascoigne?

2 Who captained the winning side in the 1967 FA Cup final?

3 Which club won the League Championship in the 1972-73 season?

4 Which player missed a penalty in the 1991 FA Cup final?

5 From which club did Spurs sign Les Ferdinand?

6 How many countries competed for the 1930 World Cup - 11, 12 or 13?

7 Which club sold Ruud Gullit to AC Milan in 1987?

8 Which Italian club lost in the final of the 1967 European Cup?

9 Which Italian club signed Graeme Souness in 1984?

10 Where do Rochdale play?

11 Which Dutch city is home to Feyenoord?

12 In which year did Spurs first win the FA Cup?

13 How many times did Bobby Moore captain England - 85, 90 or 95?

14 In which year was Pele born?

15 Which English club began life as Thames Ironworks?

## *Answers to page 144*

**1** Everton, **2** Soviet Union and Portugal, **3** Arsenal, **4** Alan Smith, **5** Dutch, **6** Italy, **7** Alan Ball, **8** 1989, **9** Joe Mercer, **10** 1994, **11** Kevin Keegan, **12** The 'Hornets', **13** Scottish, **14** Lee Dixon, **15** 1966.

# • FOOTBALL - QUIZ 26 •

*Answers on page 145*

1. Which country lost to Argentina in the semi-finals of the 1986 World Cup?
2. How many goals did Alan Shearer score on his full debut for Southampton?
3. Who knocked Italy out of the 1998 World Cup?
4. From which club did Newcastle United sign Alan Shearer in 1996?
5. Which club won the FA Cup in 1998?
6. In which year was the Scottish Football Association formed?
7. Who won the World Cup in 1958?
8. What nationality is David Ginola?
9. Who managed Arsenal in the 1992-93 season?
10. Which team plays at Filbert Street?
11. Which club won the League Cup in 1975?
12. Who did England beat 5-0 in 1975?
13. Name the 12 founder members of the Football League?
14. Name Liverpool's captain in the 1965 FA Cup final?
15. What nationality is Faustino Asprilla?

---

## *Answers to page 145*

**1** Tottenham Hotspur, **2** Torquay United, **3** Danish, **4** 1963, **5** Joe Royle, **6** Newcastle United, **7** Manchester United, **8** Argentina, **9** Gary Lineker, **10** Eusebio, **11** Heart of Midlothian, **12** Celtic, **13** Leyton Orient, **14** Pele, **15** Norman Whiteside.

# • FOOTBALL - QUIZ 27 •

*Answers on page 142*

1 Who won the FA Cup in 1984?

2 Who were the losing semi-finalists in the 1966 World Cup?

3 Which English club won the Cup Winners' Cup in 1994?

4 Who scored the only goal of the game?

5 What nationality is Pierre van Hooijdonk?

6 Which country won the 1934 World Cup?

7 Who was the second England player to be sent off in an international match?

8 In which year did Nigel Clough win his first England cap?

9 Who was England's caretaker manager in 1974?

10 In which year was Bobby Charlton knighted?

11 Which Liverpool player netted two goals in the 1974 FA Cup final?

12 What is Watford's nickname?

13 What nationality is ex-Manchester United manager Tommy Docherty?

14 Which Arsenal player was sent off in an FA Cup semi-final against Spurs?

15 In which year did Everton beat Sheffield Wednesday 3-2 to win the FA Cup?

---

## *Answers to page 142*

**1** Rangers, **2** Dave Mackay, **3** Liverpool, **4** Gary Lineker, **5** Newcastle United, **6** 13, **7** PSV Eindhoven, **8** Inter Milan, **9** Sampdoria, **10** Spotland, **11** Rotterdam, **12** 1901, **13** 90, **14** 1940, **15** West Ham United.

# • FOOTBALL - QUIZ 28 •

*Answers on page 143*

**1** Which English club won the UEFA Cup in 1984?

**2** Which team plays at Plainmoor?

**3** What nationality is Michael Laudrup?

**4** Which year marked the centenary of the Football Association?

**5** Who was manager of Everton in the 1995 FA Cup final?

**6** From which club did Arsenal sign Malcolm Macdonald?

**7** Old Trafford is the home of which club?

**8** In which country do Estudiantes play?

**9** Which English striker joined Barcelona for £275 million in 1986?

**10** Which Portuguese international was known as the 'European Pele'?

**11** Which Scottish team plays at Tynecastle?

**12** Name the first British club to win the European Cup?

**13** Which English team plays at Brisbane Road?

**14** Which Brazilian scored a hat trick against France in the 1958 World Cup semi-finals?

**15** Who scored the only goal of the 1985 FA Cup final?

***The first Charity Shield was contested in 1906 - the winners that time were Manchester United.***

---

*Answers to page 143*

**1** Belgium, **2** 3, **3** France, **4**Blackburn Rovers , **5** Arsenal, **6** 1873, **7** Brazil, **8** French, **9** George Graham, **10** Leicester City, **11** Aston Villa, **12** Cyprus, **13** Accrington, Aston Villa, Blackburn Rovers, Bolton Wanderers, Burnley, Derby County, Everton, Notts County, Preston North End, Stoke City, West Bromwich Albion and Wolverhampton Wanderers, **14** Ron Yeats, **15** Colombian.

# • FOOTBALL - QUIZ 29 •

*Answers on page 148*

**1** Ivor Allchurch won 68 caps for which country?

**2** How many Scotland caps did Dave Mackay win - 12, 22 or 32?

**3** Which team lost 2-0 in the 1984 FA Cup final?

**4** In which city was Peter Shilton born?

**5** Which team beat Liverpool 2-1 in the 1977 FA Cup final?

**6** How many times did Celtic win the Scottish Cup during the 1980s?

**7** How many goals did Peter Shilton concede in his international career?

**8** Which team plays at Stamford Bridge?

**9** Which club won the first Scottish League Championship?

**10** In which year did West Bromich Albion first lift the FA Cup - 1878, 1888 or 1898?

**11** Name Scotland's manager at the 1982 World Cup?

**12** With which two clubs did Brian Clough spend his playing career?

**13** Tottenham Hotspur won the League Cup in 1972 True or false?

**14** Which English club is known as the 'Pirates'?

**15** Who won the 1990 FA Cup?

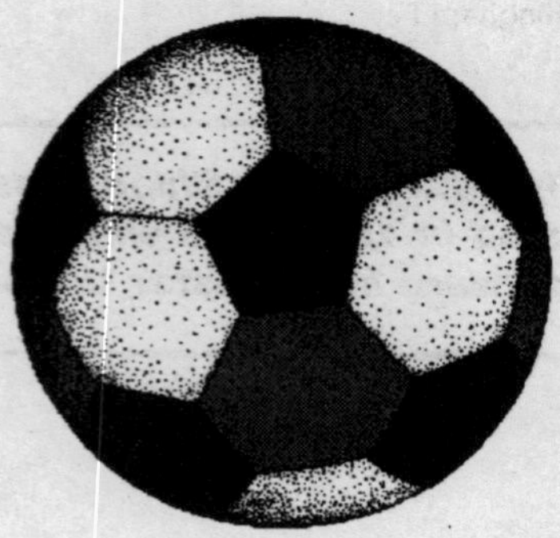

## *Answers to page 148*

**1** Newcastle United, **2** Manchester City, **3** Danny Wilson, **4** John Aldridge, **5** Everton, **6** Gerd Muller, **7** 1937, **8** Watford, **9** Amsterdam, **10** Phil Neal, **11** Lawrie McMenemy, **12** Michel Platini, **13** Ole Gunnar Solskjaer, **14** The 'Clarets', **15** Johan Neeskens (1974).

# • FOOTBALL - QUIZ 30 •

*Answers on page 149*

**1** Who was elected World Footballer of the Year in 1986?

**2** In which year was Peter Schmeichel born?

**3** Who scored a hat trick in the 1953 FA Cup final?

**4** From which club did Liverpool sign Peter Beardsley?

**5** Who did Manchester United beat in the final of the 1991 Cup Winners' Cup?

**6** Who scored both Manchester United goals?

**7** Which Danish player was voted European Footballer of the Year in 1977?

**8** Which club paid £85 million for Stan Collymore in June 1995?

**9** From which club did they buy him?

**10** Who won the FA Cup in 1961?

**11** Which player retired in 1961 after scoring 229 goals in 537 games for Liverpool?

**12** Who managed Holland at the 1974 World Cup?

**13** In which year did Sir Stanley Rous become FIFA President?

**14** Who was Southampton's manager at the start of the 1998-99 season?

**15** Where do Nottingham Forest play?

---

## *Answers to page 149*

**1** Nolberto Solano, **2** Sheffield United, **3** Australian, **4** Viv Anderson, **5** Italy, **6** Karl-Heinz Rummenigge, **7** 3, **8** Leicester City, **9** Argentina, **10** Ronaldo, **11** Peter Rodrigues, **12** France, **13** Liverpool, **14** Lev Yashin, **15** Kenny Dalglish.

# • FOOTBALL - QUIZ 31 •

*Answers on page 146*

1 From which club did Blackburn Rovers sign Darren Peacock?

2 Which club lifted the League Cup in 1970?

3 Who started the 1998-99 season as manager of Sheffield Wednesday?

4 Who was the first player to miss a penalty in an FA Cup final at Wembley?

5 For which club did Dixie Dean score sixty goals in the 1927-8 season?

6 Which West German striker was known as 'Der Bomber'?

7 In which year was Bobby Charlton born?

8 At which club did John Barnes turn professional?

9 In which Dutch city was Ruud Gullit born?

10 Which Liverpool player made 366 consecutive league appearances between 1974-1983?

11 Who was Southampton's manager at the 1976 FA Cup final?

12 Who captained France in the final of the 1984 European Championships?

13 Which Manchester United substitute scored 4 goals against Nottingham Forest in February 1999?

14 What is Burnley's nickname?

15 Who scored the first-ever World Cup final penalty?

***Dan Petrescu, Romanian and Chelsea footballer, loves life at Stamford Bridge so much he has named his baby daughter Chelsea.***

## *Answers to page 146*

**1** Wales, **2** 22, **3** Watford, **4** Leicester, **5** Manchester United, **6** Four, **7** 80, **8** Chelsea, **9** Dumbarton (1890-91), **10** 1888, **11** Jock Stein, **12** Middlesbrough and Sunderland, **13** False, **14** Bristol Rovers, **15** Manchester United.

# • FOOTBALL - QUIZ 32 •

*Answers on page 147*

1 Name the first Peruvian to score in the English Premier League?

2 Which English club plays at Bramall Lane?

3 What nationality is goalkeeper Mark Schwarzer?

4 Name the first black player to win a full England cap?

5 Who knocked Brazil out of the 1982 World Cup?

6 Which West German striker scored three goals against Mexico at the 1978 World Cup?

7 How many FA Cups did Spurs win during the 1960s?

8 Which club won the 1997 League Cup?

9 Which country knocked Brazil out of the 1990 World Cup?

10 Who was World Footballer of the Year in 1997?

11 Who skippered Southampton in the 1976 FA Cup final?

12 Which nation knocked Brazil out of the 1986 World Cup?

13 Which English club won the UEFA Cup in 1976?

14 Which Russian was voted European Footballer of the Year in 1963?

15 Who was the first Scotland player to win 100 caps?

---

## *Answers to page 147*

**1** Diego Maradona, **2** 1963, **3** Stan Mortensen, **4** Newcastle United, **5** Barcelona, **6** Mark Hughes, **7** Allan Simonsen, **8** Liverpool, **9** Nottingham Forest, **10** Tottenham Hotspur, **11** Billy Liddell, **12** Rinus Michels, **13** 1962, **14** Dave Jones, **15** City Ground.

# • FOOTBALL - QUIZ 33 •

*Answers on page 152*

1 In which stadium was the 1986 World Cup final held?

2 Name the losing semi-finalists of the 1994 World Cup?

3 Which club won the 1953 FA Cup?

4 Who scored the only goal of the 1996 FA Cup final?

5 Who was West Germany's manager at the 1982 World Cup?

6 From which club did Aston Villa sign Paul Merson?

7 Which team beat Liverpool 2-1 to win the 1987 League Cup final?

8 Newcastle United beat Newport County 13-0 in a Division 2 match in 1946 True or false?

9 Who was European Footballer of the Year in 1988 and 1989?

10 Who did England thrash 9-3 at Wembley in 1961?

11 Who skippered West Germany in the 1974 World Cup final?

12 What is Fulham's nickname?

13 Who was manager of West Germany from 1963-78?

14 In which country do Anderlecht play?

15 What nationality is manager George Graham?

---

## *Answers to page 152*

**1** Dutch, **2** England 3, Poland 0, **3** Sweden, **4** Bescot Stadium, **5** Chesterfield, **6** Roker Park, **7** Greece, **8** Pat Rice, **9** Toulouse, **10** Stockport County, **11** 1961, **12** Howard Wilkinson, **13** True, **14** Billy McNeill, **15** 29.

# • FOOTBALL - QUIZ 34 •

*Answers on page 153*

1 Who won the 1954 World Cup?

2 What was the score when England played West Germany in the 1982 World Cup?

3 Which English team plays its home matches at Moss Rose?

4 In which year was Tommy Lawton born - 1919 or 1929?

5 Which Dutch player was World Footballer of the Year in 1987 and 1989?

6 Which country beat England 4-1 in 1980?

7 Which English club plays at the New Den?

8 Who scored Chelsea's winner in the 1970 FA Cup final replay?

9 Where was the replay held?

10 Which Liverpool and England international was known as 'Crazy Horse'?

11 Who did England beat 6-0 at Wembley in 1993?

12 Who won the FA Cup in 1963?

13 Which England internationals had a chart hit with 'Diamond Lights'?

14 Fratton Park is the home of which club?

15 Which Dutch player scored against England in the 1996 European Championships?

---

## *Answers to page 153*

**1** Marseille, **2** Mart Poom, **3** Italian, **4** Bristol City, **5** 1974, **6** Everton, **7** Arsenal, **8** Two, **9** Bob Stoke, **10** Everton, **11** Johan Cruyff, **12** 824, **13** Boundary Park, **14** Peru, **15** Brazil.

# • FOOTBALL - QUIZ 35 •

*Answers on page 150*

**1** What nationality is Ronald Koeman?

**2** What was the score when England played Poland in the 1986 World Cup?

**3** With whom did England draw 3-3 in an international match at Elland Road in 1995?

**4** At which ground do Walsall play?

**5** Which English club is known as the 'Spireites'?

**6** Name Sunderland's former stadium?

**7** Who did England beat 5-0 at Wembley in 1994?

**8** Who captained Arsenal in the 1979 FA Cup final?

**9** Which city hosted England's 1998 World Cup match with Romania?

**10** Which club's ground is called Edgeley Park?

**11** In which year was Ian Rush born?

**12** Who acted as manager of England for one match in February 1999?

**13** Brian Clough became manager of Hartlepool United in 1965 True or false?

**14** Who captained Celtic in the 1967 European Cup final?

**15** How many Scottish caps did he win?

---

## *Answers to page 150*

**1** Azteca, **2** Sweden and Bulgaria, **3** Blackpool, **4** Eric Cantona, **5** Jupp Derwall, **6** Middlesbrough, **7** Arsenal, **8** True, **9** Marco van Basten, **10** Scotland, **11** Franz Beckenbauer, **12** The 'Cottagers', **13** Helmut Schoen, **14** Belgium, **15** Scottish.

# • FOOTBALL - QUIZ 36 •

*Answers on page 151*

1 Which city hosted England's opening match of France '98?

2 Name the Estonian goalkeeper signed by Derby County in 1997?

3 Which national side is known as the 'Azurri'?

4 From which club did Newcastle United sign Andy Cole?

5 In which year did Bobby Moore join Fulham - 1974 or 1975?

6 Who won the League Championship in the 1984-85 season?

7 Who won the English Premier League in the 1997-98 season?

8 How many FA Cup finals did Bolton Wanderers reach during the 1950s?

9 Who was Sunderland's manager at the 1973 FA Cup final?

10 Which English club won the Cup Winners' Cup in 1985?

11 Who was European Footballer of the Year in 1973 and 1974?

12 How many League appearances did Terry Paine make - 724, 824 or 924?

13 Name Oldham Athletic's home ground?

14 Who beat Scotland 3-1 in the 1978 World Cup finals?

15 Which country knocked Chile out of the 1998 World Cup?

***Mexican striker Cuauhtemoc Blanco introduced a new move to football during the 1998 World Cup. The Blanco Bounce involves trapping the ball between his ankles and bouncing past defenders.***

---

*Answers to page 151*

**1** West Germany, **2** 0-0, **3** Macclesfield, **4** 1919, **5** Ruud Gullit, **6** Wales, **7** Millwall, **8** David Webb, **9** Old Trafford, **10** Emlyn Hughes, **11** San Marino, **12** Manchester United, **13** Chris Waddle and Glenn Hoddle, **14** Portsmouth, **15** Patrick Kluivert.

# • FOOTBALL - QUIZ 37 •

*Answers on page 156*

**1** From which club did Nottingham Forest sign Pierre Van Hooijdonk in 1997?

**2** In which year did Ruud Gullit sign for Chelsea?

**3** Which country beat Belgium 2-1 in the final of the 1980 European Championships?

**4** Which Manchester United player scored two penalties in the 1994 FA Cup final?

**5** Against which club?

**6** Which city is home to both Celtic and Rangers?

**7** Juventus is Italy's oldest club True or false?

**8** What is Wimbledon's nickname?

**9** Who played in goal for Sunderland in the 1973 FA Cup final?

**10** Pontus Kaamark won a League Cup medal with Leicester City in 1997 What is his nationality?

**11** Which team plays at Gresty Road?

**12** Which England international left French team Marseille to join Scottish club Rangers in 1991?

**13** Which club is known as the 'Cherries'?

**14** Which club sold David Batty to Leeds United during the 1998-99 season?

**15** How many caps did George Best win for Northern Ireland - 37, 47 or 57?

---

## *Answers to page 156*

**1** 3-2, **2** Villa Park, **3** Ricardo (Ricky) Villa, **4** False (Cardiff City, 1927), **5** Kenny Dalglish, **6** Turin, **7** Newcastle United, **8** Willie Ormond, **9** Hungary, **10** Blackburn Rovers, **11** Holland, **12** Alan Shearer and Paul Gascoigne, **13** Mark Stein, **14** 1960, **15** Luxembourg.

# • FOOTBALL - QUIZ 38 •

*Answers on page 157*

**1** In which year was Dennis Bergkamp born?

**2** Who captained Manchester United in the 1991 Cup Winners' Cup final?

**3** Which city hosted the final?

**4** Which player scored most goals at the 1982 World Cup?

**5** Who lost 5-1 to England at Wembley in 1975?

**6** Who lost to West Germany in the semi-finals of the 1986 World Cup?

**7** How many England caps did Glenn Hoddle win?

**8** Which team plays at St Andrews?

**9** From which club did Norman Whiteside join Everton?

**10** Which country knocked England out of the 1962 World Cup?

**11** How many matches were played in the 1994 World Cup finals?

**12** From which English club did Rangers sign Ally McCoist?

**13** Who captained West Bromwich Albion in the 1968 FA Cup final?

**14** Which country did Zico play for?

**15** How many of England's matches in the 1990 World Cup went to extra time?

## *Answers to page 157*

**1** 14, **2** 112, **3** 1953, **4** France (1992), **5** Jock Stein, **6** 1955, **7** Bristol Rovers, **8** Alan Ball, **9** 1970, **10** Denmark, **11** Northumberland , **12** Kenny Dalglish, **13** 1949, **14** Manchester City, **15** Everton.

# • FOOTBALL - QUIZ 39 •

*Answers on page 154*

1 By what score did Scotland beat Holland in the 1978 World Cup?

2 Which ground hosted the Scotland v Holland match in the 1996 European Championships?

3 Which Argentinian scored two goals in the 1981 FA Cup final replay?

4 No Welsh club has ever won the FA Cup True or false?

5 Who succeeded Kevin Keegan as Newcastle United manager?

6 In which Italian city are Juventus based?

7 Who lost in the final of the 1976 League Cup?

8 Who managed Scotland at the 1974 World Cup?

9 Which country trounced England 6-3 at Wembley in 1953?

10 Which club bought Jason McAteer for £4 million in 1999?

11 Which country lost to Brazil in the semi-finals of France '98?

12 Who scored England's goals in the 2-0 win over Scotland during Euro 96?

13 Which Chelsea player scored in seven consecutive League matches in the 1993-94 season?

14 When was the Football League Cup introduced?

15 Who lost 9-0 to England at Wembley in 1982?

***Luca Vialli's first match as Chelsea player-manager started with a glass of champagne in the dressing room. "I wanted to have a toast to wish good luck to the players," he said.***

## *Answers to page 154*

**1** Celtic, **2** 1995, **3** West Germany, **4** Eric Cantona, **5** Chelsea, **6** Glasgow, **7** False - Genoa is, **8** The 'Dons', **9** Jim Montgomery, **10** Swedish, **11** Crewe Alexandra, **12** Trevor Steven, **13** Bournemouth, **14** Newcastle United, **15** 37.

# FOOTBALL - QUIZ 40

*Answers on page 155*

**1** How many goals did Gianni Rivera score in 60 games for Italy - 4, 14, or 24?

**2** How many Italian caps did Dino Zoff win?

**3** In which year was Graeme Souness born?

**4** Against which country did Alan Shearer score on his senior England debut?

**5** Who managed Celtic in the 1967 European Cup final?

**6** In which year was Michel Platini born?

**7** Which English team plays at the Memorial Ground?

**8** Who was the second England player to be sent off in an international match?

**9** In which World Cup were substitutes first allowed?

**10** Which country did ex-Manchester United player Jesper Olsen play for?

**11** In which English county were Jack and Bobby Charlton born?

**12** Who was the only player to have scored 100 goals in English football and 100 goals in Scottish football?

**13** In which year was Peter Shilton born?

**14** Which English club began life as West Gorton?

**15** From which club did Newcastle United sign Gary Speed?

---

*Answers to page 155*

**1** 1969, **2** Bryan Robson, **3** Rotterdam, **4** Paolo Rossi, **5** Scotland, **6** France, **7** 53, **8** Birmingham City, **9** Manchester United, **10** Brazil, **11** 52, **12** Sunderland, **13** Graham Williams, **14** Brazil, **15** 3.

# • FOOTBALL - QUIZ 41 •

*Answers on page 160*

1 Which Brazillian was World Footballer of the Year in 1983?

2 Which Chelsea player scored in every round of the 1970 FA Cup?

3 Which Italian club won the European Cup in 1964 and 1965?

4 Which club won the 1987 FA Cup?

5 Against which country did Bryan Robson score after 27 seconds in the 1982 World Cup?

6 Which manager led Newcastle United to the 1998 FA Cup final?

7 Name the five clubs managed by Brian Clough?

8 Which German club signed Tony Woodcock in 1986?

9 In which year was the Croatian Football Federation formed?

10 Which country lost in the final of the 1984 European Championships?

11 Which club is known as the' Silkmen'?

12 Steve Bull won his first England cap while a Second Division player True or false?

13 Which club won the League Cup in 1989 and 1990?

14 Which country hosted the 1958 World Cup?

15 In which year did Jack Charlton become Middlesbrough manager?

---

## *Answers to page 160*

**1** England, **2** 1910, **3** Brazil and Scotland, **4** Manchester United, **5** Manchester United, **6** 10, **7** Ron Saunders, **8** 1986, **9** Bill Shankly, **10** True, **11** 1968, **12** Manchester City, **13** The 'Robins', **14** Australian, **15** Karl-Heinz Rummenigge.

# • FOOTBALL - QUIZ 42 •

*Answers on page 161*

1 In which year was Billy Bremner appointed Leeds manager?

2 In which year was Alf Ramsey born - 1920 or 1925?

3 In which decade were Jack and Bobby Charlton born?

4 Which country knocked Romania out of the 1990 World Cup?

5 In which decade did referees first use whistles?

6 When was Kevin Keegan born?

7 In which year did Bobby Charlton play his last England international?

8 How long was Brian Clough manager of Leeds United?

9 Which team beat Newcastle United 8-1 in a First Division match in the 1985-86 season?

10 In which German city was Franz Beckenbauer born?

11 In which year was FIFA formed?

12 Who scored England's 80th minute equaliser against West Germany in the 1990 World Cup semi-finals?

13 How many caps did Bobby Charlton win for England?

14 In which year was the Football Association formed?

15 Which Juventus player scored the winning goal in the 1996 World Club Championship?

## *Answers to page 161*

**1** 1975, **2** Kenny Dalglish, **3** Lazio, **4** Burnley, **5** A plastic pitch, **6** Four, **7** Arsenal, **8** Borussia Moenchengladbach, **9** Brazil 0, England 2, **10** Ferenc Puskas, **11** Alan Mullery , **12** 1983, **13** Penarol, **14** Uruguay, **15** Nottingham Forest.

# • FOOTBALL - QUIZ 43 •

*Answers on page 158*

**1** Which country won the World Cup in 1966?

**2** In which year did Newcastle United first win the FA Cup?

**3** Which countries played in the opening match of France '98?

**4** Which club won the FA Cup in 1983?

**5** Which club sold Paul Ince to Inter Milan in June 1995?

**6** How many games did England lose under Ron Greenwood?

**7** Who was Aston Villa's manager prior to Tony Barton?

**8** When did Sir Stanley Rous die?

**9** Who was manager of Liverpool from 1959-74?

**10** England played all six of their 1966 World Cup games at Wembley True or false?

**11** When was George Best voted European Footballer of the Year?

**12** Who won the 1969 FA Cup?

**13** By what nickname is Swindon Town known?

**14** What nationality is ex-Liverpool star Craig Johnston?

**15** Who was European Footballer of the Year in 1980 and 1981?

***The most widely quoted cup score is 36-0, in September 1885 when Arbroath beat Bon Accord. Jon Petrie put 13 into the Bon Accord net.***

## *Answers to page 158*

**1** Zico, **2** Peter Osgood, **3** Inter Milan, **4** Coventry City, **5** France, **6** Kenny Dalglish, **7** Hartlepool United, Derby County, Brighton, Leeds United and Nottingham Forest, **8** Cologne, **9** 1991, **10** Spain, **11** Macclesfield, **12** False - he was a Third Division player, **13** Nottingham Forest, **14** Sweden, **15** 1973.

# • FOOTBALL - QUIZ 44 •

*Answers on page 159*

**1** In which year did Charlie George join Derby County?

**2** Name the first Scottish player to win 100 caps?

**3** With which Italian club did Paul Gascoigne play?

**4** Which Lancashire club won the League Championship in the 1959-60 season?

**5** What was installed at Loftus Road in 1981?

**6** In how many World Cups did Diego Maradona play?

**7** From which club did Nottingham Forest sign Kevin Campbell?

**8** Which club lost in the final of the 1977 European Cup?

**9** What was the score in England's match against Brazil in 1984?

**10** Who captained Hungary in the 1954 World Cup final?

**11** Who was the first England player sent off in an international?

**12** In which year did Dario Gradi become boss of Crewe Alexandra?

**13** To whom did Aston Villa lose the 1982 World Club Championship?

**14** In which country do Penarol play?

**15** Which club appointed Ron Atkinson as boss during the 1998-99 season?

---

### *Answers to page 159*

**1** 1985, **2** 1920, **3** 1930's, **4** Republic of Ireland, **5** 1870's, **6** 1951, **7** 1970, **8** 44 days, **9** West Ham United, **10** Munich, **11** 1904, **12** Gary Lineker, **13** 106, **14** 1863, **15** Alessandro Del Piero.

# • FOOTBALL - QUIZ 45 •

*Answers on page 164*

**1** Which club plays at Carrow Road?

**2** Which FIFA President gave his name to the original World Cup trophy?

**3** What was his nationality?

**4** In which year did Kevin Keegan make his England debut?

**5** Who scored a late goal at Anfield in 1989 to secure the League Championship for Arsenal?

**6** Which club is known as the 'Minstermen'?

**7** Which nation lost in the final of the 1988 European Championships?

**8** Who captained Manchester United in the 1977 FA Cup final?

**9** Which stadium hosted the 1994 World Cup final?

**10** Which club won the Football League Cup in 1961?

**11** Who scored two of Nottingham Forest's three goals in the 1979 League Cup final?

**12** Which team formerly played at Ayresome Park?

**13** Which was Pele's first World Cup?

**14** Which club won the 1924 FA Cup?

**15** Which Scandinavian nation lost 4-0 at Wembley in 1980?

---

## *Answers to page 164*

**1** France, **2** Alessandro Altobelli, **3** Tranmere Rovers, **4** True (Gianpiero Combi in 1938 and Dino Zoff in 1982), **5** Tom Finney, **6** Wycombe, **7** Manchester United, **8** Bodo Illgner, **9** Benfica, **10** True, **11** Argentina v. Cameroon, **12** 95, **13** Real Madrid, **14** Southend United, **15** 1985.

# • FOOTBALL - QUIZ 46 •

*Answers on page 165*

1 Which club is known as the 'Saddlers'?

2 From which club did Manchester United sign Roy Keane?

3 Who lost 3-2 to Luton Town in the 1988 League Cup final?

4 Who knocked Germany out of the 1994 World Cup?

5 Which Spanish club won their sixth European Cup in 1966?

6 For which country did Lou Macari play?

7 How many goals did Gary Lineker score for England?

8 From which club did Manchester United sign Steve Bruce?

9 Which country won the 1996 European Championships?

10 Which city is home to both Hibs and Hearts?

11 Who played for Ipswich Town and Arsenal in consecutive FA Cup finals in the 1970s?

12 Who scored England's first goal against Argentina in the 1998 World Cup?

13 In which year did Kenny Dalglish join Liverpool from Celtic?

14 Which Brazilian joined Newcastle United in 1987?

15 Name Scotland's manager at the 1978 World Cup?

## *Answers to page 165*

**1** Gillingham, **2** 1926, **3** Panathanaikos, **4** Chelsea, **5** Three, **6** Newcastle United, **7** Uruguay, **8** Argentina, **9** Birmingham City, **10** Just Fontaine (France), **11** Leicester City, **12** Scunthorpe, Liverpool, Hamburg, Southampton and Newcastle United, **13** Leeds United, **14** 1967, **15** Andy Roxburgh.

# • FOOTBALL - QUIZ 47 •

*Answers on page 162*

**1** Which country won the 1984 European Championships?

**2** Who scored Italy's third goal in the 1982 World Cup final?

**3** Which English team plays at Prenton Park?

**4** Two of Italy's World Cup winning teams were captained by Juventus goalkeepers True or false?

**5** Who was nicknamed the 'Preston Plumber'?

**6** Which English club is known as the 'Chairboys'?

**7** Which club lost successive FA Cup finals during the 1950s?

**8** Who kept goal for West Germany in the 1990 World Cup final?

**9** Which team lost in the final of the 1968 European Cup?

**10** Tommy Docherty managed Scotland True or false?

**11** What was the opening match of Italia '90?

**12** For how many games was Bobby Robson manager of England?

**13** Which club lost 2-1 to Aberdeen in the 1983 Cup Winners' Cup final?

**14** From which club did Nottingham Forest buy Stan Collymore in 1993?

**15** When did the Bradford City fire disaster happen?

---

## *Answers to page 162*

**1** Norwich City, **2** Jules Rimet, **3** French, **4** 1972, **5** Michael Thomas, **6** York City, **7** USSR, **8** Martin Buchan, **9** Rose Bowl, Pasadena, **10** Aston Villa, **11** Gary Birtles, **12** Middlesbrough, **13** 1958, **14** Newcastle United, **15** Norway.

# • FOOTBALL - QUIZ 48 •

*Answers on page 163*

**1** Which Division Three club beat Chesterfield 10-0 on 5 September 1987?

**2** In which year was Ferenc Puskas born - 1926 or 1936?

**3** Which team did he coach to the 1971 European Cup Final?

**4** Which club signed Tony Hateley for £100,000 in 1966?

**5** How many times was Johan Cruyff voted European Footballer of the Year?

**6** From which club did Alan Kennedy join Liverpool?

**7** For which country did Enzo Francescoli play at the 1986 World Cup?

**8** In which country do Boca Juniors play?

**9** From which club did Trevor Francis join Nottingham Forest in 1979?

**10** Who scored 13 goals in the 1958 World Cup finals?

**11** With which club did Gary Lineker make his profesional debut?

**12** Name the five clubs Kevin Keegan played for during his career?

**13** Which club won the League Championship in the 1973-74 season?

**14** In which year was Paul Gascoigne born?

**15** Who managed Scotland at the 1990 World Cup?

***The first FA Cup Final was played at the Kennington Oval on a pitch without a centre circle or penalty area, and the crossbar was a tape stretched across the two posts.***

---

## *Answers to page 163*

**1** Walsall, **2** Nottingham Forest, **3** Arsenal, **4** Bulgaria, **5** Real Madrid, **6** Scotland, **7** 48, **8** Norwich City, **9** Germany, **10** Edinburgh, **11** Brian Talbot, **12** Alan Shearer, **13** 1977, **14** Mirandinha, **15** Ally Macleod.

# FOOTBALL - QUIZ 49

*Answers on page 168*

**1** Which team plays at the Vetch Field?

**2** In which year was the English Premier League created?

**3** How many England caps did Bobby Robson win as a player?

**4** Who was Brazil's coach at the 1994 World Cup?

**5** In which year was the Munich air disaster?

**6** Name the Dutch goalkeeper who saved a penalty in the final of the 1988 European Championships?

**7** Name England's most capped player?

**8** What is Barnet's nickname?

**9** Which two countries beat Brazil in the 1998 World Cup finals?

**10** Who was Tottenham's captain in the 1961 and 1962 FA Cup finals?

**11** Which country did he captain at the 1958 World Cup?

**12** Who managed West Germany at the 1974 World Cup?

**13** Who won the League Championship in 1980-81?

**14** How many Argentinian players were sent off in the final of the 1990 World Cup?

**15** Denis Law missed the 1968 European Cup final because of injury True or false?

---

## *Answers to page 168*

**1** Nagoya Grampus Eight, **2** 1986, **3** Eusebio, **4** Parma, **5** 80, **6** Josef 'Sepp' Maier, **7** Olympic Stadium, Munich, **8** Inter Milan, **9** Terry McDermot, **10** True, **11** Lothar Matthaus, **12** Chilean, **13** Czechoslovakia, **14** Switzerland, **15** Mexico.

# • FOOTBALL - QUIZ 50 •

*Answers on page 169*

**1** Which Manchester City player scored an own goal in the 1981 FA Cup final?

**2** Name Manchester United's goalkeeper in the 1968 European Cup final?

**3** Who won the 1967 European Cup?

**4** Which club won the League Championship in the 1967-68 season?

**5** Who was Brazil's captain in the 1994 World Cup final?

**6** Name the losing semi-finalists of the 1990 World Cup?

**7** Which Second Division side won the FA Cup in 1980?

**8** Who captained Napoli to their first-ever Italian League title?

**9** Which Spurs player scored 27 League goals during the 1968-69 season?

**10** In which year was Jack Charlton appointed Republic of Ireland boss?

**11** Jimmy Greaves scored 44 goals in 57 games for England True or false?

**12** Which club won three successive League Championships during the 1980's?

**13** From which Italian club did Newcastle United sign Faustino Asprilla?

**14** Who played in goal for Leicester City in the 1969 FA Cup final?

**15** In which year was Stanley Matthews knighted?

---

## *Answers to page 169*

**1** Five, **2** 55, **3** Belgium, **4** Everton, **5** Alan Mullery, **6** Tommy Docherty, **7** 119, **8** Four, **9** Kilmarnock, **10** 1992, **11** Zinedine Zidane, **12** 1989, **13** 26, **14** 1983-84, **15** Liverpool and Arsenal.

# • FOOTBALL - QUIZ 51 •

*Answers on page 166*

**1** Which Japanese club did Gary Lineker play for?

**2** In which year did Luton Town ban visiting supporters from Kenilworth Road?

**3** Who was voted European Footballer of the Year in 1965?

**4** Which Italian club won the Cup Winners' Cup in 1993?

**5** How many England caps did Gary Lineker win - 70, 80 or 90?

**6** Who kept goal for West Germany in the 1974 World Cup final?

**7** Which stadium hosted the final?

**8** Which Italian club won the 1994 UEFA Cup?

**9** Who scored Liverpool's opening goal in the 1977 European Cup final?

**10** Gianfranco Zola was born in Sicily True or false?

**11** Who captained West Germany in the 1990 World Cup final?

**12** George Robledo scored Newcastle United's winning goal in the 1952 FA Cup final. What was his nationality?

**13** For which country did Tomas Skuhravy play at the 1990 World Cup?

**14** In which country do Grasshoppers play?

**15** Which country hosted the 1970 World Cup finals?

---

## *Answers to page 166*

**1** Swansea City, **2** 1992, **3** 20, **4** Carlos Alberto Parreira, **5** 1958, **6** Hans van Breukelen, **7** Peter Shilton, **8** The 'Bees', **9** Norway and France, **10** Danny Blanchflower, **11** Northern Ireland, **12** Helmut Schoen, **13** Aston Villa, **14** Two, **15** True.

# • FOOTBALL - QUIZ 52 •

*Answers on page 167*

1 How many League Championships did Arsenal win during the 1930s?

2 For how many games did Ron Greenwood manage England?

3 Against which country did David Platt score his first England goal?

4 From which club did Newcastle United sign Duncan Ferguson in 1998?

5 Who skippered Fulham in the 1975 FA Cup final?

6 Which Manchester United manager was sacked in 1977?

7 How many international appearances did Pat Jennings make for Northern Ireland - 99, 109 or 119?

8 For how many matches was Kevin Keegan contracted to manage England for in February 1999?

9 Which Scottish team plays at Rugby Park?

10 In which year did Kevin Keegan become manager of Newcastle United?

11 Which player was voted World Footballer of the Year in 1998?

12 In which year did Gary Lineker sign for Spurs?

13 How many Scottish caps did Alan Hansen win - 26, 46 or 66?

14 In which season were the British Home Internationals last played?

15 Name the two teams who scored three goals in FA Cup finals during the 1970s?

***It was the most discussed goal in World Cup history. Diego Maradona called it the 'Hand of God' as he flipped the ball past Peter Shilton to score for Argentina in the 1986 quarter-finals.***

---

*Answers to page 167*

**1** Tommy Hutchison, **2** Alex Stepney, **3** Celtic, **4** Manchester City, **5** Dunga, **6** England and Italy, **7** West Ham United, **8** Diego Maradona, **9** Jimmy Greaves, **10** 1986, **11** True, **12** Liverpool, **13** Parma, **14** Peter Shilton, **15** 1965.

# • FOOTBALL - QUIZ 53 •

*Answers on page 172*

**1** Which Spanish club lost to Aberdeen in the final of the 1983 Cup Winners' Cup?

**2** Who won the European Cup in 1969?

**3** What is Brentford's nickname?

**4** Which country hosted the 1978 World Cup finals?

**5** From which club did Spurs sign Paul Gascoigne?

**6** Who scored Arsenal's winning goal in the 1971 FA Cup final?

**7** Who was England's manager at the 1982 World Cup?

**8** Who scored England's goals in the 2-0 win over Tunisia at the 1998 World Cup?

**9** Who was the first player to be sent off in an FA Cup final at Wembley?

**10** In which year did Italy win their third World Cup?

**11** Which countries lost in the semi-finals of the 1978 World Cup?

**12** Which country knocked Jack Charlton's Republic of Ireland out of the 1990 World Cup?

**13** Which club is nicknamed the 'Gunners'?

**14** Who won the League Cup in 1977?

**15** In which year did Pat Jennings join Arseanl?

---

## *Answers to page 172*

**1** Manchester United, **2** Alex Ferguson, **3** 5, **4** Sammy McIlroy, **5** Northern Ireland, **6** Benfica, **7** Dino Zoff, **8** Southampton, **9** 113, **10** Queen's Park, **11** Igor Belanov, **12** Spain, **13** Rangers, **14** Bolton Wanderers, **15** West Ham United.

# • FOOTBALL - QUIZ 54 •

*Answers on page 173*

1 In which country do River Plate play?

2 Who scored the only goal of the 1978 European Cup final?

3 Who managed Scotland at the 1998 World Cup?

4 How many goals did Hristo Stoichkov score at the 1994 World Cup?

5 Wales have not qualified for the World Cup finals since 1958 True or false?

6 How many League Championships did Everton win during the 1980s?

7 Graeme Souness won 94 Scottish caps True or false?

8 How many games did England lose under manager Bobby Robson -9, 19 or 29?

9 How many FA Cup finals did Arsenal reach during the 1930s?

10 How many England caps did Bryan Robson win -70, 80 or 90?

11 Name Argentina's coach at the 1998 World Cup?

12 Who scored Brazil's goal v England in the 1970 World Cup?

13 Which Welsh club is known as the 'Bluebirds'?

14 Which club won the 1968 FA Cup?

15 Jack Charlton was player/manager of Preston North End during the 1970s True or false?

## *Answers to page 173*

**1** David Beckham and Darren Anderton, **2** The 'Seagulls', **3** Nou Camp, **4** Spain, **5** True, **6** Bobby Stokes, **7** Zinedine Zidane, **8** Italy, **9** Gianluca Pagliuca, **10** Manchester City, **11** Harry Redknapp, **12** Chile and Yugoslavia, **13** Czechoslovakia, **14** Arsenal, **15** Frank Stapleton.

# • FOOTBALL - QUIZ 55 •

*Answers on page 170*

**1** Which club won the European Cup in 1968?

**2** Who managed Scotland at the 1986 World Cup?

**3** How many games did England play at the 1986 World Cup?

**4** Who scored Manchester United's second goal in the 1979 FA Cup final?

**5** Which country did he play for?

**6** Which Portuguese club play at the 'Stadium of Light'?

**7** Who captained Italy in the 1982 World Cup final?

**8** From which club did West Ham sign Eyal Berkovic?

**9** How many games did Alf Ramsey win as England manager - 93, 103 or 113?

**10** Which Scottish club plays its home matches at Hampden Park?

**11** Name the 1986 European Footballer of the Year?

**12** In which country were the 1982 World Cup finals staged?

**13** Which Scottish club is known as the 'Gers'?

**14** Which club won the first FA Cup final staged at Wembley?

**15** Who did they beat?

***Rangers have won the Scottish League Cup 20 times, more than twice as many as their nearest and deadliest rivals Celtic, on nine wins.***

---

## *Answers to page 170*

**1** Barcelona, **2** AC Milan, **3** The 'Bees', **4** Argentina, **5** Newcastle United, **6** Charlie George, **7** Ron Greenwood, **8** Alan Shearer and Paul Scholes, **9** Kevin Moran, **10** 1982, **11** Brazil and Italy, **12** Italy, **13** Arsenal, **14** Aston Villa, **15** 1977.

# • FOOTBALL - QUIZ 56 •

*Answers on page 171*

**1** Who scored England's goals in the 2-0 victory over Colombia during France '98?

**2** What is Brighton's nickname?

**3** What is the name of Barcelonaís stadium?

**4** Which country were beaten by England in a penalty shoot-out during Euro '96?

**5** An African nation has never won the World Cup True or false?

**6** Who scored the only goal of the 1976 FA Cup final?

**7** Who scored two of Franceís goals in the 1998 World Cup Final?

**8** Who lost in the final of the 1994 World Cup?

**9** Which Italian was sent off in the 1994 World Cup match with Norway?

**10** Which team lifted the League Cup in 1976?

**11** Name the West Ham manager who signed Paolo Di Canio during the 1998-99 season?

**12** Who were the losing semi-finalists in the 1962 World Cup?

**13** Who lost in the 1962 World Cup final?

**14** Which English club was once known as Dial Square FC?

**15** Which Republic of Ireland striker scored for both Arsenal and Manchester United in FA Cup finals?

---

## *Answers to page 171*

**1** Argentina, **2** Kenny Dalglish, **3** Craig Brown, **4** Six, **5** True, **6** Two, **7** False - 54, **8** 19, **9** Three, **10** 90, **11** Daniel Passarella, **12** Jairzinho, **13** Cardiff City, **14** West Bromwich Albion, **15** False - it was Bobby Charlton.

# • FOOTBALL - QUIZ 57 •

*Answers on page 176*

**1** Which club is known as the 'Tigers'?

**2** Which team plays at Anfield?

**3** For whom did Frank Sinclair play in the 1998 World Cup?

**4** Which team lost 3-0 in the 1974 FA Cup final?

**5** Which Romanian scored two goals against Argentina in the 1994 World Cup?

**6** Gordon Banks missed England's quarter-final match with West Germany in the 1970 World Cup final Why?

**7** Who replaced him?

**8** In which year did John Barnes sign for Liverpool?

**9** Name the winners of the 1979 FA Cup?

**10** In which year did Oxford United win the League Cup?

**11** Who started the 1998-99 season as manager of Sunderland?

**12** Which club is nicknamed 'Pompey'?

**13** In which year was the FA Cup Final known as the 'Matthews Final'?

**14** From which club did Barcelona sign Ronald Koeman?

**15** Who captained the winning side in the 1963 FA Cup final?

## *Answers to page 176*

**1** Gordon Durie, **2** 1896, **3** Diego Maradona, **4** Brazil, **5** Len Shackleton, **6** Ajax, **7** Mansfield Town, **8** Alan Shearer, **9** Sampdoria, **10** Brazil, **11** Eusebio, **12** True, **13** Danny Blanchflower,. **14** Serie A, **15** Denis Law.

# • FOOTBALL - QUIZ 58 •

*Answers on page177*

1 Which Premiership team beat Manchester United 5-0 in the 1996-97 season?

2 Which country lost 3-2 in the final of the 1954 World Cup?

3 Which Dutch player scored a hat trick against England in the 1988 European Championships?

4 Who managed Manchester United to the FA Cup in 1983?

5 How many England caps did Alf Ramsey win as a player - 22, 32 or 42?

6 In which Uruguayan city was the 1930 World Cup final held?

7 Who captained France in the 1998 World Cup final?

8 Which stadium hosted the 1992 European Cup final?

9 In which year was Notts County founded?

10 Who kept goal for Brazil in the 1998 World Cup final?

11 Which Arsenal double-winning player later managed Millwall?

12 Which club won the Scottish Cup in three successive seasons during the 1980's?

13 The Pools Panel was introduced in 1961 True or false?

14 Where was the 1984 League Cup final replay held?

15 Which Watford striker was sold to AC Milan for £1 million during the 1980s?

---

*Answers to page 177*

**1** Torino, **2** 1936?, **3** Germany, **4** West Germany, **5** 1982, **6** 1987, **7** Dennis Tueart, **8** Peterborough United, **9** Nat Lofthouse, **10** False, **11** Brian Stein, **12** 1887, **13** Norman Hunter, **14** Italy, **15** Marco van Basten.

# • FOOTBALL - QUIZ 59 •

*Answers on page 174*

**1** Which Rangers player scored a hat trick in the 1996 Scottish Cup final?

**2** When was Stanley Rous born - 1896 or 1906?

**3** Who captained Argentina in the 1986 World Cup final?

**4** Who beat Scotland 4-1 at the 1982 World Cup?

**5** Who scored six goals on his debut for Newcastle United in 1946?

**6** Which Dutch club won three successive European Cups?

**7** Which club plays at Field Mill?

**8** Which player was top goalscorer at the 1996 European Championships?

**9** Which Italian club signed Trevor Francis in 1982?

**10** Who won the World Cup in 1970?

**11** Which Portuguese player scored four goals against North Korea in the 1966 World Cup?

**12** West Ham fielded eleven English players in the 1975 FA Cup final True or false?

**13** Who captained Spurs to the League and Cup 'double' in 1961?

**14** What is the top division in Italy called?

**15** Who was 1964 European Footballer of the Year?

---

## *Answers to page 174*

**1** Hull City, **2** Liverpool, **3** Jamaica, **4** Newcastle United, **5** Ilie Dumitrescu, **6** Suspected food poisoning, **7** Peter Bonetti, **8** 1987, **9** Arsenal, **10** 1986, **11** Peter Reid, **12** Portsmouth, **13** 1953, **14** PSV Eindhoven, **15** Noel Cantwell.

# • FOOTBALL - QUIZ 60 •

*Answers on page 175*

**1** Which Italian club did Denis Law join in 1961?

**2** When was Duncan Edwards born - 1936 or 1938?

**3** In which country do Hamburg play?

**4** Which country hosted the 1974 World Cup finals?

**5** In which year was goalkeeper Peter Shilton transferred to Southampton?

**6** In which year was he transferred to Derby County?

**7** Which Manchester City player scored with an overhead kick in the 1976 League Cup final?

**8** Which English club is known as the 'Posh'?

**9** Who skippered Bolton in the 1958 FA Cup final?

**10** England did not qualify for the 1970 World Cup True or false?

**11** Which Luton Town player scored two goals in the 1988 League Cup final?

**12** In which year did Aston Villa first win the FA Cup?

**13** Which tough-tackling Leeds and England defender was nicknamed ' Bites Yer Leg'?

**14** Which nation won the 1968 European Championships?

**15** Which Dutch player was voted World Footballer of the Year in 1988 and 1992?

***A Romanian football club sold a player for 500kg of pork worth £1,750 to players' wages.***

---

*Answers to page 175*

**1** Newcastle United, **2** Hungary, **3** Marco van Basten, **4** Ron Atkinson, **5** 32, **6** Montevideo, **7** Didier Deschamps, **8** Wembley, **9** 1862, **10** Taffarel, **1** George Graham, **12** Aberdeen, **13** False - 1963, **14** Maine Road, **15** Luther Blisset.

# FOOTBALL - QUIZ 61

*Answers on page 180*

1 Who won the FA Cup in 1971?

2 In which season did Brian Clough manage Derby County to the League Championship title?

3 Which Manchester United player was sent off in the 1994 League Cup final?

4 Which Newcastle United player scored after 45 seconds of the 1955 FA Cup final?

5 Who was France's manager at the 1998 World Cup?

6 Who knocked Holland out of the 1994 World Cup?

7 Which Swedish club lost 1-0 in the final of the 1979 European Cup?

8 From which club did Blackburn Rovers sign goalkeeper Tim Flowers?

9 Which player scored the first goal of France '98?

10 Which English club began life as Small Heath?

11 In which year was Alan Shearer born?

12 Which team won the first FA Cup in 1872?

13 Which English team plays at the Manor Ground?

14 Who scored Liverpool's goal in the 1977 FA Cup final?

15 What nationality is Romario?

## *Answers to page 180*

**1** Uruguay, **2** Brazil, **3** Joao Havelange, **4** Brazilian, **5** Celtic, **6** 88, **7** 1941, **8** Republic of Ireland, **9** Fulham, **10** Chile, **11** Blackburn Rovers, **12** Flamengo, **13** Newcastle United, **14** Juventus, **15** Nottingham Forest.

# • FOOTBALL - QUIZ 62 •

*Answers on page 181*

1 Which Arsenal striker scored both goals in Franceís 2-0 victory over England in February 1999?

2 Who was the first goalkeeper to save a penalty in an FA Cup final at Wembley?

3 Who won the Football League Cup in 1974?

4 In which year was the Heysel Stadium disaster?

5 Who were the losing semi-finalists at the 1998 World Cup?

6 Name the two players sent off in the 1974 FA Charity Shield?

7 In which year was Matt Busby born?

8 Who captained Newcastle United in the 1974 FA Cup final?

9 Name Manchester City's manager at the start of the 1998-99 season?

10 Name the Newcastle United manager who signed Kevin Keegan in 1982?

11 Against which country did Bryan Robson make his England debut in 1980?

12 Which English club is nicknamed the 'Grecians'?

13 From which club did Liverpool sign Ray Kennedy?

14 Which team lost in the final of the 1969 FA Cup?

15 Who did England thrash 8-3 at Wembley in 1963?

## *Answers to page 181*

**1** European Cup, League Championship, League Cup, **2** True, **3** Howard Kendall, **4** Mansfield Town, **5** Ray Wilson, **6** ,Manchester United **7** Harald Schumacher, **8** Victoria Park, **9** Paul Breitner, **10** Sunderland, **11** Hamburg, **12** Parma, **13** Sol Campbell, **14** Emilio Butragueno, **15**Middlesbrough .

# • FOOTBALL - QUIZ 63 •

*Answers on page 178*

1 Who won the 1950 World Cup?
2 Who did they beat in the final?
3 Who succeeded Sir Stanley Rous as FIFA President in 1974?
4 What is his nationality?
5 Which club won the Scottish Cup in 1967?
6 How many caps did Teofilo Cubillas win for Peru - 68, 88 or 108?
7 When was Bobby Moore born?
8 For which country did ex-Liverpool star Ronnie Whelan play?
9 Which team lost 10-0 to Liverpool in a League Cup match in 1986?
10 In which country was the 1962 World Cup staged?
11 From which club did Spurs sign Tim Sherwood in 1999?
12 Which team beat Liverpool in the 1981 World Club Championship?
13 With which club is the 'Blaydon Races' associated?
14 Which club won the 1985 European Cup?
15 From which club did Sheffield Wednesday sign Des Walker?

***In 1966 the World Cup went missing, rather embarrassingly for England. It was eventually found by a pooch called Pickles in someone's front garden!***

---

*Answers to page 178*

**1** Arsenal, **2** 1971-72, **3** Andrei Kanchelskis, **4** Jackie Milburn, **5** Aime Jacquet, **6** Brazil, **7** Malmo, **8** Southampton, **9** Cesar Sampaio (Brazil), **10** Birmingham City, **11** 1970, **12** Wanderers, **13** Oxford United, **14** Jimmy Case, **15** Brazilian.

# • FOOTBALL - QUIZ 64 •

*Answers on page 179*

**1** Which three major trophies did Liverpool win in 1984?

**2** Welsh striker Mark Hughes has never played in the World Cup finals True or false?

**3** Who was Everton's manager in the 1984 FA Cup final?

**4** Which club is known as the 'Stags'?

**5** Which England World Cup-winner left football to become a funeral director?

**6** Which team lost in the final of the 1995 FA Cup?

**7** Name the West German goalie who knocked Patrick Battiston unconscious at the 1982 World Cup?

**8** Name Hartlepool United's ground?

**9** Which West German player scored in the 1982 World Cup final?

**10** Which club, in 1985, lost to Norwich City in the League Cup final and were also relegated from the First Division?

**11** Which team lost in the final of the 1980 European Cup?

**12** From which club did Leeds United sign Tomas Brolin?

**13** Which England defender had a 'goal' disallowed against Argentina in the 1998 World Cup?

**14** Who scored four goals for Spain against Denmark in the 1986 World Cup?

**15** With which club did Brian Clough start his professional playing career?

---

### *Answers to page 179*

**1** Nicolas Anelka, **2** Dave Beasant, **3** Wolverhampton Wanderers, **4** 1985, **5** Croatia and Holland, **6** Billy Bremner and Kevin Keegan, **7** 1909, **8** Bob Moncur, **9** Joe Royle, **10** Arthur Cox, **11** Switzerland, **12** Exeter City, **13** Arsenal, **14** Leicester City, **15** Northern Ireland.

# • FOOTBALL - QUIZ 65 •

*Answers on page 184*

1 Who scored 9 goals for Bournemouth in a 1st round FA Cup tie in 1971?

2 Which English clubs played in the final of the UEFA Cup in 1972?

3 Who managed Newcastle United to the 1974 FA Cup final?

4 Which club won the European Cup in 1986?

5 What nationality is Paul Peschisolido?

6 How many times did Trevor Brooking play for England?

7 Who captained Ipswich Town in the 1978 FA Cup final?

8 Which English team beat Atletico Madrid 5-1 to win the 1963 Cup Winners' Cup?

9 What nationality is Alan Hansen

10 Which team lost 9-0 to Middlesbrough in a League match in 1958?

11 In which year was Tommy Docherty born - 1928 or 1932?

12 Which team defeated Liverpool in the 1984 World Club Championship?

13 Who was voted World Footballer of the Year in 1995?

14 What nationality is he?

15 How many caps did Denis Law win for Scotland?

## *Answers to page 184*

**1** Cesar Luis Menotti, **2** Nottingham Forest, **3** True, **4** Crystal Palace, **5** Alf Ramsey, **6** Peter Barnes, **7** 1893, **8** Atletico Madrid, **9** 30, **10** Emlyn Hughes, **11** Kevin Keegan, **12** 48, **13** Spurs, **14** Real Madrid, **15** True.

# FOOTBALL - QUIZ 66

*Answers on page 185*

**1** In which Scottish city was Kenny Dalglish born?

**2** Which countries played in the first official international match in 1872?

**3** From which club did Duncan Ferguson join Rangers in 1993?

**4** Who did Italy beat at the quarter-final stage of the 1990 World Cup?

**5** What is the German league known as?

**6** From which English club did Fiorentina sign Andre Kanchelskis?

**7** Which West German team won the European Cup in 1975?

**8** Who scored the only goal of the 1973 FA Cup final?

**9** Which English club won the Cup Winners' Cup in 1965?

**10** Andy Gray scored in the 1984 FA Cup final True or false?

**11** From which club did Barcelona sign Romario in 1993?

**12** Who kept goal for Scotland at the 1998 World Cup?

**13** In which country do Benfica play?

**14** Which club won the European Cup in 1987?

**15** What nationality was Sir Matt Busby?

---

## *Answers to page 185*

**1** Newcastle United, **2** 1969, **3** Costa Rica, **4** Nery Pumpido, **5** Antonio Goycochea, **6** 1972, **7** True, **8** Bordeaux, **9** The 'Pilgrims', **10** Phil Parkes, **11** Mexico, **12** Steve Morrow, **13** Norwich City, **14** Lou Macari, **15** False - 108.

# • FOOTBALL - QUIZ 67 •

*Answers on page 182*

1 Who was Argentina's coach at the 1978 World Cup?

2 Which club won the League Cup in 1989 and 1990?

3 Brian Clough never won the FA Cup as a player or manager True or false?

4 From which club did Blackburn Rovers sign Matt Jansen in 1999?

5 Who was manager of England from 1963-1974?

6 Who scored Manchester City's first goal in the 1976 League Cup final?

7 In which year did Wolves first win the FA Cup?

8 Which Spanish club plays its home matches at the Vicente Calderon Stadium?

9 How many goals did Kenny Dalglish score for Scotland?

10 Who captained Liverpool in the 1974 FA Cup final?

11 Which Newcastle manager signed Alan Shearer in 1996?

12 How many goals did Gary Lineker score for England?

13 Which club won the 100th FA Cup?

14 Which Spanish club side plays at the Bernabeu Stadium?

15 Alfredo Di Stefano scored 49 European Cup goals for Real Madrid True or false?

***Pele knows a good thing when he sees it. Asked who his favourite Manchester United player, he replied "Micheal Owen." No comment!***

## *Answers to page 182*

**1** Ted MacDougall, **2** Wolves and Spurs, **3** Joe Harvey, **4** Steaua Bucharest, **5** Canadian, **6** 47, **7** Mick Mills, **8** Spurs, **9** Scottish, **10** Brighton and Hove Albion, **11** 1928, **12** Independiente, **13** George Weah, **14** Liberian, **15** 55.

# FOOTBALL - QUIZ 68

*Answers on page 183*

1 From which club did Coventry City sign Darren Huckerby?

2 In which year did Bobby Robson become boss of Ipswich Town?

3 Scotland lost 1-0 in their first game of the 1990 World Cup Who beat them?

4 Name the Argentinian goalkeeper who suffered a broken leg at the 1990 World Cup?

5 Who replaced him for the remainder of the tournament?

6 When was Tommy Docherty appointed as manager of Manchester United?

7 The FA Cup is the oldest football tournament in the world True or false?

8 Which city hosted the Scotland v Norway match during France '98?

9 What is Plymouth Argyle's nickname?

10 Which goalkeeper did QPR sign from Walsall in 1970?

11 Which country hosted the 1986 World Cup finals?

12 Name the Arsenal player injured during post-match celebrations at the 1993 League Cup final?

13 From which club did Nottingham Forest sign Justin Fashanu?

14 Who succeeded John Lyall as manager of West Ham United?

15 Bobby Moore won 98 England caps True or false?

---

## *Answers to page 183*

**1** Glasgow, **2** England and Scotland, **3** Dundee United, **4** Republic of Ireland, **5** Bundesliga, **6** Everton, **7** Bayern Munich, **8** Ian Porterfield, **9** West Ham United, **10** True, **11** PSV Eindhoven, **12** Jim Leighton, **13** Portugal, **14** Porto, **15** Scottish.

# • FOOTBALL - QUIZ 69 •

*Answers on page 188*

1 Who won the European Cup in 1988?

2 Who succeeded Lou Macari as West Ham's manager?

3 Which Bolton-born striker scored 22 goals in 23 appearances for England between 1938-1948?

4 Wanderers won the FA Cup five times during the 1870's True or false?

5 Which striker scored two goals in the 1978 World Cup final?

6 From which club did Aston Villa sign utility player Steve Watson in 1998?

7 To whom did Celtic lose 2-1 in the 1970 European Cup final?

8 Who captained Spurs in the 1991 FA Cup final?

9 Who scored five goals for England v Cyprus in 1975?

10 Name the first foreign manager to win the FA Cup?

11 Which city hosted the England v Tunisia match during France '98?

12 What nationality is striker Hugo Sanchez?

13 How many nations competed in the 1998 World Cup finals?

14 Which club lost 10-0 to West Ham United in a League Cup match in 1983?

15 Bobby Robson was sacked as manager of Fulham in 1968 True or false?

## *Answers to page 188*

**1** Coventry City, **2** Steve Perryman, **3** Preston North End (1888-89), **4** Liverpool, **5** Leeds United, **6** Derby County, **7** False (Arsenal, 1950), **8** 1962, **9** Lawrie Sanchez, **10** Turkey, **11** Bristol City, **12** Sheffield Wednesday, **13** Arsenal, **14** Michael Owen, **15** Leicester City.

# FOOTBALL - QUIZ 70

*Answers on page 189*

1 Which club won the League Championship in the 1966-67 season?

2 Who won the League Cup in 1988?

3 Who was the manager of Spurs when they won the 'double'?

4 Kenilworth Road is the home of which English club?

5 In which World Cup were substitutes first allowed?

6 Which Scottish winger was kicked out of the 1978 World Cup for failing a dope test?

7 For which country did Mike England play?

8 How many FA Cup finals did Everton reach during the 1960's?

9 Who succeeded Bobby Robson as England manager?

10 Who lost to Brazil in the 1958 World Cup final?

11 Which club won the 1979 League Cup?

12 Which stadium hosted the 1970 World Cup final?

13 How many goals did England score at the 1982 World Cup?

14 Who was leading scorer in Italia '90?

15 Which country did he play for?

---

*Answers to page 189*

**1** Liverpool, **2** Brian Clough, **3** 4, **4** Italy, **5** Omam Biyik, **6** Brazil 4, Italy 1, **7** Osvaldo Ardilles, **8** Argentina, **9** Paul Ince, **10** Moscow, **11** The 'Hatters', **12** 49, **13** 1967, **14** 1954, **15** Pele.

# • FOOTBALL - QUIZ 71 •

*Answers on page 186*

1 Which English team is known as the 'Sky Blues'?

2 Who captained Spurs to FA Cup triumphs in 1981 and 1982?

3 Which club won the first Football League Championship?

4 Which club won the European Cup in 1977?

5 From which club did Coventry City sign Noel Whelan?

6 Which club formerly played at the Baseball Ground?

7 No London club won the FA Cup during the 1950s True or false?

8 When did Bobby Moore make his England debut?

9 Who scored the only goal of the 1988 FA Cup final?

10 Which country lost 8-0 to England at Wembley in 1987?

11 Which English team plays at Ashton Gate?

12 Which club lost in the final of the 1993 FA Cup?

13 Which club won the League Championship in the 1990-91 season?

14 Who scored England's goal in the 1998 World Cup match with Romania?

15 For which club did Gary Lineker make his professional debut?

---

## *Answers to page 186*

**1** PSV Eindhoven, **2** Billy Bonds, **3** Tommy Lawton, **4** True, **5** Mario Kempes, **6** Newcastle United, **7** Feyenoord, **8** Gary Mabbutt, **9** Malcolm Macdonald, **10** Ruud Gullit (1997), **11** Marseille, **12** Mexican, **13** 32, **14** Bury, **15** True.

# • FOOTBALL - QUIZ 72 •

*Answers on page 187*

**1** Which team won the 1981 Football League Cup?

**2** Who labelled Jan Tomaszewski a 'clown'?

**3** In how many World Cup finals did Pele play?

**4** Which country missed a penalty in the final of the 1982 World Cup?

**5** Which player scored the opening goal of Italia '90?

**6** What was the score in the 1970 World Cup final?

**7** Which Argentinian managed Newcastle United?

**8** In which country was Alfredo Di Stefano born?

**9** Which England player was sent off against Sweden in 1998?

**10** In which Russian city was goalkeeper Lev Yashin born?

**11** What is Luton Town's nickname?

**12** How many England goals did Bobby Charlton score?

**13** In which year was Paul Gascoigne born?

**14** In which year did Hungary thrash England 7-1?

**15** Which famous Brazilian was born Edson Arantes do Nascimento?

***Manchester United's only European Cup triumph, in 1968 against Benfica at Wembley, lived long in the memory of 100,000 spectators, thanks to an extra-time thriller.***

---

*Answers to page 187*

**1** Manchester United, **2** Luton Town, **3** Bill Nicholson, **4** Luton Town, **5** 1970, **6** Willie Johnston, **7** Wales, **8** 2, **9** Graham Taylor, **10** Sweden, **11** Nottingham Forest, **12** Azteca, **13** 6, **14** Salvatore 'Tito' Schillaci, **15** Italy.

# • FOOTBALL - QUIZ 73 •

*Answers on page 191*

**1** How many countries played in the finals of the 1966 World Cup?

**2** Who lost to England in the quarter-finals of Italia '90?

**3** How many goals did Denis Law score for Scotland?

**4** How many England caps did Bryan Robson win?

**5** Who was manager of Northern Ireland at the 1982 World Cup?

**6** Which Second Division club lost in the 1982 FA Cup final?

**7** Which country beat Italy 1-0 at Ayresome Park in the 1966 World Cup?

**8** Which Spanish club won the European Cup in 1998?

**9** When was Bobby Charlton voted European Footballer of the Year?

**10** Who won the 1954 FA Cup?

**11** Who replaced Roy Hodgson as manager of Blackburn Rovers in 1998?

**12** How many England caps did Gordon Banks win - 53, 73 or 93?

**13** From which club did Southampton sign Mark Hughes?

**14** Which Leeds and Scotland star was nicknamed 'Hot Shot'?

**15** Who played in the 1980 FA Cup final aged 17 years 256 days?

***Portsmouth FC faced an outstanding £800 bill for mince pies ordered by Terry Venables and given away to supporters at Christmas 1996.***

---

## *Answers to page 191*

**1** Brazil, **2** Edinburgh, **3** Argentinian, **4** Wrexham, **5** Dan Petrescu, **6** Scottish, **7** Cameroon, **8** Ruud Gullit and Marco van Basten, **9** West Ham United, **10** Holland, **11** Rotherham United, **12** Newcastle United, **13** Hearts, **14** 1923, **15** Every four years.

# • FOOTBALL - QUIZ 74 •

*Answers on page 190*

1 Who beat England 5-1 in 1964?

2 In which Scottish city was Graeme Souness born?

3 What nationality is striker Gabriel Batistuta?

4 Which Welsh club plays at the Racecourse Ground?

5 Who scored Romania's winner against England in the 1998 World Cup?

6 What nationality was Bill Shankly?

7 Who beat Argentina in the opening match of Italia '90?

8 Name Holland's two scorers in the 1988 European Championships final?

9 From which club did Wimbledon sign John Hartson?

10 In which country do PSV Eindhoven play?

11 Which English club is known as the 'Merry Millers'?

12 Name the first club to win successive FA Cup finals at Wembley?

13 Which Scottish team is known as the 'Jam Tarts'?

14 When was the FA Cup final first staged at Wembley?

15 How often are the World Cup finals held?

---

## *Answers to page 190*

**1** 16, **2** Cameroon, **3** 30, **4** 90, **5** Billy Bingham, **6** Queen's Park Rangers, **7** North Korea, **8** Real Madrid, **9** 1966, **10** West Bromwich Albion, **11** Brian Kidd, **12** 73, **13** Chelsea, **14** Peter Lorimer, **15** Paul Allen.

# GOLF

# GOLF - QUIZ 1

*Answers on page 196*

1 Which shot has odds of 40,000 to 1?

**2** Who was Masters Champion in 1989 and 1990?

**3** Who was the first US Women's Open champion?

**4** Who won his only Open title at St Andrews in 1946?

**5** Which club has a loft of 20 degrees?

**6** Who, in 1980, came within a few putts of becoming the first oriental to win a Grand Slam tournament?

**7** Who, at 18, finished fourth in the 1998 Open?

**8** Which golfing legend led the US to consecutive Walker Cup wins in 1928 and 1930?

**9** For what is pin a slang term?

**10** Who won his first US PGA title in 1962?

**11** Which course's first hole is Tea Olive?

**12** In which year was the US Open first televised nationally?

**13** Where did Mark Calcavecchia win his open title?

**14** In which country is Tryall Golf Club?

**15** Who won his fourth US Open title at Baltusrol in 1980?

***Playing in a 1998 Volvo PGA Championship, Sandy Lyle hit a ball into a man's pocket. On retrieving the ball, Sandy joked, "I'm not really a pickpocket."***

---

## *Answers to page 196*

**1** 1981, **2** Hoylake, **3** Albatross, **4** Augusta, **5** 1958, **6** Willie Anderson, **7** Left, **8** Bobby Locke, **9** Gleneagles Kings, **10** 1860, **11** No 7 Iron, **12** Sandy Lyle, **13** John Beck, **14** Apron, **15** Seattle.

# GOLF - QUIZ 2

*Answers on page197*

1 Who won the US PGA championship in 1928 and 1929?

2 Which course's 10th hole is South America?

3 Which year saw the only Walker Cup tie?

4 What does the club hit during an air shot?

5 Which course is also known as the PGA National?

6 Who was the first Welshman to win a major championship?

7 Who was the 1997 US Women's Open Champion?

8 Near which US city is the Oakland Hills course?

9 In which year was the US Open first held?

10 Over how long must par 5 holes be?

11 What was the first Asian course?

12 In which year did Bernhard Langer win his first Masters title?

13 Which US president installed the White House putting green?

14 Who won his second Open title at Sandwich in 1993?

15 Which course retains an old barometer with no hands, just a notice saying 'see goats'?

---

*Answers to page 197*

**1** US PGA, **2** Six Iron, **3** Andy North, **4** Patty Sheehan, **5** Back marker, **6** Royal Hong Kong, **7** Sigel and Giles, **8** Round robin, **9** Crooked Stick, **10** Ian Baker-Finch, **11** 1979, **12** Georgia, **13** 1981, **14** Prestwick, **15** Mark McCormack.

# GOLF - QUIZ 3

*Answers on page 194*

1 In which year did Larry Nelson win his first US PGA title?

2 Where, in 1930, did Bobby Jones win his last Open title?

3 What is a score of three under par called?

4 The 11th, 12th and 13th holes of which course are called Amen Corner?

5 In which year did Arnold Palmer win his first Masters title?

6 Who was the first player to win the US Open four times?

7 To which side of the target does a pulled ball fly?

8 Which Open champion lost the sight of one eye when his car was struck by a train?

9 Which course's 7th hole is Kittle Kink?

10 Which year saw the first Open Championship?

11 Which club has a loft of 39 degrees?

12 Who declared himself a Scot for team purposes despite being born in Shrewsbury?

13 Who captained the first British Walker cup win, in 1938?

14 What is the mown area immediately surrounding the green called?

15 At which US city is the Sahalee course?

## *Answers to page 194*

**1** Hole in one, **2** Nick Faldo, **3** Patty Berg, **4** Sam Snead, **5** No 2 Iron, **6** Isao Aoki, **7** Justin Rose, **8** Bobby Jones, **9** Flagstick, **10** Gary Player, **11** Augusta, **12** 1954, **13** Royal Troon, **14** Jamaica, **15** Jack Nicklaus.

# GOLF - QUIZ 4

*Answers on page 195*

**1** Which of the Majors did Jerry Barber win in 1961?

**2** Which club did Alan Shepard use on the moon?

**3** Who won his second US Open title in 1985?

**4** Who was 1992 and 1994 US Women's Open champion?

**5** What is the player with the lowest handicap called?

**6** Which Asian club has Old, New and Eden courses?

**7** Which two Walker Cup-winning captains' surnames are anagrams of each other?

**8** In which match play competition does every competitor play all the others?

**9** Where did John Daly win his US PGA title in 1991?

**10** Which 6' 4" Australian golfer wears glasses?

**11** In which year was Fuzzy Zoeller Masters champion?

**12** In which US state is the Augusta course?

**13** Which year saw Bill Rogers win the Open at Sandwich?

**14** Which course's 16th hole is Cardinals Black?

15 Which golfing manager formed the multi-million dollar International Management Group?

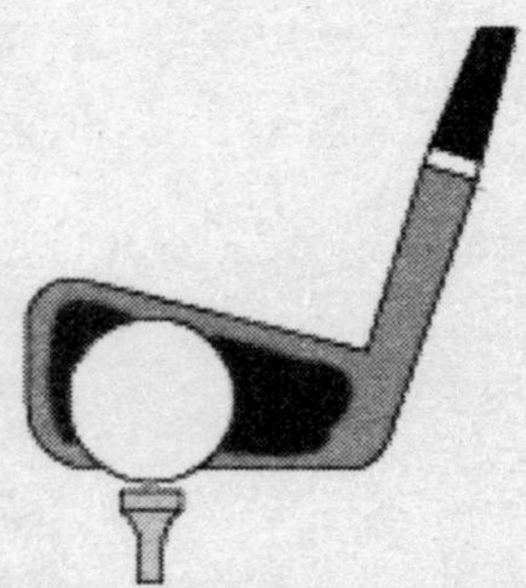

---

### *Answers to page 195*

**1** Leo Diegel, **2** Carnoustie, **3** 1965, **4** Nothing, **5** Palm Beach, **6** Ian Woosnam, **7** Alison Nicholas, **8** Detroit, **9**1895 , **10** 475 yds/434 m, **11** Royal Calcutta, **12** 1985, **13** Dwight Eisenhower, **14** Greg Norman, **15** Lahinch.

# GOLF - QUIZ 5

*Answers on page 200*

1. Which 1970 Masters champion was non-playing US Ryder Cup captain in 1979?
2. For which number wood is the baffy an obsolete equivalent?
3. When was the first Masters Tournament held?
4. Who was the 1989 US PGA champion?
5. Of what nationality is 1963 British Open champion Bob Charles?
6. What is a controlled left-to-right flight called?
7. Who was the first Open champion?
8. Who won ten tournaments in 1950?
9. What handicap does a scratch player have?
10. In which year did Jack Nicklaus win his first Open title?
11. Where did Lee Trevino win the first of his 3 successive Open wins?
12. Who led the winning US team in the first Walker Cup?
13. Which course's 2nd hole is Ord?
14. Which year saw Fuzzy Zoeller win the US Open?
15. Whose nickname is the Great White Shark'?

## *Answers to page 200*

**1** Steve Jones, **2** Birdie, **3** Swedish, **4** 1998, **5** Mark O'Meara, **6** Foursomes, **7** St Andrews, **8** 3, **9** Ben Crenshaw, **10** Byron Nelson, **11** Royal Troon, **12** Jack Nicklaus, **13** 1991, **14** St Andrews Old Course, **15** Kel Nagle.

# GOLF - QUIZ 6

*Answers on page 201*

1 Where did Sandy Lyle win his Open title in 1985?

**2** Who was 1989 and 1990 US Women's Open champion?

**3** How much does a golf ball weigh?

**4** In which year did Ray Floyd win his first US PGA title?

**5** Who only just missed winning both Opens in 1973 by coming second to Tom Weiskopf in the British?

**6** In which country is Royal Selangor course?

**7** Which Scottish golfer got a golf scholarship to Houston Baptist University?

**8** Which club is specifically designed for bunker shots?

**9** Who won his first Open title in 1979?

**10** Which course's 8th hole is the Postage Stamp?

**11** Which great American woman golfer won a record six times in 1935?

**12** Who won his second US Open title in 1997?

**13** Which seven major title-winner was known as 'Slammin' Sam'?

**14** In which year did Tom Watson win his first Masters title?

**15** Who led the US Walker Cup team to a record five wins?

***In 1973, David Russell, a 19 year-old amateur, and 71 year-old American Gene Sarazen scored a hole in one at the Royal Troon eighth hole within an hour of each other.***

---

*Answers to page 201*

**1** 1988, **2** Bisque, **3** Putter, **4** Paul Azinger, **5** Standard Scratch Score, **6** Hale Irwin, **7** Turnberry, **8** Dave Stockton, **9** Interlachen, **10** No 8 iron, **11** Tom Weiskopf, **12** 1987, **13** Jose-Maria Olazabal, **14** Royal Birkdale, **15** Andy North.

# GOLF - QUIZ 7

*Answers on page 198*

1 Who was the 1996 US Open champion?

2 What is a score of one below par called?

3 Of what nationality is 1988 US Women's Open champion Liselotte Neumann?

4 In which year did Vijay Singh win the US PGA, his first major title?

5 Which Open champion was the 1979 US amateur champion?

6 What may be American, Canadian or Rye?

7 Where did Britain win their first Walker Cup, in 1938?

8 To which number wood is the spoon an old equivalent?

9 Whose 60-foot putt on the 10th at Augusta made him 1984 Masters champion?

10 Who won 19 tournaments in 1945?

11 Where, in 1982, did Tom Watson win his fourth Open title?

12 Who returned repeatedly to his old instructor Jack Grout?

13 In which year did Jim Gabrielsen lead America to Walker Cup victory at Portmarnock?

14 Which course's 5th hole is 'hole o' cross-out'?

15 Who, in 1960, became the second Australian to win the Open?

## *Answers to page 198*

**1** Billy Casper, **2** 4, **3** 1934, **4** Payne Stewart, **5** New Zealand, **6** Fade, **7** Willie Park Snr, **8** Sam Snead, **9** Zero, **10** 1966, **11** Merion, **12** William Fownes, **13** Royal Durnoch, **14** 1984, **15** Greg Norman.

# GOLF - QUIZ 8

*Answers on page 199*

1 In which year was Sandy Lyle Masters champion?

2 What is a handicap stroke that can be claimed at any hole during a match?

3 Which club is called a Texas wedge when used unconventionally?

4 Who was the 1993 US PGA champion?

5 What do the letters SSS stand for?

6 Who won his first US Open title in 1974?

7 Which course's 9th hole is Bruce's Castle?

8 Who was the 1970 US PGA champion?

9 Where was the Walker Cup held in 1993?

10 Which club has a loft of 43 degrees?

11 Who won the Open at Troon in 1973?

12 In which year was Laura Davies US Women's Open champion?

13 Which Masters champion was 1984 amateur champion?

14 Where did Mark O'Meara win the Open in 1998?

15 Who, in a 20 year career, has won two US Opens, one other professional tournament and nothing else?

*Answers to page 199*

**1** Royal St George's ( Sandwich), **2** Betsy King, **3** 45.92 grams/1.6 oz, **4** 1969, **5** Johnny Miller, **6** Malaysia, **7** Colin Montgomerie, **8** Sand iron, **9** Seve Ballesteros, **10** Royal Troon, **11** Glenna Collett Vare, **12** Ernie Els, **13** Sam Snead, **14** 1977, **15** Francis Ouimet.

# GOLF - QUIZ 9

*Answers on page 204*

1 Which of the Majors did Ralph Guldahl win in 1937 and 1938?
2 Who won his first US PGA title in 1974?
3 What is the striking area of an iron club called?
4 Where, in 1965, did Peter Thomson win his fifth Open?
5 Who led Britain to Walker Cup victory in 1989?
6 Which feline describes a golfer of high ability?
7 Who was 1994 Masters champion?
8 In which country is the Valderrama Golf Club?
9 Who won the Open in 1997?
10 What do Americans describe as traps?
11 In which year was the first US Amateur Championship held?
12 Who has played in a record ten successive Ryder Cup matches?
13 Which course's 5th hole is Magnolia?
14 Who won his first US Open title in 1993?
15 Which type of ball preceded the gutty?

***Reigning champions of the US Masters hold a dinner for fellow competitors before the tournament starts and traditionally decide on the menu.***

## *Answers to page 204*

**1** Ben Hogan, **2** Bogey, **3** 1946, **4** Rolf Muntz, **5** 1976, **6** Valley of Sin, **7** Ray Floyd, **8** Jack Nicklaus, **9** Madrid, **10** Park, **11** 1971, **12** Carnoustie, **13** Mark Brooks, **14** Gary Player, **15** 1995.

# GOLF - QUIZ 10

*Answers on page 205*

**1** Which course's 16th hole is Wee Bogle?

**2** In which year did Ben Crenshaw win his first Masters title?

**3** For what is a blaster a slang name?

**4** Which player has won the most Major titles?

**5** Who won the US Open at Pebble Beach in 1992?

**6** After how many holes has one reached the 'turn'?

**7** Who led the US to consecutive Walker Cup wins in 1957 and 1959?

**8** In which year was the first US PGA held?

**9** Who was the first European US Women's Open champion?

**10** Who won the Open at St Andrews in 1964?

**11** Which course near Pittsburgh has been called 'the toughest course in the world'?

**12** Which Walker Cup-winning captain was US amateur champion in 1982 and 1983?

**13** In which decade did the first golf bag appear?

**14** Who won his Open title at Sandwich in 1985?

**15** How much did Young Tom Morris win for his fourth Open title in 1872?

---

*Answers to page 205*

**1** Payne Stewart, **2** 2, **3** Shinnecock Hills, **4** Jay Sigel, **5** Walker Cup, **6** Ben Hogan, **7** 1994, **8** Pau, **9** Harold Hilton, **10** Mary Queen of Scots, **11** Inverness, **12** Ken Venturi, **13** Muirfield, **14** 1901, **15** Ian Baker-Finch.

# GOLF - QUIZ 11

*Answers on page 202*

1 Who won his first US Open title at Oakmont in 1953?

2 What is a score of one over par called?

3 In which year was the first US Women's Open championship held?

4 Which Dutchman was amateur champion in 1990?

5 In which year was Ray Floyd Masters champion?

6 What is the hollow in front of St Andrews Old Course's 18th green called?

7 Who in 1960, had to choose between a golfing career and joining the Cleveland Indians baseball club?

8 Who won his first Open at Muirfield in 1966?

9 Near which city is La Puerta de Hierro golf course?

10 What was the surname of Open-winning brothers Wilkie and Mungo?

11 In which year did Michael Bonallack lead Britain to Walker Cup victory?

12 Which course's 14th hole is Spectacles?

13 Who was the 1996 US PGA champion?

14 Who played under armed guard in the 1969 PGA Championship?

15 Which year saw John Daly win the Open?

---

## *Answers to page 202*

**1** US Open, **2** Lee Trevino, **3** Blade, **4** Royal Birkdale, **5** Geoffrey Marks, **6** Tiger, **7** Jose-Maria Olazabal, **8** Spain, **9** Justin Leonard, **10** Bunkers, **11** 1895, **12** Christy O'Connor, **13** Augusta, **14** Lee Janzen, **15** Featherie.

# • GOLF - QUIZ 12 •

*Answers on page 203*

1. Who won the US Open in 1991?
2. For which number wood is brassie a former name?
3. Where did Ray Floyd win the US Open?
4. Who led the US to consecutive Walker Cup wins in the 1980's?
5. Which biennial amateur team match plays Britain and Ireland against the US?
6. Who was the first player to hold three major titles at the same time?
7. In which year was Jose-Maria Olazabal Masters champion?
8. What is the oldest golf course in continental Europe?
9. Who was the first Briton to be US amateur champion?
10. Which historical figure is credited with being the first woman golfer?
11. Where did Paul Azinger win the US PGA in 1993?
12. Who nearly died of dehydration during the 1964 US Open?
13. Where, in 1992, did Nick Faldo win his third Open?
14. Which year saw the formation of the PGA?
15. Who won the Open at Royal Birkdale in 1991?

---

*Answers to page 203*

**1** Gleneagles Kings, **2** 1984, **3** Wedge, **4** Jack Nicklaus, **5** Tom Kite, **6** Nine, **7** Charles Coe, **8** 1916, **9** Catherine Lacoste, **10** Tony Lema, **11** Oakmont, **12** Jay Sigel, **13** 1880s, **14** Sandy Lyle, **15** £8.

# GOLF - QUIZ 13

*Answers on page 208*

1. Which year saw Peter Thomson win his fifth Open?
2. Who won the Open at Royal Birkdale in 1976?
3. What is a driver with a convex face called?
4. The R&A is the governing body of golf in the entire world except America and where else?
5. In which year was Ian Woosnam Masters champion?
6. Which course's 5th hole is Fin' me oot?
7. Who won the US Open in 1995?
8. What is a number one wood called?
9. Which year saw Bob Tway win the US PGA?
10. Near which city is the Walton Heath course?
11. Whose shot at Royal Birkdale's 15th (now 16th) in 1961 is marked by a plaque?
12. Where was the Walker Cup held in 1987?
13. How many times was Bobby Jones US amateur champion?
14. In which year was the first Women's British Open held?
15. What is the surname of the father and son who created Oakmont?

---

## *Answers to page 208*

**1** Tom Watson, **2** 1993, **3** Calloway, **4** Ohio, **5** The Open, **6** Gary Player, **7** South African, **8** Links, **9** Harold Hilton, **10** Jack Nicklaus, **11** Four, **12** 1961, **13** Old Course St Andrews, **14** Mark Calcavecchia, **15** Romans.

# GOLF - QUIZ 14

*Answers on page 209*

**1** Who won consecutive US Open titles in 1988 and 1989?

**2** What is the highest number of clubs a professional may carry?

**3** Who was the 1988 US PGA champion?

**4** What started life as the Dum Dum Club?

**5** With what is a bunker filled?

**6** Who was Rookie of the Year in 1968 and leader of the Order of Merit in 1969?

**7** How many times was young Tom Morris Open Champion?

**8** At which city's course did Nick Price win his only Major title, the US PGA?

**9** Of what are fescue, bermuda and bent varieties?

**10** Who was Open Champion of 1995?

**11** What was described as 'The Scottish palace in the glen - the playground of the gods' when it opened in 1924?

**12** Who led the US to Walker Cup victory at St Andrews in 1975?

**13** Who was 1969 Open champion?

**14** In which year was Craig Stadler Masters champion?

**15** Which New Jersey course's 7th hole includes 'Hell's Half Acre' of scrub?

***Nick Faldo's obsession with golf started at the age of 13, when he saw Jack Nicklaus on TV playing in the 1973 Masters.***

---

*Answers to page 209*

**1** David Graham, **2** Ian Woosnam, **3** Carry, **4** Jock Hutchison, **5** Royal Birkdale, **6** Rough, **7** Dick Siderowf, **8** Hamburg, **9** Ben Hogan, **10** Two, **11** Hubert Green, **12** Royal Troon, **13** Seve Ballesteros, **14** Sandy Lyle, **15** Edward III.

# GOLF - QUIZ 15

*Answers on page 206*

1 Who won the US Open at Pebble Beach in 1982?

2 In which year did Bernhard Langer win his second Masters title?

3 Which handicapping system determines a player's score by his worst holes?

4 In which US state did Jack Nicklaus build Muirfield Village?

5 What, in 1907, did Arnaud Massy become the first Frenchman to win?

6 Who won his third Open at Lytham in 1974?

7 Of what nationality is Alison Shead, the first non-British women's British Open champion?

8 What term for sandy soil has come to mean seaside golf courses?

9 Which twice winner of the British Open was the first editor of Golf Monthly?

10 Who won his second US PGA title in 1971?

11 How many handicap bands are there?

12 In which year did Jack Westland lead the US to Walker Cup victory?

13 Which course's 4th hole is Ginger Beer?

14 Who was 1989 Open Champion?

15 Whose 'paganica' is thought to have been a forerunner of golf?

## *Answers to page 206*

**1** 1965, **2** Johnny Miller, **3** Bulger, **4** Mexico, **5** 1991, **6** Turnberry, **7** Corey Pavin, **8** Driver, **9** 1986, **10** London, **11** Arnold Palmer, **12** Sunningdale, **13** 5, **14** 1976, **15** Fownes.

# • GOLF - QUIZ 16 •

*Answers on page 207*

**1** Which Australian won the US Open in 1981?

**2** Who was the first European Tour player to win £1 million worldwide in a single year?

**3** What is the term for the distance from where the ball is hit to where it lands?

**4** Who was the first American to win the Open?

**5** Where did Ian Baker-Finch become Open Champion in 1991?

**6** What part of the course is not tee, fairway, green or hazards?

**7** Who led the US to Walker Cup victory at Muirfield in 1979?

**8** Near which city is Falkenstein Golf Course?

**9** Which golfing legend was known as the 'Ice Man'?

**10** How many players play a single?

**11** Who won the US PGA at Cherry Hills in 1985?

**12** Which course's 2nd hole is Black Rock?

**13** Who won his third Open at Lytham in 1988?

**14** Who was 1988 Masters champion?

**15** Whose edict of 1363 prohibited sports including 'Cambuca', a forerunner of golf?

---

*Answers to page 207*

**1** Curtis Strange, **2** 14, **3** Jeff Sluman, **4** Royal Calcutta, **5** Sand, **6** Bernard Gallacher, **7** 4, **8** St Louis, **9** Grass, **10** John Daly, **11** Gleneagles Hotel, **12** Ed Updegraff, **13** Tony Jacklin, **14** 1982, **15** Pine Valley.

# GOLF - QUIZ 17

*Answers on page 212*

**1** In which year did Nick Faldo win his third Masters title?

**2** What is a short low-running shot called?

**3** Who was the first Briton to win the US Open?

**4** Which course's 6th hole is Elysian Fields?

**5** Who played Ben Hogan in the film of the golfer's life?

**6** Who won the first Open at Muirfield in 1959?

**7** What term is used for the nervous trauma that inhibits the ability to putt?

**8** Who won the US Open at Winged Foot in 1984?

**9** Which British king appeared, club in hand, on the cover of Golf Illustrated?

**10** Who was the first golfer win all four of golf's current Majors?

**11** In which year did Jack Nicklaus win his fourth US PGA title?

**12** Who was the first American Women's British Open champion?

**13** Which year saw Tom Lehman win the Open?

14 Who led the US to Walker Cup victory at Shinnecock Hills in 1977?

**15** From what did trophy-donating Samuel Ryder make his fortune?

***Tiger Woods on becoming pro, at 20 years-old, signed a £25 million dollar contract with Nike. 1n 1997, he won the US Masters at Augusta.***

---

*Answers to page 212*

**1** 1983, **2** Lee Trevino, **3** 2, **4** Wayne Grady, **5** Augusta, **6** 1989, **7** Tom Kite, **8** 1979, **9** Gary Player, **10** Right, **11** St Andrews, **12** New Jersey, **13** Jack Nicklaus, **14** Kasumigaseki, **15** 1995.

# GOLF - QUIZ 18

*Answers on page 213*

1 Which year saw Nick Price win the Open?

2 Who was the Ryder Cup's youngest-ever competitor when he first took part in 1977?

3 What is a cleat?

4 Where is the headquarters of the European PGA?

5 Who won his first Open at Carnoustie in 1975?

6 Who was the 1993 Women's world champion?

7 Who, in 1920, became only the second Briton to win the US Open?

8 Which club has a loft of 14 degrees?

9 Who was the first British player since Harry Vardon to hold the US Open and British Open titles simultaneously?

10 In which year did Charlie Yates lead the US to Walker Cup victory?

11 Who won the US PGA in 1991?

12 Which course lies between the Irish Sea and the Mountains of Mourne?

13 Which Ryder Cup captain was the first Director General of the PGA European Tour?

14 In which year was Tiger Woods Masters champion?

15 Where, in 1993, did Lee Janzen win his first US Open?

---

### *Answers to page 213*

**1** Ailsa Craig, **2** Hale Irwin, **3** 330, **4** Annika Sorenstam, **5** 1980, **6** Joe Carr, **7** Sand wedge, **8** Tony Jacklin, **9** 1963, **10** Seve Ballesteros, **11** Henry Cotton, **12** Harry Vardon, **13** Carnoustie, **14** 1970, **15** Bobby Jones.

# GOLF - QUIZ 19

*Answers on page 210*

1 Which year saw Larry Nelson win the US Open?

2 Which golfing legend served in the Marines in Okinawa?

3 Of what number iron is the cleet an old equivalent?

4 Who was the second Australian to win the US PGA?

5 Which course's 4th hole is Flowering Crab Apple?

6 In which year did Nick Faldo win his first Masters title?

7 Up to spring 1993, who had won more tournament prize money than any other in history?

8 In which year did the Ryder Cup team become a European team?

9 Who, in 1961, became the first non-American Masters champion?

10 To which side of the target is the player's body aimed in a closed stance?

11 Where, in 1957, did Bobby Locke win his fourth and last Open?

12 In which US state is Baltusrol course?

13 Who won his second Open title at St Andrews in 1970?

14 Which Japanese course has two greens for every hole, one for summer, one for winter?

15 In which year did William C Campbell lead the US to Walker Cup victory?

---

## *Answers to page 210*

**1** 1996, **2** Chip, **3** Harry Vardon, **4** Prestwick, **5** Glen Ford, **6** Gary Player, **7** The Yips, **8** Fuzzy Zoeller, **9** Edward VIII, **10** Gene Sarazen, **11** 1975, **12** Debbie Massey, **13** 1996, **14** Lou Oehmig, **15** Flower seeds.

# • GOLF - QUIZ 20 •

*Answers on page 211*

**1** What is the name of the granite boulder that dominates Turnberry's courses?

**2** Who won his third US Open title in 1990?

**3** How many dimples are there, on average, on a golf ball?

**4** Who was women's world champion in 1995 and 1996?

**5** Which year saw Jack Nicklaus's fifth US PGA win?

**6** Who captained the British team at the Walker Cup tie of 1965?

**7** Which club has a loft of 58 degrees?

**8** Who is Scunthorpe's golfing legend?

**9** Which year saw New Zealander Bob Charles win the Open?

**10** Who, in 1980, became only the second non-American Masters champion?

**11** Who was Open champion in 1934 and 1937?

**12** Which golfing legend has a grip named after him?

**13** What is the most northerly of Scotland's Open Championship courses?

**14** In which year was Billy Casper Masters champion?

**15** Who joined Benjamin Franklin as the only American to be given the f reedom of the Burgh (Edinburgh)?

---

*Answers to page 211*

**1** 1994, **2** Nick Faldo, **3** Metal stud for golf shoes, **4** The Belfry, **5** Tom Watson, **6** Dottie Mochrie, **7** Ted Ray, **8** No 3 wood, **9** Tony Jacklin, **10** 1953, **11** John Daly, **12** Royal County Down, **13** John Jacobs, **14** 1997, **15** Baltusrol.

# GOLF - QUIZ 21

*Answers on page 216*

1 Where was the first US Open held?

2 Which four times Open champion called himself Bobby after Bobby Jones despite being born Arthur D'Arcy?

3 What is a hole designed with an angled fairway called?

4 Who won his second US PGA title in 1972?

5 Who ranked first among US president golfers with a 7-10 handicap?

6 Which club has a loft of 52 degrees?

7 Who won consecutive Opens in 1982 and 1983?

8 Whose Open win in 1979 made him the youngest champion since Young Tom Morris in 1872?

9 What is a controlled right-to-left curving flight called?

10 Who led America to three consecutive Walker Cup wins in the 1920s?

11 What was the venue for the 1957 Canada, now World, Cup, won by Japan?

12 Which golfing journalist wrote It Was Good While It Lasted?

13 Where did Roberto de Vicenzo win his Open title in 1967?

14 What is the term for a ball that comes to rest level with the flagstick?

15 Who won his sixth Masters title 23 years after his first?

## *Answers to page 216*

**1** Prestwick, **2** No 9 iron, **3** Larry Nelson, **4** Singapore, **5** 1938, **6** Dog licence, **7** 1980, **8** Merion, **9** Jack Nicklaus, **10** Right, **11** Bobby Jones, **12** Lahinch, **13** , **14** Beth Daniel, **15** Cary Middlecoff.

# GOLF - QUIZ 22

*Answers on page 217*

1 In which year was Jeff Sluman US PGA champion?
2 Who famously described golf as 'a good walk spoiled'?
3 To which side of the target line does a duck hook curve?
4 What is Sandy Lyle's real first name?
5 Who was the 1994 US Men's Amateur champion?
6 What was the first golf club established outside the UK?
7 Who was US Women's Open champion in 1995 and 1996?
8 What nationality is Vijay Singh?
9 Where did Tom Watson win his second Open title?
10 What, in golfing terms, is a rabbit?
11 At which course was the Walker Cup tied in 1965?
12 Which course's 3rd hole is Jockey's Burn?
13 Who was the first US Open champion?
14 Who was the architect of Cypress Point and Augusta courses?
15 In which year did Mark Calcavecchia win the Open?

***Tom Morris Snr. was the oldest winner of the Open at a mere 46 years and 99 days when he won in 1867.***

---

*Answers to page 217*

**1** Andy North, **2** Eagle, **3** 1980, **4**Baltusrol , **5** Davis Love III, **6** Ryder Cup, **7** William, **8** 4 1/4 in / 108mm, **9** Deane Beman, **10** St Andrews, **11** Johnny Miller, **12** 1922, **13** US Masters, **14** Bill Rogers, **15** Gleneagles Kings.

# GOLF - QUIZ 23

*Answers on page 214*

1 Where were the 1992first 12 Opens held?

2 Which club has a loft of 47 degrees?

3 Who won his second US PGA title in 1987?

4 Which Asian course was designed by James Braid, who hated travel and never set foot on it?

5 In which year did Britain finally win the Walker Cup?

6 What is slang for a 7/6 result in a match play contest?

7 Which year saw Tom Watson win his third Open title?

8 Where did David Graham become the first Australian to win the US Open?

9 Who is nicknamed the 'Golden Bear'?

10 To which side of the target does a pushed ball fly?

11 Who won his fourth US Open title in 1930?

12 Which course has been dubbed 'the St Andrews of Irish golf'?

13 In which year was Fred Couples Masters champion?

14 Who was 1994 Women's World Champion?

15 Which twice US Open champion was a qualified dentist?

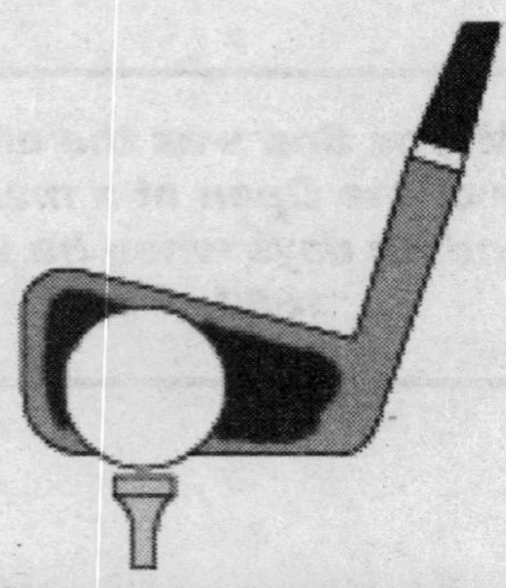

## *Answers to page 214*

**1** Newport, **2** Bobby Locke, **3** Dog-leg, **4** Gary Player, **5** JFK, **6** Pitching wedge, **7** Tom Watson, **8** Seve Ballesteros, **9** Draw shot, **10** Robert A Gardner, **11** Kasumigaseki, **12** Henry Longhurst, **13** Hoylake, **14** Pin high, **15** Jack Nicklaus.

# GOLF - QUIZ 24

*Answers on page 215*

**1** Who won the first of his two US Open titles in 1978?

**2** What is a score of two shots under par called?

**3** In which year did Seve Ballesteros win his first Masters title?

**4** Which US course is named after a farmer who was murdered by thieves in 1831?

**5** Who was 1997 US PGA champion?

**6** Which biennial team match is between players from the PGA European Tour and the US PGA Tour?

**7** What was Ben Hogan's real first name?

**8** What is the diameter of a golf hole?

**9** Which US PGA chief is the longest-running commissioner in American sport?

**10** Where, in 1978, did Jack Nicklaus win his third Open title?

**11** Who, in 1974, became the first player to win the first three tournaments of the season?

**12** In which year was the first Walker Cup held?

**13** Which tournament's winners get to wear the Green Jacket?

**14** Who won the Open at Sandwich in 1981?

**15** Which course's 1st hole is Dun Whinny?

---

*Answers to page 215*

**1** 1988, **2** Mark Twain, **3** Left, **4** Alexander, **5** Tiger Woods, **6** Royal Calcutta, **7** Annika Sorenstam, **8** Fijian, **9** Turnberry, **10** Novice player, **11** Baltimore, **12** Carnoustie, **13** Horace Rawlins, **14** Alister Mackenzie, **15** 1989.

# GOLF - QUIZ 25

*Answers on page 220*

1 Who was the 1998 US PGA champion?

2 In which year was Ray Floyd US Open champion?

3 Who is the most successful player with 88 professional wins in America's LPGA history?

4 What is the ridge along the base of an iron club called?

5 Where was the first Walker Cup held?

6 Who beat his father to win the 1868 Open?

7 How many players are involved in greensomes?

8 Where was the Open first played over 72 holes?

9 What is a putting method with gripping hands kept apart called?

10 Who famously said that he never longed to be a millionaire, just to live like one?

11 Who won the Open in 1994?

12 Which course's 14th hole is Goosedubs?

13 Who was the first Masters champion?

14 In which year was the first Championship played over 72 holes?

15 Which Masters champion's name is the plural of a previous Masters champion's name?

## *Answers to page 220*

**1** Royal Birkdale, **2** Bobby Jones, **3** Nick Faldo, **4** Gimme, **5** Joseph C Dey Jnr, **6** Royal Durnoch, **7** Willie Dunn, **8** Nick Price, **9** 1987, **10** Portmarnock, **11** Oakmont, **12** Greg Norman, **13** Fife, **14** Lee Janzen, **15** 1961.

# GOLF - QUIZ 26

*Answers on page 221*

**1** Which year saw the first US Ryder Cup victory on British soil?

**2** Where did Nick Faldo win his first Open title in 1987?

**3** What does a golfer shout to alert others in danger of being hit?

**4** Which American golfer is nicknamed 'the Walrus'?

**5** Of what nationality was Jan Stephenson, the 1983 US Women's Open champion?

**6** Who won consecutive Opens in 1961 and 1962?

**7** Which fourball team game is usually played off 1/8 of the combined handicaps of the partners?

**8** Where did Jim Gabrielsen lead the US to Walker Cup victory in 1981?

**9** What is the base of the clubhead called?

**10** Who came second in the Masters in 1971, 1975 and 1981?

**11** In which year did Ray Floyd win his second US PGA title?

**12** Merion golf course is near which US city?

**13** Which three-times British Open champion retired to the Algarve in 1977 with his wife 'Toots'?

**14** Which Open champion was the 1992 US Amateur champion?

**15** Which year saw Ernie Els's first US Open win?

***Jack Nicklaus, the Great Bear, has won eighteen major titles including the Open, which he won in 1966, 1970, 1978.***

---

*Answers to page 221*

**1** Vinney Giles, **2** St Andrews, **3** Curtis, **4** Haskell, **5** 1885, **6** Kobe, **7** Christy O'Connor, **8** Hale Irwin, **9** Takeaway, **10** Canada Cup, **11** Walter Hagen, **12** Muirfield, **13** Nick Faldo, **14** 1987, **15** Persimmon.

# GOLF - QUIZ 27

*Answers on page 218*

1 Where, in 1971, did Lee Trevino win his first Open?

2 Who was the first player, in 1930, to win a Grand Slam?

3 Who was 1996 Masters champion?

4 What is an unmissable putt called?

5 Who, in 1975, was only the second American to be elected captain of the R & A?

6 Which course's 12th hole is Sutherland?

7 Which 1894 US Open champion was known as Young Willie?

8 Who was US PGA champion in 1992 and 1994?

9 Which year saw the first European Ryder Cup victory on American soil?

10 Where was the Walker Cup held in 1991?

11 Which course features a series of eight bunkers known as the 'Church Pews'?

12 Who won his first Open at Turnberry in 1986?

13 Where was the Lundin Ladies Golf Club, believed to be the oldest, formed in 1891?

14 Who won his second US Open title in 1998?

15 In which year did Gary Player win his first Masters title?

## *Answers to page 218*

**1** Vijay Singh, **2** 1986, **3** Kathy Whitworth, **4** Flange, **5** National Golf Links, **6** Young Tom Morris, **7** Four, **8** Muirfield, **9** Split hand, **10** Walter Hagen, **11** Nick Price, **12** Prestwick, **13** Horton Smith, **14** 1892, **15** Woods.

# GOLF - QUIZ 28

*Answers on page 219*

1 Who was the winning captain at the 1993 Walker Cup?

2 Where, in 1984, did Seve Ballesteros win his second Open title?

3 What was the surname of sisters Harriot and Margaret, who gave their name to an annual trophy?

4 Which forerunner of the modern ball replaced the gutty?

5 In which year was the first Amateur Championship held?

6 Where was the first golf club in Japan?

7 Which Irish golfer is known to his fans as 'Himself'?

8 Who won his second US Open title in 1979?

9 What is the start of the backswing called?

10 How was the World Cup formerly known?

11 Who is the only player to have won four consecutive US PGA titles?

12 What is the course of the Honourable Company of Edinburgh Golfers?

13 Who won his second Open at St Andrews in 1990?

14 In which year was Larry Mize Masters champion?

15 Which American wood was the last natural material used to make clubheads?

## *Answers to page 219*

**1** 1937, **2** Muirfield, **3** Fore, **4** Craig Stadler, **5** Australian, **6** Arnold Palmer, **7** Texas Scramble, **8** Cypress Point, **9** Sole, **10** Johnny Miller, **11** 1982, **12** Philadelphia, **13** Sir Henry Cotton, **14** Justin Leonard, **15** 1994.

# GOLF - QUIZ 29

*Answers on page 224*

**1** Who won his second US PGA title in 1984?

**2** In which year was the Curtis Cup first held?

**3** What is traditionally referred to as the home of golf?

**4** Who won his fourth Open title in 1958?

**5** From which material, developed by the Du Pont Company, is the one piece ball made?

**6** Who, in 1951, became the first non-British person to be made captain of the PGA?

**7** In which year did Tony Jacklin win the Open?

**8** What is the situation of the ball at rest termed?

**9** Who was 1992 Masters champion?

**10** Near which city is the Compiegne golf course?

**11** Which year saw Payne Stewart win the US Open?

**12** Where did Geoffrey Marks lead Britain to Walker Cup victory in 1989?

**13** What is the name of the PGA European Tour ranking system?

**14** Which golfing legend was US Amateur champion in 1954?

**15** What is won by the winner of the Order of Merit?

***One of the all-time greats, Ben Hogan, played only once in he British Open and won!***

---

*Answers to page 224*

**1** 1977, **2** Glenna Collett Vare, **3** Double Bogey, **4** Ray Floyd, **5** 1981, **6** Billy Joe Patton, **7** Approach, **8** Bobby Jones, **9** Lee Trevino, **10** Jack Nicklaus, **11** Michael Bonallack, **12** 1986, **13** Pebble Beach, **14** 1983, **15** Nick Price.

# GOLF - QUIZ 30

*Answers on page 225*

1 Which year saw Hale Irwin's third US Open win?

2 Who was the first US PGA champion?

3 What is the socket in which the shaft joins the clubhead called?

4 Which golf guru was most associated with Nick Faldo until 1998?

5 Where, in 1990, did Nick Faldo win his second Open?

6 In which year did Ben Crenshaw win his second Masters title?

7 Who led Britain and Ireland to successive Curtis Cup victories in 1986 and 1988?

8 Which golfing legend was US Amateur champion in 1959 and 1961?

9 Which slang term describes the back or side edge of the hole?

10 Who won his third Open at Muirfield in 1980?

11 Which course's 17th hole is Rabbit?

12 Who was the first person to win the Masters four times?

13 Which year saw the 'Million Pound Open'?

14 Who led Britain to Walker Cup victory in 1971?

15 Which is the oldest golf course in Italy?

---

*Answers to page 225*

**1** 1976, **2** Loft, **3** Ian Woosnam, **4** Jersey, **5** Double-Eagle, **6** Jack Nicklaus, **7** Grapefruit or Sunshine Circuit, **8** Jess Sweetser, **9** 1936 and 1958, **10** Walter Travis, **11** Royal Birkdale, **12** N. Carolina, **13** Wayne Grady, **14** £25, **15** Sam Snead.

# GOLF - QUIZ 31

*Answers on page 222*

1. Which year saw Hubert Green win the US Open?
2. Who led the US Curtis Cup team to three victories and one draw?
3. What is a score of two over par called?
4. Who, at 43, succeeded Ted Ray as the oldest US Open champion?
5. In which year did Tom Watson win his second Masters title?
6. Who led the US to Walker Cup victory at Milwaukee in 1969?
7. What is the shot played to the green called?
8. After whom is the 10th hole at the Old Course St Andrews called?
9. Who won consecutive Open titles in 1971 and 1972?
10. Who held three of the Grand Slam titles in 1972?
11. Who was Amateur champion five times from 1961 to 1970?
12. Which year saw Greg Norman win his first Open?
13. Which course's 6th hole is played on a headland over Stillwater Cove?
14. In which year was Hal Sutton US PGA champion?
15. Which US PGA champion served in the Rhodesian Air Force?

## *Answers to page 222*

**1** Lee Trevino, **2** 1932, **3** St Andrews, **4** Peter Thomson, **5** Surlyn, **6** Francis Ouimet, **7** 1969, **8** Lie, **9** Fred Couples, **10** Paris, **11** 1991, **12** Peachtree, **13** Order of Merit, **14** Arnold Palmer, **15** Harry Vardon Trophy.

# GOLF - QUIZ 32

*Answers on page 223*

**1** In which year was Johnny Miller Open champion?

**2** What is the angle of the clubface called?

**3** Who was 1991 Masters champion?

**4** Where were golfing legends Harry Vardon and Ted Ray both born?

**5** What is the American term for an albatross?

**6** Who was the last player to win the US Open four times?

**7** How is the winter tour of America's southern states known?

**8** Who led the US to Walker Cup victory in 1967 and 1973?

**9** Which two years saw a Curtis Cup draw?

**10** Who was the first American to be Amateur champion?

**11** Where, in 1983, did Tom Watson win his fifth Open?

**12** In which US state is the winter golf resort of Pinehurst?

**13** Who won the US PGA at Shoal Creek in 1990?

**14** What was the cost of The Belt, the prize for the first Open?

**15** Who is the only player other than Ray Floyd to have won on both US PGA and Senior Tours in the same year?

---

## *Answers to page 223*

**1** 1990, **2** Jim Barnes, **3** Hosel, **4** David Leadbetter, **5** St Andrews, **6** 1995, **7**Diane Bailey , **8** Jack Nicklaus, **9** Tradesman's entrance, **10** Tom Watson, **11** Royal Troon, **12** Arnold Palmer, **13** 1993, **14** Michael Bonallack, **15** Roma.

# GOLF - QUIZ 33

*Answers on page 228*

1 Who was the first non-American to win the US PGA?
2 What is the national body for the development of junior golf?
3 What is the minimum depth of a golf hole?
4 Which successful golfer is affectionately nicknamed 'Big Momma'?
5 How many years separated Harry Vardon's first and last Open wins?
6 Who was the first Australian to win the US Open?
7 Which year saw Scott Simpson win the US Open?
8 What is the privilege of playing first from the tee called?
9 In which year did Nick Faldo win his second Open?
10 In which county is Royal St George's course?
11 Who led the US to Walker Cup victory at Sunningdale in 1987?
12 Who was the 1967 Open champion?
13 Which course's 4th hole is Woe-be-tide?
14 In which year did Seve Ballesteros win his second Masters title?
15 Who missed a 3-foot putt on the last green at the 1978 Masters to tie the winner, Gary Player?

## *Answers to page 228*

**1** Bernhard Langer, **2** 5, **3** Fanny Sunesson, **4** 1992, **5** Hale Irwin, **6** 1959, **7** Peter Thomson, **8** Slice, **9** Fred Couples, **10** 13, **11** 1963, **12** Jack Nicklaus, **13** Tom Morris, **14** Turnberry, **15** Ernie Els.

# • GOLF - QUIZ 34 •

*Answers on page 229*

**1** Who was the first Italian to play for Europe in the Ryder Cup?

**2** What nationality is golfer David Frost?

**3** What term is used for the natural objects a player may remove?

**4** In which did Tom Watson win his first Open?

**5** Gleneagles Hotel is just south of which city?

**6** In which year did Ed Updegraff lead the US to Walker Cup victory?

**7** Who was 1995 Masters champion?

**8** From which rubber-like substance were balls formerly made?

**9** For whom did the US LPGA amend its constitution to give her automatic membership?

**10** What was the site of the first Open played in England?

**11** Who won his third Open at St Andrews in 1978?

**12** Of whom did Tommy Armour famously remark 'He could relax on a hot stove'?

**13** Which year saw Jack Nicklaus win his first US PGA title?

**14** Which links course is 10 miles north of Dublin?

**15** Who was the first player to win the Open 5 times?

***Sandy Lyle, the son of a golf pro, was the first man to represent his country at boy, youth and senior levels.***

---

*Answers to page 229*

**1** Bobby Locke, **2** Ernie Els, **3** Stroke play, **4** 1979, **5** Julius Boros, **6** Ben Hogan, **7** Sweet Spot, **8** Ben Crenshaw, **9** Muirfield, **10** Nancy Lopez, **11** Argentinian, **12** Prestwick, **13** 1995, **14** John Daly, **15** William IV.

# GOLF - QUIZ 35

*Answers on page 226*

1 Who was 1993 Masters champion?

2 To which number iron is the mashie an old equivalent?

3 Who is Nick Faldo's famous caddy?

4 Which year saw Tom Kite win the US Open?

5 Who, at the age of 45, became the oldest US Open champion?

6 In which year did Gary Player first win the Open?

7 Who was the first Australian to win the Open?

8 What is the opposite of a hook?

9 Whose nickname is 'Boom Boom'?

10 How many Articles were in the original Rules of Golf?

11 In which year did Richard Tufts lead the US to Walker Cup victory?

12 Who won the third US PGA title at Canterbury in 1973?

13 After whom is Old Course St Andrews 18th hole called?

14 Where, in 1986, did Greg Norman win his first Open?

15 Which South African has won the World Match-play Championship three times in a row?

## *Answers to page 226*

**1** Gary Player, **2** Golf Foundation, **3** 4 in (100mm), **4** Joanne Carner, **5** 18, **6** David Graham, **7** 1987, **8** Honour, **9** 1990, **10** Kent, **11** Fred Riley, **12** Roberto de Vicenzo, **13** Turnberry, **14** 1983, **15** Hubert Green.

# GOLF - QUIZ 36

*Answers on page 227*

1 Who was the first South African to win the Open?

2 Who won his first US Open title in 1994?

3 What is medal play more correctly called?

4 In which year did Dick Siderowf lead the US to Walker Cup victory?

5 Who won the US Open in 1963?

6 Who went on to win six Grand Slam titles after surviving a terrible car crash in 1949?

7 Which point on the clubface will deliver maximum mass at impact?

8 Who was 1984 Masters champion?

9 Where, in 1980, did Tom Watson win his third Open?

10 Who won her state championship at 12 and nine tournaments in her first year as a pro?

11 Of what nationality was Roberto de Vicenzo, 1967 Open champion?

12 Which course hosted the first Open Championship in 1860?

13 Which year saw Steve Elkington win the US PGA?

14 Who won the US PGA in 1991, having come in as ninth reserve at the last minute?

15 Which king granted St Andrews its Royal status?

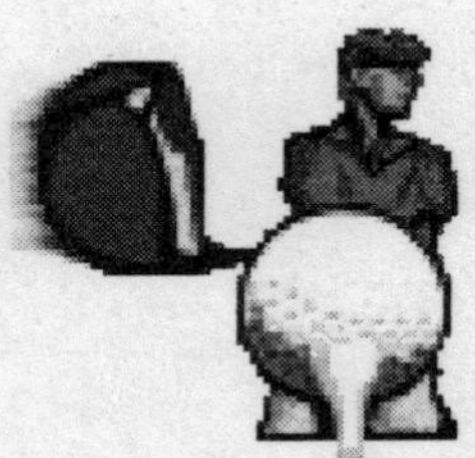

## *Answers to page 227*

**1** Costantino Rocca, **2** South African, **3** Loose impediments, **4** 1975, **5** Perth, **6** 1975, **7** Ben Crenshaw, **8** Gutta Percha, **9** Laura Davies, **10** St George's, **11** Jack Nicklaus, **12** Walter Hagen, **13** 1963, **14** Portmarnock, **15** James Braid.

# GOLF - QUIZ 37

*Answers on page 232*

1. Who won his second Open at St Andrews in 1984?
2. In which year was Tommy Aaron Masters champion?
3. What term is used for allowing a player, dissatisfied with a first drive, to hit a second?
4. Who was the first Australian to win the US PGA?
5. Which cup sees the US LPGA play the women's PG European Tour?
6. Who finished third in the 1974 US PGA at the age of 62?
7. In which year did Lou Oehmig lead the US to Walker Cup victory?
8. At which course is the Masters held?
9. Who became, in 1970, the first British Player to win the US Open since Ted Ray in 1920?
10. Which year saw Justin Leonard win the Open?
11. In which country was the first Johnnie Walker World Championship held?
12. Who won the US Open in 1987?
13. What do Americans call plus fours?
14. Who was the first South African to win the US Open?
15. Which club has a loft of 35 degrees?

---

## *Answers to page 232*

**1** Fuzzy Zoeller, **2** St Andrews, **3** 8, **4** Dave Marr, **5** Cypress Point, **6** Tom Watson, **7** The Dell, **8** Larry Nelson, **9** Australian, **10** Harry Vardon, **11** Bernhard Langer, **12** 1990, **13** Jack Nicklaus, **14** 1932, **15** Royal Troon.

# GOLF - QUIZ 38

*Answers on page 233*

1 Which year saw Tom Weiskopf win the Open at Troon?

2 Who won both Opens and both Amateurs in 1930?

3 What is the term for dividing one round into three matches for betting purposes?

4 Who was the first player to amass $1 million in one year?

5 Where did Jay Sigel lead the US to Walker Cup victory for the second time?

6 Who won his US Open at Shinnecock Hills in 1986?

7 Who was 'The Babe', Olympic athlete and 1948, 1950 and 1954 US Women's Open champion?

8 Which golfing legend stood for parliament in Melbourne?

9 In which Irish county is Ballybunion?

10 Who won the US PGA at Inverness in 1986?

11 Which course is also called simply 'Sandwich'?

12 Who, in 1970, became only the third Briton to win the US Open?

13 In which year was Charles Coody Masters champion?

14 Who could be said to be the first properly trained and qualified golf course architect?

15 Who was 1998 Open champion?

***William Park was the first winner of the British Open in 1860.***

---

*Answers to page 233*

**1** Steve Elkington, **2** 1978, **3** 250yds / 228m, **4** Tom Watson, **5** Gleneagles, **6** Lawson Little, **7** The Open, **8** 1996, **9** No 5 iron, **10** John Fischer, **11** Women's Open, **12** Surrey, **13** Tony Lema, **14** Nick Faldo, **15** 1975.

# GOLF - QUIZ 39

*Answers on page 230*

1 Which Masters champion's real first names are Frank Urban?

2 Where was the Walker Cup first held in Britain?

3 Of which number iron is the niblick an old equivalent?

4 Which late golf commentator won the US PGA championship in 1965?

5 Which course's Pacific-side 16th is reckoned to be the most photographed hole?

6 Which golfing legend's middle name is Sturges?

7 What is the name of Lahinch's 6th hole, the only one left of the original Old Tom Morris design?

8 Who won the US Open at Oakmont in 1983?

9 Of what nationality is Corinne Dibnah, 1988 Women's Open champion?

10 Who is the only player to win the Open six times?

11 Who missed the critical 8-foot putt in the 1991 Ryder Cup against Hale Irwin?

12 In which year did Nick Faldo win his second Masters title?

13 Who was the first player to produce personal yardage charts of golf courses?

14 Which year saw Gene Sarazen's only Open win?

15 Which royal course features both the longest and the shortest hole on the Open championship rota?

## *Answers to page 230*

**1** Seve Ballesteros, **2** 1973, **3** Mulligan, **4** David Graham, **5** Solheim Cup, **6** Sam Snead, **7** 1977, **8** Augusta, **9** Tony Jacklin, **10** 1997, **11** Jamaica, **12** Sctt Simpson, **13** Knickers, **14** Gary Player, **15** No. 6 iron.

# GOLF - QUIZ 40

*Answers on page 231*

**1** Who was the 1995 US PGA champion?

**2** In which year did Gary Player win his last Masters title?

**3** Up to how long are holes rated as par 3s?

**4** Who won his second Open at Turnberry in 1977?

**5** Which venue has a King's, a Queen's and a Monarch course?

**6** Who won both the British and the US Amateur Championships in successive years, 1934 and 1935?

**7** What did Tom Weiskopf win in 1973, his only major title?

**8** Which year saw Steve Jones win the US Open?

**9** Which club has a loft of 31 degrees?

**10** Who captained the US team in the Walker Cup tie of 1965?

**11** Which tournament did Ayako Okamoto win at Woburn in 1984?

**12** In which county is Wentworth?

**13** Which Open champion died in a plane crash in 1966?

**14** Who won his first Open at Muirfield in 1987?

**15** Which year was Carnoustie's last as an Open venue?

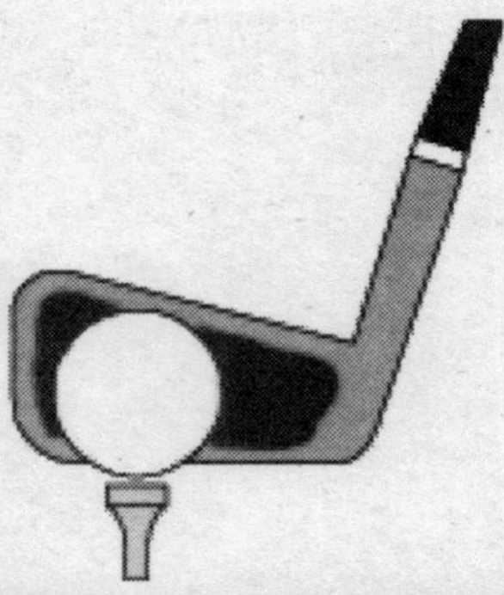

## *Answers to page 231*

**1** 1973, **2** Bobby Jones, **3** Nassau, **4** Curtis Strange, **5** Pine Valley, **6** Ray Floyd, **7** Babe Zaharias, **8** Peter Thomson, **9** Kerry, **10** Bob Tway, **11** Royal St George's, **12** Tony Jacklin, **13** 1971, **14** Robert 'Trent' Jones, **15** Mark O'Meara.

# HORSE RACING

# •HORSE RACING - QUIZ 1•

*Answers on page 239*

1 Which American Triple Crown race is run at Pimlico, Baltimore?

2 On which horse did Willie Ryan win the Derby in 1997?

3 In which month is Royal Ascot?

4 Which horse won the Derby in 1971?

5 Who won the Prix de l'Arc de Triomphe three years in succession 1985-87?

6 What connects the 1997 and 1998 Irish 2000 Guineas-winning horses?

7 Where in London were the first regular race meetings held in the 12th century?

8 In which year was Garden Path the last filly to win the 2000 Guineas?

9 When do thoroughbreds celebrate their birthday in the Northern hemisphere?

10 Who has been champion jockey a record 26 times?

11 Where is the Cambridgeshire run?

12 Whose sixth and last Oaks win was on Circus Plume in 1984?

13 Which horse won the 1998 Ascot Gold Cup?

14 Where are the Nunthorpe Stakes run?

15 Who rode Cherokee Rose to victory in the 1995 Haydock Park Sprint Cup?

---

## *Answers to page 239*

**1** Newmarket, **2** The St Leger, **3** The 12th Earl of Derby, **4** Sheikh Mohammed, **5** Oh So Sharp, **6** 1 mile, **7** Shantou, **8** 1809, **9** Epsom, **10** Nijinsky, **11** Cheveley Park Stakes, **12** The Melbourne Cup, **13** Pat Shanahan, **14** Intrepidity, **15** Marcus Armytage.

# •HORSE RACING - QUIZ 2•

*Answers on page 239*

1 Which horse won the 1998 Grand National?

2 Who was National Hunt champion jockey a record 8 times?

3 Where is the Cesarewitch run?

4 Which race was first won by Diomed in 1780?

5 Which year saw the formation of the Jockey Club?

6 Which horse, ridden by Lester Piggott, was the last to win the Prix de l'Arc de Triomphe twice?

7 Which five times Derby-winning jockey shot himself in 1886?

8 Who owns Ascot race course?

9 How old is a yearling?

10 Which horse won the St Leger in 1997?

11 What is the oldest of America's Triple Crown races?

12 What is a bet on the Lincoln Handicap and the Grand National called?

13 Which trainer has had the most 2000 Guineas wins with 7?

14 In which year did Declan Gillespie win the Irish 2000 Guineas on Prince of Birds?

15 Which Sandown Park race was first run in 1886 and is named after a horse?

## *Answers to page 239*

**1** Carl Llewellyn, **2** The Triple Crown, **3** Dr Devious, **4** Ayr, **5** Sleepytime, **6** Aintree, **7** Freddie Head, **8** Dubai World Cup, **9** Bets, **10** Jem Robinson, **11** Tic tac, **12** Swain, **13** St Leger, **14** 1779, **15** Dream Well.

# •HORSE RACING - QUIZ 3•

*Answers on page 236*

1 Where was the Oaks run during both World Wars?

2 What is the oldest of the five Classics?

3 After whose Epsom home is the Oaks named?

4 Who was Leading Owner for the 10th time in 1997?

5 Which horse gave Steve Cauthen his only 1000 Guineas win in 1985?

6 Over what distance is the 1000 Guineas run?

7 Which horse won the St Leger in 1996?

8 In which year was the 2000 Guineas first run?

9 Where is the Derby run?

10 Which was the last horse to win the English Triple Crown?

11 Which race is run over the last 6 furlongs of the Bunbury Mile at Newmarket?

12 What is the name of Australia's most important race?

13 Who rode Zagreb to win the 1996 Irish Derby?

14 Which horse won the Oaks in record time in 1993?

15 Who was the last amateur jockey to win the Grand National?

***Red Rum won the Grand National three times and was second twice. Retired after his 1977 success, he thrived on his fame and had public engagements, opening supermarkets and going on a round of celebrity appearances.***

## *Answers to page 236*

**1** Preakness Stakes, **2** Benny the Dip, **3** June, **4** Mill Reef, **5** Pat Eddery, **6** Desert (King and Prince), **7** Smithfield, **8** 1944, **9** January 1, **10** Gordon Richards, **11** Newmarket, **12** Lester Piggott, **13** Kayf Tara, **14** York, **15** Cash Asmussen.

# •HORSE RACING - QUIZ 4•

*Answers on page 237*

1 Who rode Party Politics to Grand National victory in 1992?

2 How are the 2000 Guineas, the Derby and the St Leger collectively known?

3 Which horse gave John Reid his first Derby win?

4 Where was the St Leger run in 1989, due to damage to the Doncaster track?

5 Which horse did Kieren Fallon ride to victory in the 1997 1000 Guineas?

6 Where is the Grand National run?

7 Who rode Pas de Response to win the Cheveley Park Stakes in 1996?

8 What is the richest race, run on a dirt course over 1 mile 2 furlongs?

9 What are yankees, yaps and union jacks?

10 Which jockey has won the 2000 Guineas a record 9 times?

11 What is the bookmakers' sign language called?

12 Which horse won consecutive King George VI & Queen Elizabeth Diamond Stakes in 1997 and 1998?

13 France's Prix Royal Oak is roughly the equivalent of which English race?

14 In which year was the Oaks first run?

15 Which horse won the 1998 Irish Derby?

---

## *Answers to page 237*

**1** Earth Summit, **2** Peter Scudamore, **3** Newmarket, **4** The Derby, **5** 1750, **6** Alleged, **7** Frederick Archer, **8** The Queen, **9** Between one and two years, **10** Silver Patriarch, **11** Belmont Stakes, **12** The Spring Double, **13** John Scott, **14** 1988, **15** The Eclipse Stakes.

# •HORSE RACING - QUIZ 5•

*Answers on page 242*

**1** Of which English race is France's Poule d'Essai des Pouliches the equivalent?

**2** Which horse gave Lester Piggott his first 1000 Guineas win?

**3** Which race did Sagaro win a record three times?

**4** In what is a horse's pedigree listed?

**5** Which horse ran the St Leger in equal record time in 1934?

**6** Where was England's first Sunday flat meeting held in 1992?

**7** Who won his fourth and last Oaks on Salsabil in 1990?

**8** Who fell at the first Grand National, giving his name to one of its features?

**9** Whose 1902 coronation does the Coronation Cup commemorate?

**10** Which horse gave Steve Cauthen his only 2000 Guineas win, in 1979?

**11** Which jockey holds the record for the most Derby wins, with 9?

**12** Which was the last horse to win the Dubai Champion Stakes twice in a row?

**13** Who won the Derby six times between 1915 and 1925?

**14** Which race is run at Churchill Downs, Louisville?

**15** How long is the Grand National?

---

## *Answers to page 242*

**1** Whitbread Gold Cup, **2** 3 years, **3** Pat Eddery, **4** Las Meninas, **5** 1807, **6** Pat Taafe, **7** Epsom, **8** Shahrastani, **9** Nurseries, **10** Ezzoud, **11** The National Hunt Committee, **12** Thierry Jarnet, **13** 66, **14** Shahtoush, **15** 1988.

# •HORSE RACING - QUIZ 6•

*Answers on page 243*

1 Which horse gave Billy Newnes his first Oaks win in 1982?

2 Which race did Olivier Peslier win on Xaar in 1997?

3 After whom is the Cesarewitch named?

4 Which horse did Michael Roberts ride to Coronation Cup victory in 1993?

5 How many stewards are appointed to oversee a race meeting?

6 At which course is the Melbourne Cup run?

7 Who rode One in a Million to win the 1000 Guineas in 1979?

8 Which race was known until 1985 as the Benson & Hedges Gold Cup?

9 Which horse won the Derby by a record 10 lengths in 1981?

10 Which horse did Jason Titley ride to win the 1995 Grand National?

11 Who rode Snurge to his first St Leger win in 1990?

12 Over what distance is the Oaks run?

13 Which horse gave Pat Eddery his third 2000 Guineas win, in 1993?

14 The French Classics are run at Longchamps and where else?

15 Which horse was the first winner of the Grand National?

## *Answers to page 243*

**1** Rough Quest, **2** Bill Scott, **3** Dick Francis, **4** Sedgefield, **5** 1974, **6** Royal Ascot, **7** King of Kings, **8** Fred Rimell, **9** George Duffield, **10** The Jockey Club, **11** Musical Bliss, **12** The Derby, **13** Mr Frisk, **14** Newmarket, **15** Brett Doyle.

# •HORSE RACING - QUIZ 7•

*Answers on page 240*

1 Which race, when inaugurated in 1957, was the first to attract major commercial sponsorship?

2 To what age are horses in the Classic races restricted?

3 Who rode Toulon to win the 1991 St Leger?

4 Which horse won the 1000 Guineas in record time in 1994?

5 Which year saw the first Ascot Gold Cup?

6 Who is the only jockey to have won the Cheltenham Gold Cup four times?

7 Where is the Oaks run?

8 Which horse gave Walter Swinburn his last Derby win in 1986?

9 What are handicap races for two-year-olds called?

10 Which horse won consecutive International Stakes in 1993 and 1994?

11 What is the controlling body for the National Hunt?

12 Who rode Pennekamp to 2000 Guineas victory in 1995?

13 What record number took part in the 1927 Grand National?

14 Which horse won the Oaks in 1998?

15 In which year did Rhyme'N'Reason win the Grand National?

## *Answers to page 240*

**1** 1000 Guineas, **2** Humble Duty, **3** Ascot Gold Cup, **4** The General Stud Book, **5** Windsor Lad, **6** Doncaster, **7** Willie Carson, **8** Captain Becher, **9** Edward VII, **10** Tap on Wood, **11** Lester Piggott, **12** Triptych, **13** Steve Donoghue, **14** The Kentucky Derby, **15** Four miles and four furlongs.

# •HORSE RACING - QUIZ 8•

*Answers on page 241*

**1** Which horse did Mick Fitzgerald ride to win the 1996 Grand National?

**2** Which jockey holds the record for the most St Leger wins, with 9?

**3** Who rode the royal horse that collapsed in the 1956 Grand National?

**4** Where did three horses die in one race in February 1999?

**5** In which year did Brian Taylor ride Snow Knight to win the Derby?

**6** Where is the St James's Palace Stakes run?

**7** Which horse won the 1998 2000 Guineas?

**8** Who is the only trainer to have had 4 Grand National winners at Aintree?

**9** Who rode User Friendly to Oaks victory in 1992?

**10** What is the controlling body for flat racing?

**11** Which horse gave Walter Swinburn his first 1000 Guineas win, in 1989?

**12** France's Prix de Jockey Club is the equivalent of which English race?

**13** Which horse ran the Grand National in record time in 1990?

**14** Where is the 1000 Guineas run?

**15** Who rode the winner Sayyedati in the 1995 Sussex Stakes?

***For a colt to win the Triple Crown, he must win the Derby, St.Ledger and Two Thousand Guineas.***

---

## *Answers to page 241*

**1** Time Charter, **2** Dewhurst Stakes, **3** Tsar Nicholas II of Russia, **4** Opera House, **5** 4, **6** Flemington Park, **7** Joe Mercer, **8** Juddmonte International Stakes, **9** Shergar, **10** Royal Athlete, **11** Richard Quinn, **12** 1.5 miles, **13** Zafonic, **14** Chantilly, **15** Matthew.

# •HORSE RACING - QUIZ 9•

*Answers on page 246*

1 Which horse gave Richard Dunwoody his 2nd Grand National win, in 1994?

2 Over what distance is the Derby run?

3 Whom did Classic Cliche give his first St Leger win, in 1995?

4 Which horse ran the Derby in record time in 1995?

5 Who rode Jet Ski Lady to Oaks victory in 1991?

6 Which major race did Real Quiet win in 1998?

7 Which horse gave Michael Kinane the first of his 2000 Guineas wins, in 1990?

8 Which Ascot race was first run in 1973 as the Green Shield Stakes?

9 Where is the Prix de l'Arc de Triomphe run?

10 Which trainer won the 1000 Guineas a record 9 times?

11 Which horse won consecutive Eclipse Stakes in 1995 and 1996?

12 Who won the Grand National on Aldaniti?

13 Which ploughhorse won the Grand National in 1908?

14 In which year was the earliest recorded steeplechase run in Co Cork?

15 Who rode Tarascon to win the 1998 Irish 1000 Guineas?

## *Answers to page 246*

**1** 1916, **2** The Autumn double, **3** Sceptre, **4** Ayr, **5** John Murtagh, **6** Jayne Thompson, **7** Sun Princess, **8** 30, **9** Goodwood, **10** Willie Carson, **11** Seagram, **12** Bosra Sham, **13** Royal Applause, **14** H H Aga Khan III, **15** Moonax.

# •HORSE RACING - QUIZ 10•

*Answers on page 247*

1 Who rode Red Rum to consecutive Grand National wins in 1973 and 1974?

2 Who holds the record of most 1000 Guineas wins, with 7?

3 How long is Newmarket's July Cup?

4 Which horse did Lester Piggott ride to 2000 Guineas victory in 1970?

5 Which suffragette was killed at the Derby in 1913?

6 Which jockey won consecutive St Legers in 1980 and 1981?

7 Which was the last horse to win the Fillies Triple Crown?

8 Where are the Irish Classics run?

9 Who was Leading Trainer for a record 9th time in 1990?

10 Which horse won the Derby in 1990?

11 Which year saw a dead heat in the Nunthorpe Stakes?

12 Who rode High-Rise to win the Derby in 1998?

13 Which filly won the Irish Derby in 1994?

14 Where is the King George VI Chase run?

15 Which horse won the 1989 Oaks, only to be disqualified the following year?

***Answers to page 247***

**1** 5-2, **2** Greville Starkey, **3** 30, **4** Foinavon, **5** Richard Hills, **6** Devon Loch, **7** 1993, **8** Doncaster, **9** 8, **10** Moon Madness, **11** Three and over, **12** John Francome, **13** Tudor Minstrel, **14** Newmarket, **15** Frank Buckle.

# •HORSE RACING - QUIZ 11•

*Answers on page 244*

1 In which year was Fifinella the last filly to win the Derby?
2 What is a bet on the Cesarewitch and the Cambridgeshire called?
3 Which horse won all the Classics bar the Derby in 1902?
4 Where is the Scottish Grand National run?
5 Who rode to consecutive Irish Oaks wins in 1997 and 1998?
6 Which lady jockey died after a fall at Catterick in 1987?
7 Which horse won the Oaks by a record 12 lengths in 1983?
8 How many jumps are there in the Grand National?
9 Where are the Sussex Stakes run?
10 Who won his first 2000 Guineas on High Top in 1972?
11 Which horse won the 1991 Grand National under Nigel Hawke?
12 Which horse did Pat Eddery ride to win the 1996 1000 Guineas?
13 Which horse gave Walter Swinburn his first Middle Park Stakes win, in 1995?
14 Who has been Leading Owner a record 13 times?
15 Which horse won the St Leger in 1994?

***Trainer Martin Pipe's Ultimate Smoothie won at a Worcester meeting in May 1998 giving the trainer his 200th win of the season. This was the sixth time he had reached this landmark.***

## *Answers to page 244*

**1** Miinnehoma, **2** 1.5 miles, **3** Frankie Dettori, **4** Lammtarra, **5** Christy Roche, **6** The Kentucky Derby, **7** Tirol, **8** The Fillies Mile, **9** Longchamps, **10** Robert Robson, **11** Halling, **12** Bob Champion, **13** Rubio, **14** 1752, **15** Jamie Spencer.

# •HORSE RACING - QUIZ 12•

*Answers on page 245*

1 For which odds is Top of the Crust a bookmakers' term?

2 Who won his only Derby on Shirley Heights in 1978?

3 What record number of Classics has Lester Piggott won?

4 Which outsider won the 1967 Grand National?

5 Which jockey won his first 1000 Guineas on Harayir in 1995?

6 Which royal horse collapsed in the Grand National in 1956?

7 In which year was the Grand National void after a false start?

8 Where is the St Leger run?

9 How many nails are there in a horseshoe?

10 Which horse gave Pat Eddery his first St Leger win, in 1986?

11 After many changes, what age was finally settled on for horses in the Sussex Stakes?

12 Who stopped competing to draw the 1981/82 National Hunt jockey championship with the injured Peter Scudamore?

13 Which horse won the 2000 Guineas by a record 8 lengths in 1947?

14 Where are the Middle Park Stakes run?

15 Which jockey holds the record for the most Oaks wins, with 9?

---

## *Answers to page 245*

**1** Brian Fletcher, **2** George Fordham, **3** 6 furlongs, **4** Nijinsky, **5** Emily Davison, **6** Joe Mercer, **7** Oh So Sharp, **8** The Curragh, **9** Henry Cecil, **10** Quest for Fame, **11** 1997, **12** Olivier Peslier, **13** Balanchine, **14** Kempton Park, **15** Aliysa.

# •HORSE RACING - QUIZ 13•

*Answers on page 250*

1. Which horse won consecutive Ascot Gold Cups in 1992 and 1993?
2. In which year did Fairy Footsteps give Lester Piggott his 2nd 1000 Guineas win?
3. Which jockey won the Grand National a record 5 times?
4. Which horse won the Oaks in 1996?
5. How long is the hand, in which horses are measured?
6. Which horse won consecutive Grand Nationals in 1935 and 1936?
7. What is the highest fence in the Grand National?
8. Who rode Bob's Return to St Leger victory in 1993?
9. France's Poule d'Essai des Poulins is the equivalent of which English race?
10. In what year did Santa Claus win the Derby?
11. Where is the Coronation Cup run?
12. What were used for the first time at Newmarket on 8 July, 1965?
13. Where is the Steward's Cup run?
14. On which horse did Michael Hills win the Derby in 1996?
15. Who rode Medaaly to win the 1996 Racing Post Trophy?

---

## *Answers to page 249*

**1** Gerald Mosse, **2** Mark of Esteem, **3** The favourite, **4** Newmarket, **5** 1983, **6** Ben Nevis, **7** Doncaster, **8** Brian Rouse, **9** Triptych, **10** Desert Orchid, **11** Geraldine Rees, **12** Lord Gyllene, **13** Never Say Die, **14** 1975, **15** Red Rum.

# •HORSE RACING - QUIZ 14•

*Answers on page 248*

1 Which jockey won three of the French Classics in 1997?

2 Which horse gave Frankie Dettori his 2000 Guineas win in 1996?

3 What do bookmakers call the 'splonk'?

4 Where is the 2000 Guineas run?

5 In which year was Shergar kidnapped?

6 Which horse won the 1980 Grand National?

7 Where is the Racing Post Trophy run?

8 Who rode Quick As Lightning to win the 1980 1000 Guineas?

9 Which horse won consecutive Coronation Cups in 1987 and 1988?

10 Which grey won the Cheltenham Gold Cup in 1989?

11 Who was the first woman to complete the Grand National?

12 Which horse did Tony Dobbin ride to win the 1997 Grand National?

13 Which horse won the St Leger by a record 12 lengths in 1954?

14 In which year was the Diamond added to the King George VI & Queen Elizabeth Diamond Stakes?

15 Which is the only horse to have won the Grand National three times?

---

## *Answers to page 250*

**1** 1983, **2** Midway Lady, **3** Chepstow, **4** Newmarket Town Plate, **5** Trotting and pacing, **6** Golden Miller, **7** Lester Piggott, **8** 1989, **9** Benjamin Disraeli, **10** Generous, **11** Co. Kildare, **12** Gordon Richards, **13** The Oaks, **14** Shadayid, **15** Paul Cook.

# •HORSE RACING - QUIZ 15•

*Answers on page 249*

1 In which year did Corbiere win the Grand National?

2 Which horse gave Ray Cochrane his only Oaks win, in 1986?

3 Where is the Welsh Grand National run?

4 Which race was Eileen Joel the first woman to win, in 1925?

5 Which two gaits are used in harness racing?

6 Which horse won the Cheltenham Gold Cup a record five consecutive times in the 1930s?

7 Who won his first 2000 Guineas on Crepello in 1957?

8 In what year did Nashwan win the Derby?

9 Which primie minister called the Derby “the blue ribbon of the turf”?

10 Which horse was kind enough to win the Derby in 1991?

11 In which county is The Curragh race course?

12 Who was the first jockey to be knighted?

13 France's Prix de Diane Hermes is the equivalent of which English race?

14 Which horse gave Willie Carson his 2nd 1000 Guineas win in 1991?

15 Who rode Touching Wood to win the 1982 St Leger?

***On February 8th 1983 Shergar was kidnapped and £2,000,000 ransom was demanded. His owner the Aga Khan made it clear no ransom would be paid, the IRA were believed to be responsible but the real story was never told.***

## *Answers to page 248*

**1** Drum Taps, **2** 1981, **3** George Stevens, **4** Lady Carla, **5** Four inches, **6** Reynolstown, **7** The Chair, **8** Philip Robinson, **9** 2000 Guineas, **10** 1964, **11** Epsom, **12** Stalls, **13** Goodwood, **14** Shaamit, **15** Gary Hind.

# MOTOR RACING

# • FORMULA 1 - QUIZ 1 •

*Answers on page 254*

**1** In which year was the Formula 1 World Championship first held - 1950 or 1955?

**2** Which British circuit staged the first-ever World Championship Grand Prix?

**3** Which Italian driver was world champion in 1950?

**4** How many F1 Grands Prix did Jackie Stewart win - 17, 27 or 37?

**5** In 1970, which New Zealand driver was killed while testing a sports car at Goodwood?

**6** Which Stirling won the 1958 Argentine Grand Prix?

**7** In which decade was Stirling Moss born?

**8** In which year was the Constructors' Championship launched - 1958 or 1963?

**9** In which decade did Rene Arnoux make his F1 debut?

**10** Name the first man to win the opening four races of a season?

**11** In 1961, which Italian won the very first F1 Grand Prix that he entered?

**12** Which British driver won the 1956 Belgian Grand Prix?

**13** In which year did Rubens Barrichello make his F1 debut - 1989 or 1993?

**14** In which decade was French driver Jean Behra born?

**15** In which decade was Britain's Derek Bell born?

---

## *Answers to page 254*

**1** Patrese, **2** Four, **3** Estoril (Portugal), **4** McLaren-Honda, **5** Roland Ratzenberger, **6** True, **7** 1959, **8** Jordan, **9** Jacques Villeneuve, **10** 1975, **11** False - 1976, **12** 1945, **13** Four, **14** France, **15** Hill.

# • FORMULA 1 - QUIZ 2 •

*Answers on page 255*

**1** In which decade was Gerhard Berger born?

**2** Which Italian won the 1950 British Grand Prix?

**3** Which Briton won the Canadian Grand Prix in 1971 and 1972?

**4** In which country was Michele Alboreto born?

**5** In which decade was Swedish driver Joakim Bonnier born?

**6** When did Thierry Boutsen make his F1 debut - 1977 or 1983?

**7** Thierry Boutsen won his first Formula 1 Grand Prix in 1984 True or false?

**8** The FIA is the controlling body of the sport In which French city is it based?

**9** Which British driver won the 1977 Japanese Grand Prix?

**10** Who won the Constructors' Championship in 1994?

**11** From 1950 to 1960, the Indianapolis 500 formed part of the F1 World Championship True or false?

**12** In which decade was French legend Alain Prost born?

**13** Which Argentinian was world champion in 1951 and from 1954 to 1957?

**14** When was James Hunt born - 1947 or 1951?

**15** Name the Argentinian driver who won the British Grand Prix in 1951 and 1954?

***The success of the modern day MacLaren and their 1998 MP4-13 is due not only to the drivers but moreover the talents of their chief designer, Andrew Newey.***

---

*Answers to page 255*

**1** Stirling Moss, **2** 1960s, **3** Italy, **4** Johnny Herbert, **5** Stirling Moss, **6** 1970s, **7** Scheckter, **8** Silverstone, **9** France, **10** 1972, **11** Ayrton Senna, **12** Three, **13** Jack Brabham, **14** Twenty five, **15** Twelve.

# FORMULA 1 - QUIZ 3

*Answers on page 252*

1 Which Riccardo was European Formula Three champion in 1976?

2 How many times did British drivers win the Italian Grand Prix during the 1950s - 2, 4 or 6?

3 At which circuit did Ayrton Senna secure his first F1 victory?

4 Who won the Constructors' Championship in 1989 with 141 points?

5 Which Austrian was killed during qualifying at the 1994 San Marino Grand Prix?

6 Nigel Mansell won the German Grand Prix two years running during the 1990s True or false?

7 When was Martin Brundle born - 1959 or 1963?

8 For which team did Rubens Barrichello and Eddie Irvine drive during the 1995 season?

9 Which Canadian won the 1996 British Grand Prix?

10 In which year did James Hunt first win a F1 Grand Prix?

11 John Watson first won a F1 Grand Prix in 1971 True or false?

12 When was Belgian driver Jacky Ickx born - 1935 or 1945?

13 How many times did Jim Clark win the Dutch Grand Prix during the 1960s - 4, 6 or 8?

14 In which country was Jacques Laffite born?

15 Which Graham won the 1962 German Grand Prix?

## *Answers to page 252*

**1** 1950, **2** Silverstone, **3** Giuseppe Farina, **4** Twenty seven, **5** Bruce McLaren, **6** Moss, **7** 1920s, **8** 1958, **9** 1970s, **10** Ayrton Senna, **11** Giancarlo Baghetti, **12** Peter Collins, **13** 1993, **14** 1920s, **15** 1940s.

# • FORMULA 1 - QUIZ 4 •

*Answers on page 253*

**1** Which Briton won the 1958 Dutch Grand Prix - Stirling Moss or Jim Clark?

**2** In which decade was Ayrton Senna born?

**3** In which country was Riccardo Patrese born?

**4** Which Briton partnered Michael Schumacher at Benetton in 1995?

**5** Which British driver was World Championship runner-up from 1955 to 1958?

**6** In which decade did the American driver Peter Revson win the British Grand Prix?

**7** Which Jody won the British Grand Prix in 1974?

**8** Woodcote, Becketts and Hangar Straight are landmarks on which famous circuit?

**9** In which country was Jean Alesi born?

**10** When did Jean-Pierre Beltoise win the Monaco Grand Prix - 1972 or 1976?

**11** Which driver was on pole position a record 65 times in his 161 Grands Prix starts?

**12** How many times was Britain's Graham Hill runner-up in the World Championship?

**13** Name the first driver to win a F1 Grand Prix in a car of his own make?

**14** How old was Emerson Fittipaldi when he became world champion - 20, 25 or 30?

**15** How many times did Brands Hatch stage the British Grand Prix between 1964 and 1986 - 8, 12 or 16?

---

## *Answers to page 253*

**1** 1950s, **2** Giuseppe Farina, **3** Jackie Stewart, **4** Italy, **5** 1930s, **6** 1983, **7** False - 1989, **8** Paris, **9** James Hunt, **10** Williams-Renault, **11** True, **12** 1950s, **13** Juan Manuel Fangio, **14** 1947, **15** Jose Froilan Gonzalez.

# • FORMULA 1 - QUIZ 5 •

*Answers on page 258*

1 Who was the first driver to retain the F1 World Championship?

2 In which year was James Hunt's first season driving for McLaren?

3 How many races made-up the 1976 season - 12, 14 or 16?

4 How old was Juan Manuel Fangio when he won the 1957 World Championship - 36, 41 or 46?

5 Lotus-Ford won the 1970 Constructors' Championship with 59 points True or false?

6 At which German circuit did Niki Lauda have his near-fatal crash in 1976?

7 In 1977, which team marked their first-ever Grand Prix with a win?

8 What nationality was F1 driver Carlos Pace?

9 How old was Mario Andretti when he won the 1978 World Championship - 28, 38 or 48?

10 Ronnie Peterson won 10 Formula One Grands Prix during his career What nationality was he?

11 How many Grand Prix wins did Niki Lauda have during his 1977 Championship-winning season?

12 Which Briton was runner-up in the 1991 World Championship?

13 Which Brazilian won the British Grand Prix in 1975?

14 In which year did Jack Brabham win his first World Championship Grand Prix?

15 Which British driver was killed at the 1959 Moroccan Grand Prix?

***Damon Hill had some near misses before taking the World Drivers' Championship in 1996. He was third in 1993, second in 1994 and 1995.***

---

## *Answers to page 258*

**1** True, **2** Brands Hatch, **3** Belgium, **4** Colin Chapman, **5** Alberto Ascari, **6** John Surtees, **7** Jo Bonnier, **8** 2, **9** 1980s, **10** Bremgarten, **11** 1958, **12** 1950s, **13** 23, **14** Tyrell-Ford, **15** 1990s.

# • FORMULA 1 - QUIZ 6 •

*Answers on page 259*

**1** Which circuit staged the British Grand Prix from 1950 to 1954?

**2** Mike Hawthorn, in 1958, was the last world champion in a front-engined car True or false?

**3** How many times was Jacky Ickx runner-up in the World Championship?

**4** In which country was Jacky Ickx born?

**5** In which decade did the Arrows team make their F1 debut?

**6** Which team won the Constructors' Championship in 1995?

**7** In which decade did Briton's Mike Beuttler fail to win a point in 28 Grand Prix starts?

**8** How many different makes of car did Jackie Stewart drive to debut wins?

**9** Name the only driver to win a Grand Prix in his own country during 1984?

**10** In which year were drivers Graham Hill and Tony Brise killed in a plane crash?

**11** Who was the first South African driver to win a F1 Grand Prix?

**12** In which country was Nelson Piquet born?

**13** How old was Niki Lauda when he first became F1 world champion - 23, 26 or 29?

**14** In which year was the revamped Nurburgring re-opened - 1980 or 1984?

**15** In 1981, which Italian driver was acquitted of the manslaughter of Ronnie Peterson?

---

## *Answers to page 259*

**1** Chris Bristow and Alan Stacey, **2** France, **3** Nurburgring, **4** Juan Manuel Fangio, **5** Stirling Moss, **6** Niki Lauda, **7** 1970s, **8** Brazil, **9** Nigel Mansell, **10** France, **11** Forty three, **12** Forty four, **13** Seven, **14** Wolfgang von Trips, **15** Ten.

# • FORMULA 1 - QUIZ 7 •

*Answers on page 256*

**1** Mario Andretti was born in Italy True or false?

**2** Which British circuit staged the European Grand Prix in 1983 and 1985?

**3** In which country is the Zolder Grand Prix circuit?

**4** Which man founded Lotus?

**5** Which Italian driver won the British Grand Prix in 1952 and 1953?

**6** Which British driver won Grands Prix with both Ferrari and Cooper in 1966?

**7** Name the first Swedish driver to win a World Championship Grand Prix?

**8** How many British drivers scored points in the 1950 World Championship - 0, 2 or 4?

**9** In which decade did the Australian Grand Prix gain World Championship status?

**10** Which circuit was used for the Swiss Grand Prix between 1950 and 1954?

**11** In which year did Mike Hawthorn become the first British world champion?

**12** In which decade was French driver Philippe Alliot born?

**13** How old was Emerson Fittipaldi when he won his first F1 Grand Prix - 23, 25 or 27?

**14** Who won the Constructors' Championship in 1971 - Tyrell-Ford or Ferrari?

**15** In which decade did the legendary Juan Manuel Fangio die?

---

## *Answers to page 256*

**1** Alberto Ascari, **2** 1976, **3** Sicteen, **4** Forty six, **5** True, **6** Nurburgring, **7** Wolf, **8** Brazilian, **9** Thirty eight, **10** Swedish, **11** Three, **12** Nigel Mansell, **13** Emerson Fittipaldi, **14** 1959, **15** Stuart Lewis-Evans.

# • FORMULA 1 - QUIZ 8 •

*Answers on page 257*

**1** Which two Britons were killed at the 1960 Belgian Grand Prix?

**2** In which country did French legend Alain Prost win his first F1 Grand Prix race?

**3** At which German circuit did Jackie Stewart win the last of his 27 Formula 1 Grand Prix races?

**4** Which driver won the German Grand Prix three years in succession during the 1950s?

**5** Name the first home winner of the British Grand Prix?

**6** Who won the British Grand Prix in 1976, 1982 and 1984?

**7** In which decade did the Osterreichring stage its first World Championship Grand Prix?

**8** In which country is the Interlagos Grand Prix circuit?

**9** Who was prevented from winning the 1986 World Championship when his wheel exploded in the final race of the season?

**10** In which country was Didier Pironi born?

**11** How old was Giuseppe Farina when he won the 1950 World Championship - 38, 43 or 48?

**12** How old was Jack Brabham when he retired as a F1 driver - 44, 49 or 54?

**13** How many of the 10 rounds of the 1963 season did Jim Clark win?

**14** Which German driver was killed at Monza in the 1961 Italian Grand Prix?

**15** How many Grand Prix wins did the McLaren team have in 1989 - 8, 10 or 12?

---

## *Answers to page 257*

**1** Silverstone, **2** True, **3** 2, **4** Belgium, **5**1970s , **6** Benetton-Renault, **7** 1970s, **8** Three, **9** Niki Lauda, **10** 1975, **11** Jody Scheckter, **12** Brazil, **13** 26, **14** 1984, **15** .Riccardo Patrese

# • FORMULA 1 - QUIZ 9 •

*Answers on page 262*

**1** In which decade did Italian driver Lorenzo Bandini win the Austrian Grand Prix?

**2** Which Italian driver famously crashed his car into the harbour at the 1955 Monaco Grand Prix?

**3** At which circuit was Alberto Ascari killed in 1955?

**4** When did American driver Richie Ginther win the Mexican Grand Prix - 1965 or 1975?

**5** Maurice Trintignant won the Monaco Grand Prix in 1965 and 1968 True or false?

**6** How many rounds made-up the 1951 World Championship - 4, 8 or 12?

**7** Which make of car did 1950 world champion Giuseppe Farina drive?

**8** James Hunt won the British Grand Prix in 1977 True or false?

**9** For which team was he driving?

**10** In which decade did the Sauber team make their F1 debut?

**11** Which Briton won the 1989 and 1992 Brazilian Grands Prix?

**12** In how many different makes of car did Niki Lauda win F1 Grand Prix races?

**13** How many victories did British drivers have at the United States Grand Prix during the 1960s - 2, 4 or 8?

**14** Which circuit hosted the United States Grand Prix from 1961 to 1980?

**15** In which decade did Italian driver Piero Taruffi win the Swiss Grand Prix?

---

## *Answers to page 262*

**1** Four, **2** Argentina, **3** McLaren-Honda, **4** 1970s, **5** Jean-Pierre Jabouille, **6** 1960s, **7** Mosport, **8** Gilles Villeneuve, **9** Jim Clark, **10** 1980s, **11** 1930s, **12** Autria, **13** Carlos Reutemann, **14** True, **15** Ayrton Senna and Alain Prost.

# • FORMULA 1 - QUIZ 10 •

*Answers on page 263*

1 In 1965, who won their second Constructors' Championship with 54 points?

2 In which decade was Martin Brundle born?

3 In which decade was Mario Andretti born?

4 How many times was Jackie Stewart runner-up in the World Championship?

5 In which country was Jochen Mass born?

6 Name the first American driver to win a F1 Grand Prix?

7 Stirling Moss won F1 Grands Prix in five different makes of car True or false?

8 Which Italian driver made his F1 debut in the 1981 San Marino Grand Prix?

9 Name the only two drivers to win Grands Prix at the three British circuits - Silverstone, Aintree and Brands Hatch?

10 At which German circuit did John Surtees win his first Grand Prix?

11 At which Grand Prix circuit is the Brabham Straight?

12 How old was Jim Clark when he first became F1 world champion - 22, 27 or 32?

13 Name the first man to achieve fifty F1 Grand Prix wins?

14 Which Jonathan was European Formula Two champion in 1983?

15 Name the first Finnish driver to win a F1 Grand Prix?

***Only one Argentinian has ever won the Formula One Drivers' Championship, winning it five times in total. The name; Fangio.***

---

*Answers to page 263*

**1** 1980s, **2** Bruce McLaren, **3** 1, **4** Stirling Moss, **5** Jean Alesi, **6** Patrick Depailler, **7** 2, **8** South Africa, **9** 1960s, **10** Japan, **11** True, **12** Michael Schumacher, **13** Jody Scheckter, **14** Australia, **15** 1920s.

# • FORMULA 1 - QUIZ 11 •

*Answers on page 260*

**1** How many Grands Prix did Jack Brabham win during the 1966 season - 1, 4 or 7?

**2** In which country was Carlos Reutemann born?

**3** Who won the Constructors' Championship in 1988?

**4** During which decade did French driver Francois Cevert win the United States Grand Prix?

**5** In 1979, which driver become the first winner of a F1 Grand Prix in a turbo-powered car?

**6** In which decade was the Canadian Grand Prix accorded World Championship status?

**7** Which circuit staged the first Canadian Grand Prix?

**8** Which driver had a Canadian circuit named after him?

**9** Which British driver won the Belgian Grand Prix four times during the 1960s?

**10** In which decade did the Minardi team make their F1 debut?

**11** In which decade was Graham Hill born?

**12** In which country is the Osterreichring Grand Prix circuit?

**13** Which Argentinian driver won the 1978 British Grand Prix?

**14** In 1988, McLaren won 15 of the 16 Grands Prix True or false?

**15** Which two drivers drove for McLaren in 1988?

## *Answers to page 260*

**1** 1960s, **2** Alberto Ascari, **3** Monza, **4** 1965, **5** False - 1955 and 1958, **6** Eight, **7** Alfa Romeo, **8** True, **9** McLaren, **10** 1990s, **11** Nigel Mansell, **12** Three, **13** Eight, **14** Watkins Glen, **15** 1950s.

# • FORMULA 1 - QUIZ 12 •

*Answers on page 261*

1 In which decade did Enzo Ferrari die?

2 Name the first New Zealand driver to win a Formula One Grand Prix race?

3 When Keke Rosberg won the 1982 World Championship, how many Grands Prix did he win?

4 Which British driver won a race every season from 1955 to 1961?

5 Which French driver gained his first Grand Prix victory at Montreal in 1995?

6 In 1980, which French driver was killed testing an Alfa Romeo at Hockenheim?

7 How many Grand Prix victories did Patrick Depailler have?

8 In which country is the Kyalami circuit?

9 During which decade did Matra-Ford win the Constructors' Championship?

10 In which country is the Suzuka circuit?

11 Cooper-Climax won the Constructors' Championship in 1959 True or false?

12 Which winner of the 1994 Belgium Grand Prix was disqualified because the skid-block on his car was too thin?

13 Which South African driver had 10 Grand Prix wins between 1972 and 1980?

14 In which country was Jack Brabham born?

15 In which decade was Jack Brabham born?

---

## *Answers to page 261*

**1** Lotus-Climax, **2** 1950s, **3** 1940s, **4** Two, **5** Germany, **6** Johnnie Parson, **7** True, **8** Michele Alboreto, **9** Jim Clark and Jack Brabham, **10** Nurburgring, **11** Adelaide (Australia), **12** 27, **13** Alain Prost, **14** Palmer, **15** Keke Rosberg.

# • FORMULA 1 - QUIZ 13 •

*Answers on page 266*

1 How many Grand Prix wins did Graham Hill have between 1958 and 1975 - 10, 14 or 18?

2 In which decade did Jean Alesi make his F1 debut?

3 In which country was Bruce McLaren born?

4 Which driver won the 1955 British Grand Prix - Stirling Moss or John Surtees?

5 In which country is the Paul Ricard circuit?

6 Which British driver won the 1966 Belgian Grand Prix?

7 In which decade did Clay Regazzoni win the British Grand Prix?

8 In 1968, which Briton won the German Grand Prix by more than four minutes?

9 Name the first communist country to stage a F1 Grand Prix?

10 In which country was Keke Rosberg born?

11 How old was Ayrton Senna when he first became F1 world champion - 18, 23 or 28?

12 Which Rene was European Formula Two champion in 1977?

13 Which Briton was F1 world champion in 1969, 1971 and 1973?

14 When was the first World Championship Grand Prix staged in Japan - 1966 or 1976?

15 Which Italian Formula One driver won 13 Grands Prix between 1951 and 1955?

---

## *Answers to page 266*

**1** Nigel Mansell, **2** True, **3** Williams-Ford, **4** 1970s, **5** Juan Manuel Fangio, **6** Six, **7** Emerson Fittipaldi, **8** 1970s, **9** Riccardo Paletti, **10** Zandvoort, **11** 1990s, **12** Alain Prost, **13** Five, **14** True, **15** McLaren-Honda.

# • FORMULA 1 - QUIZ 14 •

*Answers on page 267*

1 When did Nigel Mansell make his F1 debut - 1977 or 1980?

2 Which French driver was killed during practice at Watkins Glen in 1973?

3 In which year did Nigel Mansell win his first Grand Prix as a Ferrari driver?

4 In which decade did Jody Scheckter become world champion?

5 In which country was Jody Scheckter born?

6 How many times was Nigel Mansell World Championship runner-up during the 1980s?

7 In which decade did Brabham-Repco win their first Constructors' Championship?

8 Nigel Mansell won the 1986 Belgian Grand Prix True or false?

9 Who won the Constructors' Championship in 1987 with 137 points?

10 Which Australian driver won the 1980 British Grand Prix?

11 In which country is the Hockenheim circuit?

12 Which British driver won the German Grand Prix in 1963 and 1964?

13 In 1972, who won the Constructors' Championship with 61 points?

14 How old was Jack Brabham when he won the 1966 World Championship - 30, 40 or 50?

15 In which decade did Elio de Angelis make his F1 debut?

***Eleven different constructors have won the title in the forty years since it's inception in 1958. The first being Vanwall, the last McLaren.***

---

*Answers to page 267*

**1** Jochen Rindt, **2** San Paulo, **3** Nigel Mansell, **4** Three, **5** 1930s, **6** 1990s, **7** Italy, **8** Hunt, **9** Jackie Stewart, **10** Lotus-Ford, **11** True, **12** James Hunt, **13** Seventeen, **14** True, **15** Thirteen.

# • FORMULA 1 - QUIZ 15 •

*Answers on page 264*

1 Name the seventh Briton to become F1 world champion?

2 Nigel Mansell won the 1992 World Championship by 52 points True or false?

3 Who won the Constructors' Championship in 1981 with 95 points?

4 In which decade did the Tyrrell team make their F1 debut?

5 Which Argentinian driver won the 1956 British Grand Prix?

6 How many of the 11 races of the 1971 season did Jackie Stewart win - 3, 6 or 9?

7 Name the first Brazilian to become world champion?

8 In which decade was Jacques Villeneuve born?

9 Which Italian driver was killed at the 1982 Canadian Grand Prix?

10 At which Dutch circuit did British driver Roger Williamson lose his life in 1973?

11 In which decade did the Pacific team make their F1 debut?

12 Name the first French driver to win the F1 World Championship?

13 How many Grand Prix wins did Jack Brabham have in 1960 - 5, 8 or 11?

14 John Watson won the 1981 British Grand Prix True or false?

15 Who won the Constructors' Championship in 1991?

## *Answers to page 264*

**1** Fourteen, **2** 1980s, **3** New Zealand, **4** Stirling Moss, **5** France, **6** John Surtees, **7** 1970s, **8** Jackie Stewart, **9** Hungary, **10** Sweden, **11** Twenty eight, **12** Arnoux, **13** Jackie Stewart, **14** 1976, **15** Alberto Ascari.

# • FORMULA 1 - QUIZ 16 •

*Answers on page 265*

1 Which Austrian driver was world champion in 1970?

2 In which Brazilian city is Ayrton Senna buried?

3 Which British driver won the 1987 Austrian Grand Prix?

4 How many times was Nelson Piquet world champion during the 1980s?

5 In which decade was John Surtees born?

6 In which decade did the Forti team make their F1 debut?

7 In which country is the Monza Grand Prix circuit?

8 Which James won the Dutch Grand Prix in 1975 and 1976?

9 In 1973, which driver set a new record of 27 Grand Prix victories?

10 Who won the Constructors' Championship in 1973 - Lotus Ford or Ferrari?

11 Ferrari made their F1 debut in 1950 True or false?

12 Who won the 1976 Spanish Grand Prix, only to be disqualified because his car was too wide and then had the win restored?

13 At what age was Ayrton Senna South American kart champion?

14 Ferrari won the Constructors' Championship in 1982 True or false?

15 How many of Jack Brabham's 126 Grand Prix starts were from pole position - 7, 13 or 19?

---

*Answers to page 265*

**1** 1980, **2** Francois Cevert, **3** 1989, **4** 1970s, **5** South Africa, **6** Two, **7** 1960s, **8**True , **9** Williams-Honda, **10** Alan Jones, **11** Germany, **12** John Surtees, **13** Lotus-Ford, **14** Forty, **15** 1970s.

# • FORMULA 1 - QUIZ 17 •

*Answers on page 270*

**1** Which British driver won the German Grand Prix in 1958 and 1959?

**2** For which team was Jody Scheckter driving when he became world champion in 1979?

**3** In which year was Gilles Villeneuve killed in practice at the Belgian Grand Prix?

**4** Which French driver won the 1979 European Formula Three crown?

**5** Which Briton won the Belgian Grand Prix in 1993 and 1994?

**6** In which decade was Britain's Tony Brooks born?

**7** When did Martin Brundle make his F1 debut - 1984 or 1988?

**8** How old was Nelson Piquet when he first became F1 world champion - 23, 26 or 29?

**9** Which Swiss driver won the 1968 British Grand Prix?

**10** Who won their first Constructors' Championship in 1974?

**11** In which year did Alain Prost first win the British Grand Prix - 1983 or 1986?

**12** In which year did James Hunt retire from F1?

**13** How many Grand Prix wins did Niki Lauda achieve between 1971 and 1985 - 15, 20 or 25?

**14** How many Grand Prix victories did Alain Prost have in the 1988 season?

**15** Which Briton won the 1986 Canadian Grand Prix?

***The Scheckter brothers, Jody and Ian and the Fittipaldi's, Emerson and Wilson were the last sets of brothers to race against each other in Formula One before the advent of the Schumachers.***

---

## *Answers to page 270*

**1** 1985, **2** Jackie Stewart, **3** Six, **4** Italian (Monza), **5** Ferrari, **6** Eight, **7** Thirty five, **8** 108, **9** 1985, **10** Italian, **11** True, **12** Denny Hulme, **13** Twenty five, **14** Jim Clark, **15** Damon Hill.

# • FORMULA 1 - QUIZ 18 •

*Answers on page 271*

**1** In which country is the Spa-Francorchamps circuit?

**2** Who won the Constructors' Championship in 1983?

**3** Which Peter won the 1958 British Grand Prix?

**4** How old was Graham Hill when he won the 1968 World Championship - 33, 38 or 43?

**5** Which Australian was world champion in 1959, 1960 and 1966?

**6** How many Grand Prix wins did the Williams team have in 1993 - 6, 9 or 12?

**7** How old was Emerson Fittipaldi when he became world champion in 1972?

**8** Which make of car did Juan Manuel Fangio drive to the 1951 World Championship?

**9** Benetton were formed in 1986 from the former Toleman team True or false?

**10** Which British driver won the 1973 Belgian Grand Prix?

**11** How many times did British drivers win the Italian Grand Prix during the 1960s -2, 4 or 6?

**12** In which decade did the McLaren team make their F1 debut?

**13** Who replaced Damon Hill at Williams in 1997?

**14** Who won the Constructors' Championship in 1993 with 168 points?

**15** Which was the last season of the turbo-charged car -1984 or 1988?

---

## *Answers to page 271*

**1** 1960s, **2** Mike Hawthorn, **3** Twenty nine, **4** James Hunt, **5** Nigel Mansell, **6** Ferrari, **7** 1970s, **8** 1976, **9** True, **10** Three, **11** Ayrton Senna, **12** Rosberg, **13** Alain Prost, **14** 1975, **15** John Surtees, Graham Hill and Jim Clark.

# • FORMULA 1 - QUIZ 19 •

*Answers on page 268*

**1** In which year did Nigel Mansell win his first F1 Grand Prix?

**2** Which British driver won the 1972 Argentine Grand Prix?

**3** How many Grand Prix victories did Jackie Stewart have during the 1971 season?

**4** At which 1971 Grand Prix did 061 of a second separate the first five cars?

**5** Who won their third Constructors' Championship in 1975?

**6** How many races made up the 1961 World Championship - 5, 8 or 11?

**7** How old was Niki Lauda when he won the 1984 World Championship - 30, 35 or 40?

**8** How many points did Nigel Mansell score during the 1992 season - 88, 98 or 108?

**9** In which year did Ayrton Senna win his first Grand Prix?

**10** What nationality was Elio de Angelis?

**11** Alberto Ascari is the only driver to win maximum points in a season True or false?

**12** Which New Zealand driver was world champion in 1967?

**13** How many Grand Prix wins did Jim Clark have between 1960 and 1968 - 25, 35 or 45?

**14** Which Briton won a Grand Prix in every season from 1962 to 1968?

**15** Which Briton won the 1994 Japanese Grand Prix?

## *Answers to page 268*

**1** Tony Brooks, **2** Ferrari, **3** 1982, **4**Alain Prost , **5** Damon Hill, **6** 1930s, **7** 1984, **8** Twenty nine, **9** Jo Siffert, **10** McLaren (Ford engine), **11** 1983, **12** 1979, **13** Twenty five, **14** Seven, **15** Nigel Mansell.

# • FORMULA 1 - QUIZ 20 •

*Answers on page 269*

**1** In which decade was the Mexican Grand Prix granted World Championship status?

**2** Which British driver won the French Grand Prix in 1958?

**3** How old was Mike Hawthorn when he became F1 world champion - 23, 26 or 29?

**4** Which British driver won the French Grand Prix in 1976?

**5** Name the only Briton to win the Hungarian Grand Prix during the 1980s?

**6** Who won their fourth Constructors' Championship in 1976?

**7** In which decade did the Williams team make their F1 debut?

**8** In which year did Britain's James Hunt become world champion?

**9** James Hunt won the 1976 World Championship by a single point True or false?

**10** How many times did Alain Prost finish as runner-up in the World Championship during the 1980s?

**11** Name the only driver to win three F1 world titles before the age of 32?

**12** Which Keke was F1 world champion in 1982?

**13** Which French driver was European Formula Three champion in 1979?

**14** In which year was Jacques Laffite European Formula Two champion - 1970 or 1975?

**15** Name the British drivers who finished 1st, 2nd and 3rd in the 1964 World Championship?

---

## *Answers to page 269*

**1** Belgium, **2** Ferrari, **3** Collins, **4** Thirty eight, **5** Jack Brabham, **6** Nine, **7** Twenty five, **8** Alfa Romeo, **9** True, **10** Jackie Stewart, **11** Six, **12** 1960s, **13** Heinz-Harald Frentzen, **14** Williams-Renault, **15** 1988.

# • FORMULA 1 - QUIZ 21 •

*Answers on page 274*

1 Name the first American to be crowned F1 world champion?

2 Which Italian driver was killed while testing his Brabham at Paul Ricard in 1986?

3 Who 'collided' with Damon Hill in the crucial final race of the 1994 season?

4 Name the first South American country to hold a World Championship Grand Prix?

5 Which Briton was F1 world champion in 1996?

6 How many times did the Aintree circuit host the British Grand Prix - 3, 5 or 7?

7 Which make of car did Juan Manuel Fangio drive to the 1955 World Championship?

8 How many F1 Grand Prix wins did Sweden's Ronnie Peterson have?

9 Who won the Constructors' Championship in 1977?

10 In which decade did the Ligier team make their F1 debut?

11 When did Ludovico Scarfiotti win the Italian Grand Prix - 1960 or 1966?

12 In which decade did the Lotus team make their F1 debut?

13 Which Mario was F1 world champion in 1978?

14 When was Patrick Depailler born - 1944 or 1950?

15 Which Michele was European Formula Three champion in 1980?

***Among Formula One's most celebrated fans' are Mick Jagger and Jimmy White and Prince Phillip.***

---

## *Answers to page 274*

**1** Alessandro Nannini, **2** Emerson Fittipaldi, **3** 1970s, **4** Austrian, **5** Holland, **6** Five, **7** Alain Prost, **8** 1970s, **9** Graham Hill, **10** McLaren-Honda, **11** True, **12** Ferrari, **13** Stirling Moss, **14** Italian, **15** Ten.

# • FORMULA 1 - QUIZ 22 •

*Answers on page 275*

1 How old was Nelson Piquet when he won the 1987 World Championship - 32, 35 or 38?

2 How many Grand Prix wins did Damon Hill have in 1996?

3 How many world championship points did Jack Brabham amass between 1955 and 1970 - 161, 261 or 361?

4 How many times was Alain Prost F1 world champion during the 1980s?

5 At which German circuit was Britain's John Taylor killed in 1966?

6 How many points did Nigel Mansell finish the 1992 season with - 88, 98 or 108?

7 Who partnered Nigel Mansell at Williams in 1992?

8 Which Brazilian driver had 23 Grand Prix wins between 1978 and 1991?

9 How old was James Hunt when he became world champion?

10 Which driver won a Grand Prix in every season from 1985 to 1993?

11 In which decade did Lella Lombardi of Italy become the first woman to finish in the top six in a F1 Grand Prix?

12 Who won the Constructors' Championship in 1978?

13 In which country was Marco Apicella born?

14 In which year did John Watson win the Belgian Grand Prix - 1978 or 1982?

15 Which Patrick was European Formula Two champion in 1974?

---

## *Answers to page 275*

**1** Fourteen, **2** Peter Gethin, **3** Fifteen, **4** Michael Schumacher, **5** Three, **6** 1960, **7** Jacques Villeneuve, **8** True, **9** Hunt the Shunt, **10** France, **11** Ferrari, **12** Jack Brabham, **13** Williams-Ford, **14** Jackie Stewart, **15** 29.

# • FORMULA 1 - QUIZ 23 •

*Answers on page 272*

1 Which Italian driver won the 1989 Japanese Grand Prix at Suzuka?

2 Which Brazilian driver won 14 Formula One Grands Prix between 1970 and 1980?

3 In which decade did Frenchman Didier Pironi make his F1 debut?

4 What nationality is Niki Lauda?

5 In which country is the Zandvoort Grand Prix circuit?

6 How many Grand Prix victories did Alain Prost have in 1985 - 5, 7 or 9?

7 Which driver won his 4th World Championship in 1993?

8 In which decade did Tyrell launch a six-wheeled F1 car?

9 Which Briton was F1 world champion in 1962 and 1968?

10 Who won the Constructors' Championship in 1986?

11 Jackie Stewart won the German Grand Prix three times as a driver True or false?

12 Who won the Constructors' Cup in 1979?

13 Which British driver won the 1961 German Grand Prix?

14 What nationality is Pierluigi Martini?

15 How many Grand Prix wins did the McLaren team have in 1992 - 7, 10 or 13?

## *Answers to page 272*

**1** Phil Hill, **2** Elio de Angelis, **3** Michael Schumacher, **4**Argentina , **5** Damon Hill, **6** Five, **7** Mercedes-Benz, **8** Ten, **9** Ferrari, **10** 1970s, **11** 1966, **12** 1950s, **13** Andretti, **14** 1944, **15** Alboreto.

# • FORMULA 1 - QUIZ 24 •

*Answers on page 273*

**1** How many successive Grand Prix wins did Ferrari have between 1952 and 1953 - 10, 14 or 18?

**2** Name the British driver who won the 1971 Italian Grand Prix?

**3** How many Grand Prix wins did the McLaren team have in 1988?

**4** Who was F1 world champion in 1995?

**5** How many Grand Prix wins did Damon Hill have with Williams in 1993?

**6** When was Damon Hill born - 1958 or 1960?

**7** Who partnered Damon Hill at Williams in 1996?

**8** Johnny Herbert won the 1995 British Grand Prix True or false?

**9** What was James Hunt's nickname?

**10** In which country was Rene Arnoux born?

**11** Who won the Constructors' Championship in 1964 - Ferrari or Vanwall?

**12** Which Australian driver had 14 Grand Prix victories between 1955 and 1970?

**13** Who won the Constructors' Championship in 1980?

**14** Which Briton won the Dutch Grand Prix in 1968, 1969 and 1973?

**15** How old was Jody Scheckter when he became world champion?

---

## *Answers to page 273*

**1** Thirty five, **2** Seven, **3** 261, **4** Three, **5** Nurburgring, **6** 108, **7** Riccardo Patrese, **8** Nelson Piquet, **9** Twenty nine, **10** Ayrton Senna, **11** 1970s, **12** Lotus-Ford, **13** Italy, **14** 1982, **15** Depailler.

# • FORMULA 1 - QUIZ 25 •

*Answers on page 278*

1 In which year did French driver Patrick Tambay win his first F1 Grand Prix?

2 Name the only driver to win a F1 Grand Prix in his native country during the 1973 season?

3 Which Australian was F1 world champion in 1980?

4 In which decade was Jackie Stewart born?

5 Which Mexican driver won the 1967 South African Grand Prix?

6 In which country is the Autodromo Hermanos Rodriguez Grand Prix circuit?

7 Which Briton won the Monaco Grand Prix five times between 1963 and 1969?

8 Name the first driver to win Formula One and Indy Car championships in successive seasons?

9 Name the first African country to stage a World Championship Grand Prix?

10 Which former world champion died in June 1993, aged 45?

11 How old was Mario Andretti when he won the 1978 World Championship - 28, 33 or 38?

12 In which year did Jackie Stewart retire from Formula 1?

13 Who won the Constructors' Championship in 1963?

14 How many Grand Prix wins did Niki Lauda have in his first F1 season?

15 In which decade did the Toleman team make their F1 debut?

---

## *Answers to page 278*

**1** Austrian, **2** Eight, **3** Herbert, **4** 1964, **5** Carel Godin de Beaufort, **6** Williams-Ford, **7** Monaco, **8** Italian, **9** Williams-Renault, **10** 1920s, **11** Jochen Rindt, **12** Monza, **13** James Hunt, **14** Eight, **15** Jacques Villeneuve.

# • FORMULA 1 - QUIZ 26 •

*Answers on page 279*

1 Which Belfast-born driver won the 1976 Austrian Grand Prix?

2 How old was Juan Manuel Fangio when he won the 1957 World Championship?

3 In which decade did the Lola team make their F1 debut?

4 Which Austrian driver suffered horrific burns in the 1976 German Grand Prix?

5 In which country was Rubens Barrichello born?

6 Which Argentinian driver had 24 Grand Prix wins between 1950 and 1958?

7 Which Briton was F1 world champion in 1963 and 1965?

8 Johnny Dumfries was British Formula Three champion in 1984 In which year did he make his F1 debut?

9 In which decade was Jacques Laffite born?

10 Name the first man to become world champion on two wheels and also four wheels?

11 Who was F1 world champion in 1990 and 1991?

12 Which Briton won the 1976 Canadian Grand Prix?

13 Which Swedish driver was European Formula Two champion in 1971?

14 How old was Ayrton Senna when he was killed?

15 How many times did Nigel Mansell win the French Grand Prix during the 1980s?

***Graham Hill, Damon's father, another of the charismatic drivers of the 1960s and 1970s, won two World Championships yet he was 24 before he learned to drive.***

*Answers to page 279*

**1** Magny Cours, **2** 1991, **3** 1960s, **4** Nelson Piquet at Imola (1980 Italian and 1981 San Marino), **5** Nigel Mansell at Brands Hatch (1985 European & 1986 British), **6** 1994, **7** True, **8** Vanwall, **9** 1990, **10** Twelve, **11** Nigel Mansell, **12** Germany, **13** 1988, **14** ,Rene Arnoux **15** Imola.

# • FORMULA 1 - QUIZ 27 •

*Answers on page 276*

1 What nationality is Gerhard Berger?

2 How many races made-up the 1951 World Championship?

3 Which Johnny was British Formula Three champion in 1987?

4 When was British driver Johnny Herbert born - 1960 or 1964?

5 Which Dutch driver lost his life at the Nurburgring in 1964?

6 Who won the Constructors' Championship in 1981?

7 At which circuit is the Monte Carlo Grand Prix staged?

8 What nationality is Andrea de Cesaris?

9 Who won the Constructors' Championship in 1992?

10 In which decade was Mike Hawthorn born?

11 In 1970, which Austrian driver became the first posthumous world champion?

12 At which Italian circuit was Jochen Rindt killed?

13 Who won the 1976 British Grand Prix but was later disqualified because his car had been illegally repaired during the race?

14 How many Grand Prix wins did McLaren have in 1991?

15 Who was F1 world champion in 1997?

---

## *Answers to page 276*

**1** 1982, **2** Emerson Fittipaldi, **3** Alan Jones, **4** 1930s, **5** Pedro Rodriguez, **6** Mexico, **7** Graham Hill, **8** Nigel Mansell, **9** Morocco, **10** James Hunt, **11** Thirty eight, **12** 1973, **13** Lotus-Climax, **14** Two, **15** 1980s.

# • FORMULA 1 - QUIZ 28 •

*Answers on page 277*

**1** At which circuit was the 1991 French Grand Prix staged?

**2** In which year did Italy's Alessandro Zanardi make his F1 debut - 1991 or 1994?

**3** In which decade was Mark Blundell born?

**4** Name the first driver to win two different F1 Grands Prix on the same circuit in successive years?

**5** Name the second driver to achieve this feat?

**6** In which year did Michael Schumacher win his first F1 World Championship?

**7** The first Australian Grand Prix was held in 1928 True or false?

**8** Who won the Constructors' Championship in 1958 - Vanwall or Ferrari?

**9** In which year was the 500th World Championship Grand Prix held?

**10** How many Grand Prix wins did the McLaren team have in 1984 - 8, 10 or 12?

**11** Which British driver won the 1994 Australian Grand Prix?

**12** In which country is the Nurburgring Grand Prix circuit?

**13** In which year did Ayrton Senna first become world champion?

**14** Which French driver had seven Grand Prix wins between 1978 and 1989?

**15** At which Grand Prix circuit was Ayrton Senna killed in 1994?

---

## *Answers to page 277*

**1** John Watson, **2** Forty six, **3** 1960s, **4** Niki Lauda, **5** Brazil, **6** Juan Manuel Fangio, **7**Jim Clark , **8** 1986, **9** 1940s, **10** John Surtees, **11**Ayrton Senna , **12** James Hunt, **13** Ronnie Peterson, **14** Thirty four, **15** Two.

# • FORMULA 1 - QUIZ 29 •

*Answers on page 282*

**1** What nationality is Thierry Boutsen?

**2** In which decade did Italian driver Vittorio Brambilla win the Austrian Grand Prix?

**3** How many Grand Prix wins did Lotus have in 1978 - 8, 10 or 12?

**4** Which Briton won the 1958 Dutch Grand Prix?

**5** How old was Niki Lauda when he won the 1984 World Championship - 35, 38 or 41?

**6** Which Swedish driver won his only Grand Prix in 1977?

**7** At which Italian circuit did Jackie Stewart score his first F1 Grand Prix win?

**8** How many Grands Prix did American driver Dan Gurney win between 1959 and 1970?

**9** Who won the Constructors' Championship in 1985?

**10** Clay Regazzoni was European Formula Two champion in 1970 True or false?

**11** In which year was the 250th Grand Prix staged?

**12** How old was Jackie Stewart when he retired from F1 in 1973?

**13** The French Grand Prix was first held in 1906 True or false?

**14** When was the first German Grand Prix held - 1926 or 1936?

**15** Pierluigi Martini was European Formula Three champion in 1973 True or false?

---

*Answers to page 282*

**1** 1978, **2** True, **3** 1920s, **4** 1988, **5** 289, **6** 281, **7** 1971, **8** Nigel Mansell, **9** Two, **10** 274, **11** German, **12** True, **13** Eighteen, **14** Jim Clark, **15** Argentina.

# • FORMULA 1 - QUIZ 30 •

*Answers on page 283*

**1** Which German driver, born in 1928, was known as 'Taffy'?

**2** In which decade did Wilson Fittipaldi - brother of Emerson - make his F1 debut?

**3** Which driver won the 1978 Canadian Grand Prix?

**4** In which decade was Gilles Villeneuve born?

**5** Which Briton won the 1986 Canadian Grand Prix?

**6** Which French driver competed in 136 Grands Prix between 1971 and 1983 without a win?

**7** Which two drivers drove for Ferrari in 1997?

**8** Which driver was F1 world champion in 1998?

**9** In which year was the 100th Grand Prix raced?

**10** How many of the 16 rounds of the 1989 season did McLaren win - 10, 12 or 14?

**11** Which Briton was world champion in 1964?

**12** In which country is the Watkins Glen Grand Prix circuit?

**13** In which season did Ayrton Senna make his F1 debut?

**14** With which team?

**15** In which position did Ayrton Senna finish in his first F1 season - 3rd, 6th or 9th?

***The dangers of Formula One are obvious and in Monaco in 1955 Alberto Ascari driving his Lancia D50 crashed through the harbour wall and Ascari had to be dragged out from the sea!***

---

*Answers to page 283*

**1** The race has been stopped, **2** All clear, **3** Brazil, **4** Thirteen, **5** 1950s, **6** 1979, **7** 1980, **8** Thirty three, **9** Six, **10** 1950s, **11** Nigel Mansell, **12** Nine, **13** 1960s, **14** Five, **15** Tony Brooks.

# • FORMULA 1 - QUIZ 31 •

*Answers on page 280*

**1** In which year was the 300th Grand Prix staged?

**2** The Belgian Grand Prix was first raced in 1925 True or false?

**3** In which decade was the first Italian Grand Prix held?

**4** When did Britain's Julian Bailey make his F1 debut -1985 or 1988?

**5** How many points did Graham Hill win during his F1 career -189, 289 or 389?

**6** How many championship points did Emerson Fittipaldi score between 1970 and 1980 - 181, 281 or 381?

**7** In which year was the 200th Grand Prix staged?

**8** Name the first driver to win the opening five races of a season?

**9** How many Grands Prix did John Surtees win in 1964?

**10** How many points did Jim Clark score in his F1 career - 274, 374 or 474?

**11** What nationality is F1 driver Heinz-Harald Frentzen?

**12** Seven British drivers scored points in the 1969 World Championship True or false?

**13** How many of Mario Andretti's 128 Grand Prix starts were from pole position - 8, 18 or 28?

**14** Which racing legend lost his life in a Formula Two race at Hockenheim in 1968?

**15** In which country was Juan Manuel Fangio born?

---

## *Answers to page 280*

**1** Belgian, **2** 1970s, **3** Eight, **4** Stirling Moss, **5** Thirty five, **6** Gunnar Nilsson, **7** Monza, **8** Four, **9** McLaren-TAG, **10** True, **11** 1978, **12** Thirty four, **13** True, **14** 1926, **15** False - 1983.

# • FORMULA 1 - QUIZ 32 •

*Answers on page 281*

1 What does a red flag signify during a Grand Prix race?

2 What does a green flag signify during a Grand Prix?

3 In which country was F1 driver Pedro Diniz born?

4 How many of Graham Hill's 176 Grand Prix starts were from pole position - 13, 19 or 25?

5 In which decade was Italian driver Roberto Moreno born?

6 In which year did the Williams team win their first F1 Grand Prix?

7 In which year did the Williams team win their first world drivers' title?

8 How many of Jim Clark's 72 Grand Prix starts were from pole position?

9 How many Grands Prix did Gilles Villeneuve win between 1977 and 1982?

10 In which decade was Piercalo Ghinzani born?

11 Which Briton was F1 world champion in 1992?

12 How many Grands Prix did Nigel Mansell win during the 1992 season?

13 In which decade was Jacky Ickx European Formula Two champion?

14 How many Grand Prix wins did Niki Lauda have in the 1975 season?

15 Which British driver won the 1959 French Grand Prix?

---

## *Answers to page 281*

**1** Wolfgang von Trips, **2** 1970s, **3** Gilles Villeneuve, **4** 1950s, **5** Nigel Mansell, **6** Jean-Pierre Jarier, **7** Michael Schumacher and Eddie Irvine, **8** Mika Hakkinen, **9** 1961, **10** Ten, **11** John Surtees, **12** USA, **13** 1984, **14** Toleman, **15** 9th.

# • FORMULA 1 - QUIZ 33 •

*Answers on page 286*

1 BRM won the Constructors' Championship in 1962 True or false?

2 Which British driver won the 1958 Belgian Grand Prix?

3 Which 20 year old Mexican finished in fourth position in the 1962 Belgian Grand Prix?

4 For which team did Ayrton Senna drive his debut Grand Prix?

5 How old was Bruce McLaren when he won his first Formula One Grand Prix - 22, 25 or 28?

6 How old was Troy Ruttman when he won the 1952 Indianapolis 500?

7 In which country is the Estoril Grand Prix circuit?

8 Which Argentinian driver scored 27714 World Championship points between 1950 and 1958?

9 How many Grand Prix wins did Benetton have in 1994?

10 In which year was Juan Fangio born - 1911 or 1921?

11 How many Grand Prix wins did Stirling Moss have between 1951 and 1961?

12 How old was Nelson Piquet when he won the World Championship in 1987 - 35, 38 or 41?

13 Jim Clark won the German Grand Prix in 1965 True or false?

14 Which Emerson was F1 world champion in 1972 and 1974?

15 In which country was Emerson Fittipaldi born?

***Stirling Moss won 16 Grands Prix during his career and was runner-up four times in the Drivers' Championship but never won it.***

## *Answers to page 286*

**1** McLaren-Porsche, **2** Damon Hill, **3** James Hunt, **4** Nine, **5** Nigel Mansell, **6** McLaren-Honda, **7** Niki Lauda, **8** Alain Prost, **9** Nelson Piquet, **10** Finland, **11** Ferrari, **12** Niki Lauda, **13** James Hunt, **14** Alan Jones, **15** Damon Hill.

# • FORMULA 1 - QUIZ 34 •

*Answers on page 287*

1 How many times did Jackie Stewart win the French Grand Prix between 1965 and 1973?

2 Which British driver won the 1993 Hungarian Grand Prix?

3 Which Briton won the 1962 Dutch Grand Prix?

4 Which Austrian driver scored 4205 points between 1971 and 1985?

5 Which New Zealand driver scored 248 points during his F1 career?

6 Name the first Belgian driver to win a Grand Prix?

7 Which driver won seven Grands Prix during the 1988 season?

8 How old was Luigi Fagioli when he won the 1951 French Grand Prix - 43, 48 or 53?

9 Which South African scored 255 world championship points between 1972 and 1980?

10 What does a yellow flag signify during a Grand Prix?

11 On which course can Sefton Straight be found?

12 How many of Alberto Ascari's 31 Grand Prix starts were from pole position - 7, 14 or 21?

13 How many F1 Grands Prix did Mario Andretti win between 1968 and 1982 - 7, 12 or 17?

14 Which Swedish driver scored 206 points between 1970 and 1980?

15 Which Australian driver won the British Grand Prix in 1959, 1960 and 1966?

---

*Answers to page 2887*

**1** Brabham-Repco, **2** Five, **3** Wolfgang von Trips, **4** Jim Clark, **5** 1930s, **6** Twelve, **7** 1992, **8** 1969, **9** 1984, **10** Stirling Moss, **11** 180, **12** 1985, **13** Rene Arnoux, **14** 360, **15** Six.

# • FORMULA 1 - QUIZ 35 •

*Answers on page 284*

1 Who won the Constructors' Championship in 1984 with 143 points?

2 Which driver won the first three Grands Prix of the 1996 season?

3 Which Briton won the German Grand Prix in 1976?

4 How many Grand Prix wins did Williams have in 1987?

5 Name the only driver to win a Grand Prix race in his own country in 1987?

6 Who won the Constructors' Championsnhip in 1990?

7 Which driver was F1 world champion in 1975, 1977 and 1984?

8 Which driver won a F1 Grand Prix in every season from 1981 to 1990?

9 Which driver won a F1 Grand Prix in every season from 1980 to 1987?

10 In which country was Mika Hakkinen born?

11 Who won their first Constructors' Championship in 1961?

12 Which Austrian driver had 25 Grand Prix victories between 1971 and 1985?

13 Which Briton amassed 179 championship points between 1973 and 1979?

14 Which Australian driver scored 206 championship points from 1975 to 1986?

15 Which British driver won the 1995 Argentine Grand Prix?

---

## *Answers to page 284*

**1** True, **2** Tony Brooks, **3** Ricardo Rodriguez, **4** Toleman, **5** Twenty two, **6** Twenty two, **7** Portugal, **8** Juan Manuel Fangio, **9** Eight, **10** 1911, **11** Sixteen, **12** Thirty five, **13** True, **14** Emerson Fittipaldi, **15** Brazil.

# • FORMULA 1 - QUIZ 36 •

*Answers on page 285*

**1** Who won the Constructors' Championship in 1967?

**2** How many Grands Prix did Emerson Fittipaldi win in 1972 - 5, 8 or 11?

**3** Which German driver won the 1961 British Grand Prix?

**4** Which British driver won the French Grand Prix in 1963 and 1965?

**5** In which decade was Jim Clark born?

**6** How many Grands Prix did Carlos Reutemann win between 1972 and 1982 - 4, 8 or 12?

**7** In which year did Michael Schumacher win his first Grand Prix?

**8** When was Michael Schumacher born -1966 or 1969?

**9** In which year was the 400th Grand Prix staged?

**10** Which Briton amassed 18664 championship points between 1951 and 1961?

**11** How many points did John Surtees amass during his F1 career - 90, 180 or 270?

**12** In which year did Ayrton Senna win his first F1 Grand Prix?

**13** Which French driver scored 179 world championship points from 1978 to 1989?

**14** How many world championship points did Jackie Stewart amass in his F1 career - 260, 360 or 460?

**15** During his three years with Lotus, how many Grands Prix did Ayrton Senna win?

---

## *Answers to page 285*

**1** Three, **2** Damon Hill, **3** Graham Hill, **4** Niki Lauda, **5** Denny Hulme, **6** Jacky Ickx, **7** Alain Prost, **8** Fifty three, **9** Jody Scheckter, **10** Danger, **11** Silverstone, **12** Fourteen, **13** Twelve, **14** Ronnie Peterson, **15** Jack Brabham.

# • FORMULA 1 - QUIZ 37 •

*Answers on page 290*

1 Who was disqualified and banned for two races for ignoring a black flag at the 1994 British Grand Prix?

2 What nationality is F1 driver Stefan Johansson?

3 In which year did Ayrton Senna join McLaren?

4 How many Grands Prix did Alan Jones win between 1975 and 1986 - 8, 12 or 16?

5 In which country was Alan Jones born?

6 Which driver won eight Grands Prix during the 1988 season?

7 Who won the Constructors' Championship in 1960?

8 How many Grand Prix wins did Williams have in 1993 - 6, 9 or 12?

9 How many times did Jim Clark win the British Grand Prix during the 1960s?

10 What does a white flag signify during a Grand Prix race?

11 In which country is the Catalunya Grand Prix circuit?

12 The 1982 Swiss Grand Prix was held in France True or false?

13 Name the first Canadian driver to win a Grand Prix?

14 How many Grands Prix did James Hunt win between 1973 and 1979 - 10, 15 or 20?

15 Who won the Constructors' Championship in 1968?

***Only one Frenchman has won the Drivers' Championship, four times in all, Alain Prost.***

---

## *Answers to page 290*

**1** 1911, **2** May, **3** 200, **4** True, **5** Borg-Warner Trophy, **6** Wheeler-Shebler Trophy, **7** True, **8** Jim Clark, **9** Graham Hill, **10** 1960s, **11** 1970s, **12** 29th, **13** Four, **14** Emerson Fittipaldi, **15** Jacques Villeneuve.

# • FORMULA 1 - QUIZ 38 •

*Answers on page 291*

1 What is the acronym for motor cycling's world governing body?

2 How many 500cc World Championships did American rider Eddie Lawson win during the 1980s - 4, 6 or 8?

3 Which British rider, born in 1940, was known as 'Mike the Bike'?

4 Which Briton won the 500cc World Championship in 1956 and from 1958 to 1960?

5 Which Italian was 500cc world champion from 1966 to 1972?

6 How many World Championships did Agostini win in the 350cc class?

7 Which Briton was 500cc world champion in 1976 and 1977?

8 In which decade did Mike Hailwood win the first of his ten World Championships?

9 Which Briton won four 250cc World Championships from 1964 to 1971?

10 Which Italian rider won the 500cc World Championship in 1981?

11 Which Briton won the World Superbike Championship in 1994?

12 In 1996, who won his 21st Isle of Man TT race at the age of 44?

13 What does TT stand for?

14 How many Grand Prix wins did Giacomo Agostini have from 1966 to 75 - 72, 122 or 172?

15 In which year did Mike Hailwood lose his life in a tragic road accident?

---

### *Answers to page 291*

**1** True, **2** 1980s, **3** Two, **4** 1968, **5** New Zealand, **6** Six, **7** Peter Collins, **8** Michael Lee, **9** Olsen, **10** Danish, **11** Three, **12** Michael Lee, **13** 1981, **14** 1985, **15** Ivan Mauger.

# •INDIANAPOLIS 500 - QUIZ 39•

*Answers on page 288*

**1** In which year was the Indianapolis 500 first held - 1911 or 1921?

**2** In which month is the race staged?

**3** How many laps of the 25 mile Indianapolis Raceway circuit is the race made-up of?

**4** All corners at the circuit are left-handers True or false?

**5** Which trophy has been awarded to the winner annually from 1936?

**6** Which trophy was awarded to winners from 1911-1935?

**7** The Indianapolis 500 formed part of the F1 World Championship between 1950 and 1960 True or false?

**8** Which Scottish driver won in 1965 Indianapolis 500 in a Lotus-Ford?

**9** Which English driver won the 1966 Indianapolis 500 in a Lola-Ford?

**10** In which decade did Mario Andretti first win the Indianapolis 500?

**11** In which decade did Janet Guthrie become the first woman driver to qualify for the Indianapolis 500?

**12** In which position did she finish - 9th, 19th or 29th?

**13** How many times did A J Foyt win the Indianapolis 500 between 1961 and 1977 - 2, 4 or 8?

**14** Which Brazilian F1 world champion driver won the Indianapolis 500 in 1989 and 1993?

**15** Which Canadian driver won the Indianapolis 500 in 1995?

---

## *Answers to page 288*

**1** Michael Schumacher, **2** Swedish, **3** 1988, **4** Twelve, **5** Australia, **6** Ayrton Senna, **7** Cooper-Climax, **8** Nine, **9** Five, **10** Slow-moving vehicle on the track, **11** Spain, **12** True, **13** Gilles Villeneuve, **14** Ten, **15** Lotus-Ford.

# • SPEEDWAY - QUIZ 40 •

*Answers on page 289*

1 The first World Championship for individual riders was held in 1936 True or false?

2 In which decade did Bruce Penhall first become individual world champion?

3 How many individual World Championships did Bruce Penhal win - 2, 4 or 6?

4 In which decade did Ivan Mauger win his first individual World Championship?

5 In which country was Ivan Mauger born?

6 How many individual World Championships did Ivan Mauger win - 3, 6 or 9?

7 Name the only British rider to win the individual World Championship during the 1970s?

8 Name the first British rider to win the Long Track World Championship?

9 Which Ole was individual world champion in 1975?

10 What nationality was Ole Olsen?

11 How many individual World Championships did Ole Olsen win?

12 Which Briton won the individual World Championship in 1980?

13 In which year did Michael Lee win the Long Track World Championship?

14 When did England's Simon Wigg first win the Long Track World Championship?

15 Which rider won the Long Track World Championship in 1971 and 1972?

---

*Answers to page 289*

**1** FIM, **2** Four, **3** Mike Hailwood, **4** John Surtees, **5** Giacomo Agostini, **6** Seven, **7** Barry Sheene, **8** 1960s, **9** Phil Read, **10** Marco Lucchinelli, **11** Carl Fogarty, **12** Joey Dunlop, **13** Tourist Trophy, **14** 122, **15** 1981.

# OLYMPICS

# • OLYMPICS - QUIZ 1 •

*Answers on page 296*

**1** In which year were the first modern Olympic Games held?

**2** Which country won all the track and field events at the 1904 Olympics?

**3** Which event had a giant version added for the first time at the 1952 Winter Olympics?

**4** Which Ethiopian, nicknamed 'the Shifter', did the 5,000 and 10,000m double in 1980?

**5** Where were the Winter Olympics held in 1998?

**6** Whose 1992 100m hurdles win made her the first Greek sportswoman to win Olympic gold?

**7** Who opened the 1956 Summer Games in Melbourne?

**8** Which country came top of the medals table in both Olympics in 1956 and 1960?

**9** Which alpine skier won three golds at the 1968 Winter Olympics?

**10** Which team's participation in Montreal in 1972 caused 22 African countries to pull out?

**11** Who was the 1996 men's 100m champion?

**12** Who, in 1948, won the US their first skiing medal?

**13** In which year's Olympics did the teams first parade in the opening ceremony?

**14** With four golds and a silver, which Romanian gymnast was 1984's most successful competitor?

**15** Who won the women's Olympic tennis title in 1988?

## *Answers to page 296*

**1** Tessa Sanderson, **2** Show jumping, **3** Peggy Fleming, **4** Melbourne, **5** Gustavo Thoni, **6** 1500m, **7** Paris, **8** Sjoukje Dijstra, **9** Rosa Mota, **10** King George I of Greece, **11** St Moritz, **12** Steve Redgrave, **13** Ed Moses, **14** 1912, **15** Sally Gunnell.

# OLYMPICS - QUIZ 2

*Answers on page 297*

1. Which 19-year-old was the 1960 light-heavyweight boxing gold medallist?
2. In which year was gender testing for women introduced at the Olympics?
3. Where were the first post-war Winter Olympics held in 1948?
4. Who was the first IOC president?
5. Who was disqualified after his 100m win in 1988?
6. At which venue's opening ceremony did a jet-propelled 'rocket man' appear?
7. Which country came top of the medal table at Chamonix in 1924?
8. Who opened the XI Winter Olympics in Sapporo in 1972?
9. In which year did curling first appear officially in the Winter Olympics?
10. Who, in 1980, became the first pentathlete to exceed 5,000 points?
11. Which US city was chosen to host the 2002 Winter Olympics?
12. Which 1904 marathon-winner collapsed four times on the last lap only to be disqualified?
13. Who won the 1992 women's 800m gold medal for Holland?
14. In which year were the Winter Olympics held in Cortina d'Ampezzo?
15. Which Finn became, in 1976, the first athlete to successfully defend his Olympic 5,000m and 10,000m titles?

***Olympia, the original site of the games that had seen so many sporting heros was ravaged by flood and earthquakes.***

---

*Answers to page 297*

**1** Greg Louganis, **2** Grenoble, **3** Pierre de Coubertin, **4** Kevin Young, **5** Long jump, **6** Harold Abrahams, **7** USA, **8** Peter Elliott, **9** Stockholm, **10** Galina Kulakova, **11** Michael Johnson, **12** 1964, **13** Bruce Jenner, **14** Los Angeles, **15** Mary Lou Retton.

# • OLYMPICS - QUIZ 3 •

*Answers on page 294*

**1** Who was the 1984 women's javelin gold medallist?

**2** In which event in 1932 were no medals awarded as no team managed to get three contestants round the circuit?

**3** Who was the 1968 women's figure skating champion?

**4** Which city was the first Olympic venue of the southern hemisphere?

**5** Which 1968 giant slalom champion went on to coach Alberto Tomba?

**6** Over which distance did Sebastian Coe win gold in 1980?

**7** Where were the Summer Games held in 1924?

**8** Whose 1964 figure skating win was Holland's first gold since 1948?

**9** Which Portuguese runner won the 1988 women's marathon?

**10** Who opened the first modern Olympic Games in Athens in 1896?

**11** Which venue was the first to hold the Winter Olympics twice?

**12** Who won his third consecutive coxless pair gold in 1996?

**13** Who won the 400m hurdles gold in 1976 with a new world record?

**14** In which year's Games were all the continents first represented?

**15** Who was the 1992 women's 400m hurdles champion?

## *Answers to page 294*

**1** 1896, **2** USA, **3** Slalom, **4** Miruts Yifter, **5** Nagano, **6** Paraskevi Patoulidou, **7** Duke of Edinburgh, **8** USSR, **9** Jean-Claude Killy, **10** New Zealand, **11** Donovan Bailey, **12** Gretchen Fraser, **13** 1904, **14** Ecaterina Szabo, **15** Steffi Graf.

# OLYMPICS - QUIZ 4

*Answers on page 295*

**1** Which 1984 double gold medallist was the first to exceed 700 points at highboard diving?

**2** Where were the 1968 Winter Olympics held?

**3** Who succeeded Dimitrios Vikelas as IOC president?

**4** Who won the 1992 men's 400m hurdles with a new world record?

**5** Which event used to have two categories, one 'standing'?

**6** Which Briton won the 100m gold in Paris in 1924?

**7** Which country caused a scandal at the 1948 Winter Olympics by sending two ice hockey teams?

**8** Who won silver in the 1,500m in 1988?

**9** Due to quarantine laws, where were the horse riding events held for the Melbourne Games?

**10** Who won three cross-country skiing golds in 1968?

**11** Who was the 1996 men's 200m and 400m champion?

**12** At which year's Winter Olympics did luge tobogganing first appear?

**13** Who was the 1976 decathlon champion?

**14** Where were the Summer Games held in 1932?

**15** Which gymnast won the gold medal in the 1984 women's individual all-around event?

---

## *Answers to page 295*

**1** Cassius Clay, **2** St Moritz, **3** Dimitrios Vikelas, **4** Ben Johnson, **5** Los Angeles, **6** Norway, **7** Emperor Hirohito, **8** 1998, **9** Nadyezda Tkatchenko, **10** Salt Lake City, **11** 1968, **12** Dorando Pietri, **13** Ellen van Langen, **14** 1956, **15** Lasse Viren.

# • OLYMPICS - QUIZ 5 •

*Answers on page 300*

1 Where were the 1988 Winter Olympics held?

2 In 1900, which American became the first athlete to win four gold medals at a single Olympic Games?

3 Which country took five of the nine available speed skating medals in 1976?

4 Who, in 1980, became the first gymnast to score a perfect 10?

5 In which track event was the world record improved three times in 1924?

6 In which year's Olympics did volleyball and judo first appear?

7 Who won the 1988 100m breaststroke gold medal?

8 What caused the number of participants in 1932 to be half that of 1928?

9 Who became, in 1968, the first swimmer to take three golds in individual events?

10 Which new Soviet grouping came top of the medals table in Barcelona in 1992?

11 Who, in 1948, was the first woman Olympic long jump champion?

12 Where were the 1976 Summer Games held?

13 Who successfully defended his 100m freestyle swimming title in 1996?

14 Which Russian won four gymnastic gold medals in 1956?

15 In which year's Games did Japan first appear?

## *Answers to page 300*

**1** Mary Rand, **2** Seoul, **3** Germany and Japan, **4** Phil and Steve Mahre, USA, **6** Shane Gould, **7** St Moritz, **8** Bob Beamon, **9** Football, **10** Georg Thoma, **11** 1912, **12** Lu Li, **13** Sonja Henie, **14** Carl Lewis, **15** John Naber.

# OLYMPICS - QUIZ 6

*Answers on page 301*

**1** Who was the 1976 men's figure skating gold medallist?

**2** Which Australian won three golds in women's athletics in Melbourne in 1956?

**3** Who was the 1980 men's 100m breaststroke gold medallist?

**4** Which country achieved top position in the gold medal table in the Paris Games of 1900?

**5** Who was the 1998 slalom and giant slalom champion?

**6** Who, with four golds, was 1948's most successful female competitor?

**7** Who won both the men's diving events in 1988?

**8** Which Ethiopian won the 1996 men's 10,000 m?

**9** Who was International Olympic Commitee president 1925-1942?

**10** Which American won the 1968 men's 100m?

**11** Who successfully defended his Olympic long jump title in 1992?

**12** Whose world record in the 1924 400m was not officially recognised until 1936?

**13** Which country was banned from the 1972 Games for its aparthied policies?

**14** Which American swimmer won four gold medals in 1964?

**15** Who were Olympic hockey champions from 1928 to 1960?

***The first Olympic games were thought to have taken place in Greece in 776BC. There was only one event - astade. This was a sprint over 19.27 metres. The prize; a Laurel Wreath.***

---

*Answers to page 301*

**1** Judo, **2** 1936, **3** Walt Disney, **4** Great Britain, **5** Johannes Sigfrid Edstrom, **6** Jan Zelezny, **7** Kristin Otto, **8** Sonja Henie, **9** Negative sex test, **10** Ravel's Bolero, **11** Gymnastics, **12** Oslo, **13** Chris Boardman, **14** 1968, **15** Nikolai Andrianov.

# OLYMPICS - QUIZ 7

*Answers on page 298*

**1** Which Briton won the long jump and came second in the pentathlon in 1964?

**2** Where were the 1988 Summer Games held?

**3** Which two countries were excluded from the 1948 Summer Games?

**4** Which brothers' 1984 silver and gold were America's first men's slalom medals?

**5** Which country came top of the gold medal table at St Louis in 1904?

**6** Which swimmer's three golds, one silver and one bronze were overshadowed by Mark Spitz's achievements in 1972?

**7** Where, in 1928, were many events in the second Winter Olympics disrupted by unseasonably mild weather?

**8** Who set a long jump record at the 1968 Games that was to be held for twenty three years?

**9** In which team sport had the USSR not won a gold medal for 32 years before becoming Olympic champions in 1988?

**10** Which German became, in 1960, the first non-Scandinavian to win a Nordic skiing event?

**11** In which year's games did women swimmers first appear?

**12** Which Chinese gymnast scored a perfect 10 on the asymmetrical bars in 1992?

**13** Who turned professional after her third consecutive Olympic figure skating championship win in 1936?

**14** Who won a fourth consecutive long jump gold in 1996?

**15** Which backstroke swimmer won in 1976 with the first sub two-minute time over 200m?

## *Answers to page 298*

**1** Calgary, **2** Alvin Kraenzlein, **3** Holland, **4** Alexander Ditiatin, **5** Men's 400m, **6** 1964, **7** Adrian Moorhouse, **8** The Depression, **9** Debbie Meyer, **10** Unified Team, **11** Olga Gyarmati, **12** Montreal, **13** Aleksandr Popov, **14** Larissa Latynina, **15** 1912.

# OLYMPICS - QUIZ 8

*Answers on page 299*

**1** In which sport did Dulzhman Wim Ruska win two gold medals in 1972?

**2** In which year were the Winter Olympics held in Garmisch-Partenkirchen?

**3** Who stage-managed the opening ceremony of the 1969 Winter Olympics?

**4** Who were the 1988 men's hockey champions?

**5** Which Swede succeeded Henry de Baillet-Latour as IOC President?

**6** Which Czech successfully defended his javelin title in 1996?

**7** Which East German won six swimming golds at the 1988 Games?

**8** Which 15-year-old Norwegian skater was the star of the 1928 Winter Olympics?

**9** Why was the 1964 women's 100m bronze medallist barred from international competition in 1967?

**10** Which piece of music did Torvill and Dean use for their winning free-dance in 1984?

**11** In which sport did American Anton Heida win five gold medals in St Louis in 1904?

**12** Where were the Winter Olympics held in 1952?

**13** Which cyclist was the 1992 4,000m individual pursuit champion?

**14** In which year's Olympics did the high jump see the first 'Fosbury Flop'?

**15** Which Russian won four gymnastic golds in 1976?

---

## *Answers to page 299*

**1** John Curry, **2** Betty Cuthbert, **3** Duncan Goodhew, **4** France, **5** Alberto Tomba, **6** Fanny Blankers-Koen, **7** Greg Louganis, **8** Haile Gebrselassie, **9** Henri de Baillet-Latour, **10** Jim Hines, **11** Carl Lewis, **12** Eric Liddell, **13** Rhodesia, **14** Don Schollander, **15** India.

# • OLYMPICS - QUIZ 9 •

*Answers on page 304*

**1** Where were the Summer Games held in 1984?

**2** Who was the 1968 Olympic heavyweight boxing champion?

**3** Which country came top of the gold medal table in London in 1908?

**4** What was the surname of the American figure-skating gold medal-winning brothers, one of whom became champion in 1956, the other in 1960?

**5** Who, in 1988, became the first Olympic women's super giant slalom champion?

**6** In which year were the Winter Olympics first held in a separate year from the Summer Olympics?

**7** At which sport did Willis Lee win five gold medals in 1920?

**8** Which New Zealander successfully defended his 800m title in 1964?

**9** Where were the 1980 Winter Olympics held?

**10** Who won Germany's first ever individual atheletics gold medal at Amsterdam in 1928?

**11** Which racket sport made its Olympic debut in 1992?

**12** Which three Olympic Games were cancelled due to war?

**13** Who successfully defended his giant slalom title in 1992?

**14** Which country took all three medals in the 1936 10,000m?

**15** Which 16-year-old German was the 1972 women's high jump champion?

***One of the more musical events added 20 years or so later was trumpet blowing - much approved of by the 20,000 plus crowds.***

---

*Answers to page 304*

**1** Great Britain, **2** Karl Schranz, **3** The Dream Team, **4** Michael Spinks, **5** The five continents, **6** Daniela Silivas, **7** Slalom or White-water, **8** Gail Devers, **9** 1928, **10** Carl Lewis, **11** Germany, **12** Helsinki, **13** Triple jump, **14** Pope John XXIII, **15** 1980.

# • OLYMPICS - QUIZ 10 •

*Answers on page 305*

**1** Of what nationality was the 1988 women's figure skating champion Kristi Yamaguchi?

**2** Which Finn successfully defended his 3,000m steeplechase title in 1936?

**3** Which country's football team successfully defended their Olympic title in 1968?

**4** Which Russian won gold in the women's floor, vault and team combined exercises in 1976?

**5** For what did Dutchman Jan Wils get a gold medal in Amsterdam in 1928?

**6** Who was the 1996 decathlon gold medallist?

**7** Who are still reigning champions in the tug-of-war, discontinued in 1920?

**8** Which speed skater won golds in the 1994 1,500, 5,000 and 10,000m, all with new world records?

**9** Who won the gold medal in the 1972 pentathlon?

**10** Where in London were the Games held in 1908?

**11** Who was the 1964 heavyweight boxing gold medallist?

**12** Who was the 1988 pole vault champion, setting a new Olympic record with his only valid attempt?

**13** Why did Greta Andersen have to be rescued in the 400m freestyle swimming event in 1948?

**14** Where were the 1984 Winter Olympics held?

**15** Which figure-skater won Olympic gold and her fifth consecutive world title in 1960?

---

## *Answers to page 305*

**1** Emil Zatopek, **2** 1984, **3** Abebe Bikila, **4** Florence Griffith-Joyner, **5** Avery Brundage, **6** Vitali Sherbo, **7** France, **8** Leon Spinks, **9** 1996, **10** Eric Heiden, **11** Erik Lundkvist, **12** Marie-Jose Perec, **13** 1936, **14** Japan, **15** Richard Meade.

# • OLYMPICS - QUIZ 11 •

*Answers on page 302*

**1** Who, in 1900, became the first Olympic cricket champions?

**2** Which Austrian skier was sent home just before the 1972 Winter Olympics for breaking amateur regulations?

**3** What was the nickname applied to the unbeatable US basketball team of the 1992 Games?

**4** Who was the 1976 middleweight boxing gold medallist?

**5** What do the Olympic flag's five rings represent?

**6** Which female Romanian gymnast won three golds in 1988?

**7** Which form of canoeing first appeared in the 1972 Games?

**8** Who successfully defended her 100m title in 1996?

**9** In which year was the Olympic flame introduced?

**10** Who, in 1984, won the same four gold medals as Jesse Owens in 1936?

**11** Which country came top of the medal table in Berlin in 1936?

**12** Where were the Summer Games of 1952 held?

**13** At which field event was Kenny Harrison 1996 men's champion?

**14** Which Pope gave his blessing at the 1960 opening ceremony in St Peter's Square?

**15** At which year's Winter Olympics was artificial snow first used?

## *Answers to page 302*

**1** Los Angeles, **2** George Foreman, **3** Great Britain, **4** Jenkins, **5** Sigrid Wolf, **6** 1994, **7** Shooting, **8** Peter Snell, **9** Lake Placid, **10** Lina Raske-Batschauer, **11** Badminton, **12** 1916, 1940, 1944, **13** Alberto Tomba, **14** Finland, **15** Ulrike Meyfarth.

# • OLYMPICS - QUIZ 12 •

*Answers on page 303*

**1** Who won the 5,000m, the 10,000m and the marathon at Helsinki in 1952?

**2** Which year's Summer Games were boycotted by the Soviet Union and its allies?

**3** Which barefoot 1960 marathon winner became the first Ethiopian gold medallist?

**4** Which flamboyant American sprinter won three golds in 1988?

**5** Which Olympic athlete was IOC president 1952-72?

**6** For which six gold-winning gymnast was the Belarussian anthem played in 1992 for the first time?

**7** Who, in 1900, became the first Olympic rugby champions?

**8** Who was the 1976 light-heavyweight boxing gold medallist?

**9** At which year's Olympic Games did women's football first appear?

**10** Who won five speed skating golds and set four Olympic records in 1980?

**11** Which Swedish sign painter won the javelin gold in 1928?

**12** Who successfully defended her 400m title in 1996?

**13** In which year was the Olympic flame first brought to the Games from Greece?

**14** Which country won all three medals in the small hill ski jump at the 1972 Sapporo Winter Olympics?

**15** Which Briton was the 1972 individual 3-day event Olympic champion?

---

## *Answers to page 303*

**1** American, **2** Volmari Iso-Hollo, **3** Hungary, **4** Nelli Kim, **5** Stadium design, **6** Dan O'Brien, **7** Great Britain, **8** Johann Olav Koss, **9** Mary Peters, **10** White City, **11** Joe Frazier, **12** Sergei Bubka, **13** She fainted, **14** Sarajevo, **15** Carol Heiss.

# • OLYMPICS - QUIZ 13 •

*Answers on page 308*

**1** At which year's Games did synchronized swimming first appear?

**2** Which country, in 1972, finally ended Hungary's reign as Olympic football champions?

**3** In which now obsolete athletics event were Sweden/Denmark the first gold medallists in 1900?

**4** Which event in the 1932 Winter Olympics was dominated by the Americans John Shea and Irving Jaffee?

**5** Who won the women's downhill and giant slalom for Switzerland in 1972?

**6** Which sport was dominated by China and Korea when introduced to the Games in 1988?

**7** Which country's men's 4x100m team was disqualified in 1960 for an illegal changeover?

**8** Who opened the Moscow Games in 1980?

**9** Where were what are now recognized as the first Winter Olympic Games held in 1924?

**10** Who became the most successful Olympic gymnast ever in 1964, having won a total of 18 medals, nine of them gold?

**11** For which country did swimmer Krisztina Egerszegy win three gold medals in 1992?

**12** In which year were canoeing and basketball introduced to the Games?

**13** At which event did Fatuma Roba win gold in 1996?

**14** Who, in 1952, became the first decathlete to successfully defend his Olympic title?

**15** Who was the 1980 men's figure skating champion?

---

## *Answers to page 308*

**1** Miloslav Mecir, **2** Beatrix Schuba, **3** Athens, **4** Paavo Nurmi, **5** 1948, **6** China and Cuba, **7** Jim Thorpe, **8** USSR, **9** 1900, **10** Innsbruck, **11** Vladimir Salnikov, **12** Canada, **13** 1976, **14** Dick McTaggart, **15** Mexico City.

# • OLYMPICS - QUIZ 14 •

*Answers on page 309*

**1** How many teams from the former Yugoslavia took part in the 1992 Summer Games?

**2** Who won four gymnastics golds to become the most successful male contestant in the Tokyo Olympics in 1964?

**3** Of what were the 'combined events' a forerunner?

**4** Who successfully defended his 500m speed skating title in 1968 with a new Olympic record?

**5** In which year's Winter Olympics did the 2-man bobsled first appear?

**6** What regained its status as a full Olympic sport in 1988 after a 64-year absence?

**7** Who won bronze in the show jumping in 1960?

**8** Who was the 1984 and 1988 110m hurdles champion?

**9** Which city became a Winter Olympic venue for the second time in 1976?

**10** Who became, in 1984, the first heptathlon gold medallist?

**11** What is the oldest Winter Olympic sport?

**12** Which country took all three medals in the decathlon of 1936?

**13** Which 18-year-old Australian woman won three sprinting gold medals at the 1956 Olympics?

**14** Which year's Summer Games were boycotted by Japan, W Germany and the USA, among others?

**15** Which 1956 triple gold medal-winning skier was known as the 'Blitz fron Kitz'?

***A Zulu named Lentauw, running for South Africa, came in 11th and had the honour of being the first black African distance runner to compete in the Olympics.***

---

*Answers to page 309*

**1** Gail Devers, **2** 1956, **3** Stockholm, **4** Ski jump, **5** Harold Osborn, **6** 800m, **7** Francisco Fernandez Ochoa, **8** Portuguese, **9** Michael Morris Killanin, **10** 1932, **11** Paris, **12** Jackie Joyner-Kersee, **13** Lidia Skoblikova, **14** David Wilkie, **15** Yugoslavia.

# • OLYMPICS - QUIZ 15 •

*Answers on page 306*

**1** Who won the Olympic men's tennis title in 1988?

**2** Which European and World champion also became Olympic women's figure skating champion in 1968?

**3** Where were the first modern Olympic Games held?

**4** Which nine gold medal-winning athlete was banned from the 1932 Games for contravening amateur regulations?

**5** Which year's Winter Olympics saw the first appearance of Chile, Iceland, Korea and the Lebanon?

**6** Which two countries refused to take part in pre-Games drugs testing in 1992?

**7** Who won the pentathlon and decathlon in 1912 only to be disqualified as a 'professional'?

**8** Which country won four consecutive Olympic ice hockey gold medals from 1964?

**9** In which year were women allowed to compete in the Olympics for the first time?

**10** To which city did 25,000 tons of snow have to be transported for the 1964 Winter Olympics?

**11** Which Russian became, in 1980, the first to break the 15-minute barrier in the 1,500m freestyle swimming event?

**12** Which country's ice hockey team won the gold in 1924 by scoring 110 and conceding only 3?

**13** At which year's Olympic Games were women's rowing, basketball and handball first introduced?

**14** Which Briton, in 1956, won not only the lightweight gold but also the Val Barker Cup for the Games' most stylish boxer?

**15** Where were the 1968 Summer Games held?

---

## *Answers to page 306*

**1** 1984, **2** Poland, **3** Tug-of-war, **4** Speed skating, **5** Marie-Therese Nadig, **6** Table tennis, **7** USA, **8** Leonid Brezhnev, **9** Chamonix, **10** Larissa Latynina, **11** Hungary, **12** 1936, **13** Women's marathon, **14** Bob Mathias, **15** Robin Cousins.

# • OLYMPICS - QUIZ 16 •

*Answers on page 307*

1 Who was the 1992 women's 100m champion?

2 At which year's Winter Olympics did Giuliana Chenal-Minuzzi become the first woman to take the Olympic oath?

3 Where were the Games held in 1912?

4 Which Winter Olympic event is divided into small hill, big hill and team?

5 Which American won the high jump and the decathlon in 1924?

6 At which distance did Steve Ovett win gold in 1980?

7 Who won the 1972 slalom to give Spain their first ever Winter Olympics gold medal?

8 Of what nationality was 1984 marathon-winner Carlos Lopes?

9 Which Irishman was IOC president 1972-80?

10 Which year's Games saw the introduction of the three-level podium?

11 Which city was the first to hold the Olympic Games twice?

12 Who was 1988's heptathlon champion?

13 Which Soviet speed skater won four golds and set three Olympic records at the 1964 Winter Olympics?

14 Who won the men's 200m breaststroke title in 1976 with a new world record?

15 Which country won the 1980 Olympic basketball title?

## *Answers to page 307*

**1** 4, **2** Yukio Endo, **3** Decathlon, **4** Erhard Keller, **5** 1932, **6** Tennis, **7** David Broome, **8** Roger Kingdom, **9** Innsbruck, **10** Glynis Nunn, **11** Figure skating, **12** USA, **13** Betty Cuthbert, **14** 1980, **15** Toni Sailer.

# • OLYMPICS - QUIZ 17 •

*Answers on page 312*

**1** In which year's Olympics did Michael Jordan first appear as a member of the gold medal-winning basketball team?

**2** Which discus thrower became, in 1968, the first Olympic athlete to win four consecutive titles in the same event?

**3** How many countries took part in the 1896 Olympics?

**4** Which Czech athlete was the 1992 decathlon champion?

**5** Which fabled Finn came top of the individual medal table in 1924?

**6** Where were the Summer Games held in 1964?

**7** Which swimmer was the 1996 100m and 200m men's butterfly champion?

**8** Who won the men's 100m and 200m in LA in 1932?

**9** In which bobsledding event, which only appeared in the 1948 Games, did Britain's John Crammond win bronze?

**10** Who won the 1976 women's high jump with a height of 193m?

**11** Which country's participation in the 1956 Games resulted in China's withdrawal?

**12** Who was the men's 100m winner in 1980?

**13** Which country's team was the target of a terrorist attack in 1972?

**14** In which year's Games did the modern pentathlon first appear?

**15** Who, in 1988, became the first East German to win the decathlon?

***The original and uncomplicated origins of the game formed in Greece fell into corruption and disrepute under the influence of the Romans. In AD 67, Emperor Nero accepted the crown for the chariot race - he was the only entrant!***

---

## *Answers to page 312*

**1** Vladimir Artemov, **2** George VI, **3** Torvill and Dean, **4** Laszlo Papp, **5** St Louis, **6** Men's 200m, **7** Mark Spitz, **8** 14, **9** Garry Herbert, **10** Single sculls, **11** USA, **12** Tennis, **13** Dorothy Hamill, **14** 1988, **15** 50k.

# • OLYMPICS - QUIZ 18 •

*Answers on page 313*

1 At which year's Winter Olympics were the downhill and slalom events introduced?

2 Which Finn won his third consecutive single sculls title in 1984?

3 Where were the 1900 Olympics held?

4 Who jumped 807m to win the 1964 men's Olympic long jump title?

5 Which sport made its first appearance since 1920 in the 1972 Games?

6 Who won both the men's 400m and 800m in 1976?

7 How long did the 1912 Greco-Roman wrestling match between the silver and bronze medallists last?

8 Which Czech gymnast won four golds and two silvers in Mexico City in 1968?

9 Which Australian successfully defended his 1,500m freestyle swimming title in 1996?

10 Which year's Games were the first to be covered by live radio broadcasts?

11 Who beat Fatima Whitbread to the javelin gold medal in 1988?

12 Who was the 1980 decathlon gold medallist?

13 In which track event in 1932 was an extra lap added by mistake?

14 Which country claimed its first-ever gold when Romas Ubertas won the discus title in 1992?

15 Which London marathon founder was the 1956 3,000m steeplechase gold medallist?

---

*Answers to page 313*

**1** Great Britain, **2** Squaw Valley, **3** Weightlifting, **4** Great Britain, **5** Johnny Weismuller, **6** Yachting, **7** Mexico City, **8** Katarina Witt, **9** 100m freestyle, **10** Antwerp, **11** Michelle Smith, **12** Mildred 'Babe' Didrikson, **13** 1972, **14** Yvonne van Gennip, **15** London.

# • OLYMPICS - QUIZ 19 •

*Answers on page 310*

**1** Which Russian was the 1988 Games' most successful gymnastic competitor with four golds?

**2** Which British king attended the opening ceremony of the Olympics in London in 1948?

**3** Who won the Olympic ice dancing gold and their fourth world championship title in 1984?

**4** Which Hungarian became, in 1956, the first boxer to win three Olympic titles?

**5** Where were the 1904 Olympics held?

**6** In which event's 1968 medal ceremony did two recipients give Black Power salutes?

**7** Which swimmer won seven gold medals and set four world records in Munich in 1972?

**8** At what age did diver Aileen Riggin become the youngest Olympic champion in 1920?

**9** Who coxed the winning men's coxed pair in Barcelona in 1992?

**10** In which event did Vyacheslav Ivanov win his third consecutive gold medal in 1964?

**11** Which country's swimming team won all six swimming relay medals in the 1996 Olympics?

**12** Which sport was reintroduced as a competitive event at the 1988 Olympics after a 64-year absence?

**13** Who, in 1976, added the Olympic figure skating title to her world title?

**14** Which year's Winter Olympics saw the first appearance of the Super G?

**15** How long was the road walk, introduced as an event in 1932?

---

## *Answers to page 310*

**1** 1984, **2** Al Oerter, **3** 14, **4** Robert Zmelik, **5** Paavo Nurmi, **6** Tokyo, **7** Denis Pankratov, **8** Eddie Tolan, **9** Skeleton bob, **10** Rosemarie Ackermann, **11** Taiwan, **12** Allan Wells, **13** Israel, **14** 1912, **15** Christian Schenk.

# • OLYMPICS - QUIZ 20 •

*Answers on page 311*

**1** Which country won the 1988 men's coxless pairs title?

**2** Where were the 1960 Winter Olympics held?

**3** Which sport was originally split into the one- and two-arm lift categories?

**4** Which country won gold in the Tornado catamaran class yachting event in 1976?

**5** Which Tarzan actor won two swimming gold medals in 1924?

**6** Which sport has Finn and Europa classes?

**7** Which Summer Olympic venue is at almost 2,240m above sea level?

**8** Who won her first Olympic figure skating gold medal in 1984?

**9** In which event did Dawn Fraser win her third consecutive gold medal in 1964?

**10** Where were the 1920 Games held?

**11** Who was the controversial 1996 women's 400m freestyle swimming champion?

**12** Who won the women's 80m hurdles and the javelin in 1932 before going on to a golfing career?

**13** Which year's Olympics saw the appearance of 17-year-old Olga Korbut?

**14** Which Dutch speed skater was the 1988 women's 1,500m, 3,000m and 5,000m champion?

**15** Which city held the Summer Olympic Games for the second time in 1948?

---

## *Answers to page 311*

**1** 1948, **2** Pertti Karppinen, **3** Paris, **4** Lynn Davies, **5** Archery, **6** Alberto Juantorena, **7** Over 11 hours, **8** Vera Caslavska, **9** Kieren Perkins, **10** 1924, **11** Petra Felke, **12** Daley Thompson, **13** 3,000m, **14** Lithuania, **15** Chris Brasher.

# • OLYMPICS - QUIZ 21 •

*Answers on page 318*

1 Who won the 1968 men's 400m hurdles with a new world record?

2 What was France's third Winter Olympic venue?

3 Which Hungarian fencer competed in the Olympics from 1932-60, winning 7 golds, 1 silver and 2 bronzes?

4 Who won the 1984 90m hill ski jump with a record jump of 116m?

5 What type of birds were released at the 1920 opening ceremony?

6 Who, in 1988, became the first woman figure skater since Sonja Henie to retain her Olympic title?

7 Who temporarily received a lifetime ban for getting a lift in the marathon in 1904?

8 Who won the lightweight judo title in front of her home crowd in 1992?

9 Where were the Summer Games held in 1928?

10 Which Briton won the women's 800m in Tokyo in 1964?

11 Who was the 1996 men's singles Olympic tennis champion?

12 Which Russian gymnast won the women's individual combined exercises, beam and asymmetrical bars in 1976?

13 Which year's Winter Olympics saw the first appearance of Australia, Greece, Spain and Turkey?

14 Which Finnish policeman was the 1972 5,000m and 10,000m champion?

15 Which country's competitors appeared in the 1960 Winter Olympics, then not again until 1994?

***Joseph Stadler, silver medallist in the standing high jump, and George Poage, third in the 200m and 400m hurdles, made history as the first two black Americans to win Olympic medals.***

---

## *Answers to page 316*

**1** Valeriy Borsov, **2** Markus Wasmeier, **3** Great Britain, **4** Middleweight, **5** 1928, **6** Lindsay Davenport, **7** Ria Mastenbroek, **8** Barcelona, **9** Eruption of Vesuvius, **10** Michael Gross, **11** Dick Button, **12** Malcolm Cooper, **13** 1920, **14** Felipe Munoz, **15** Ulrich Wehling.

# • OLYMPICS - QUIZ 22 •

*Answers on page 317*

**1** Which country won seven of the twelve boxing titles in 1992?

**2** Which decathlete equalled the world record to successfully defend his Olympic title in 1984?

**3** At which year's Games did ice hockey first appear?

**4** Who became, in 1964, the first-ever women's 400m Olympic champion?

**5** In which sport did Georges Miez win three golds in 1928 to top the individual medal table?

**6** Which German won two biathlon golds in the Winter Olympics of 1992?

**7** In which sport did Ivar Ballangrud dominate the 1936 Winter Olympics, winning three golds?

**8** Which American won the 1972 men's marathon?

**9** At which year's Olympics did beach volleyball first appear?

**10** Which Russian successfully defended his super-heavyweight weightlifting title in 1976?

**11** Where were the Games held in 1908?

**12** Who became, in 1988, the first Olympic men's super giant slalom champion?

**13** During which event in 1948 did the Dane Hans Christensen retire with a fractured leg?

**14** Which combined event first appeared in the Winter Olympics in 1960?

**15** At which year's Olympics was Britain's Chris Finnegan middleweight boxing champion?

---

## *Answers to page 317*

**1** Sapporo, **2** Linford Christie, **3** Jesse Owens, **4** Ingemar Stenmark, **5** 1904, **6** Matt Biondi, **7** Jeanette Altwegg, **8** Archery, **9** South Africa, **10** Albert I, **11** Wilma Rudolph, **12** 1976, **13** Renate Stecher, **14** 1928, **15** Sebastian Coe.

# • OLYMPICS - QUIZ 23 •

*Answers on page 314*

1 Which Russian won gold in the 1972 men's 100m and 200m?

2 Who was the 1994 men's giant slalom and Super G champion?

3 Which country, in 1900, became the first Olympic soccer champions?

4 At which weight was Floyd Patterson 1952 Olympic boxing champion?

5 In which year was the German team finally readmitted after WWI?

6 Who was the 1996 women's singles Olympic tennis champion?

7 Which swimmer, with three golds and one silver, was the most successful female competitor in the 1936 Games?

8 Where were the 1992 Summer Games held?

9 What prevented Rome from being the 1908 Olympic venue?

10 Which successful German swimmer was nicknamed 'the albatross'?

11 Who won the 1952 men's figure skating gold with a programme featuring the first-ever triple loop?

12 Which Briton retained his small-bore rifle title in 1988?

13 Which year's Games saw the first appearance of the five-ringed Olympic flag?

14 Which swimmer, in Mexico City in 1968, provided Mexico with its first-ever gold medal?

15 Which East German won his third successive skiing gold in 1980?

---

## *Answers to page 318*

**1** Heike Drechsler, **2** Marjorie Jackson, **3** 1972, **4** Greco-Roman, **5** Liechtenstein, **6** 144, **7** USA, **8** Lennox Lewis, **9** Svetlana Masterkova, **10** 11-a-side handball, **11** Anita Lonsbrough, **12** 400m hurdles, **13** Ard Schenk, **14** Marathon, **15** Juan Antonio Samaranch.

# • OLYMPICS - QUIZ 24 •

*Answers on page 315*

**1** Where were the 1972 Winter Olympics held?

**2** Who was the 1992 men's 100m champion?

**3** Who came top of the individual medal table with four golds in 1936?

**4** Who won golds in the men's slalom and giant slalom in 1980?

**5** In which year were archery, boxing, basketball and lacrosse introduced to the Games?

**6** Which American swimmer won five gold medals in 1988?

**7** Which Briton won the women's figure skating gold in 1952?

**8** At which sport was Justin Hursh the 1996 men's champion?

**9** Which nation returned to the Winter Olympics in 1994 for the first time in 34 years?

**10** Who presented the medals at Antwerp in 1920?

**11** Which triple gold medallist in Rome in 1960 was known as the 'black gazelle'?

**12** In which year was Sugar Ray Leonard light-welterweight Olympic boxing champion?

**13** Which East German won both the women's 100m and 200m in 1928?

**14** In which year were women first permitted to compete in track and field events?

**15** Who successfully defended his 1500m title in 1984?

---

## *Answers to page 315*

**1** Cuba, **2** Daley Thompson, **3** 1920, **4** Betty Cuthbert, **5** Gymnastics, **6** Mark Kirchner, **7** Speed skating, **8** Frank Shorter, **9** 1996, **10** Vasiliy Alexeyev, **11** London, **12** Franck Piccard, **13** 800m, **14** Biathlon, **15** 1968.

# • OLYMPICS - QUIZ 25 •

*Answers on page 316*

**1** Who was the 1992 women's long jump champion?

**2** Who set a new world record in the women's 100m in Helsinki in 1952?

**3** In which year's Olympics did West Germany win their first hockey gold?

**4** Which wrestling style first appeared at the Games in 1908?

**5** For which country did German-born Hanni Wenzel win three skating golds in 1980?

**6** How many arrows constitute a round of Olympic archery?

**7** Which country was top of the medal table at Lake Placid in 1932?

**8** Who was the 1988 super-heavyweight boxing gold medallist?

**9** Who won golds in the 1996 women's 800m and 1,500m?

**10** Which outdoor team sport appeared once, in Berlin in 1936?

**11** Which Briton won gold in the 1960 women's 200m breaststroke with a new world record?

**12** In which event in 1984 did Nawal El Moutawakel become the first Moroccan sportswoman to win gold?

**13** Which speed skater had to settle for three golds at the 1972 Winter Olympics after falling in the 400m?

**14** Which event did Italian Gelindo Bordin win in 1988?

**15** Who became IOC president in 1980?

***The Modern Olympics were due to take place in France in 1900 but pressure due to impatient members saw Athens picked and the first games staged in 1896.***

## *Answers to page 314*

**1** David Hemery, **2** Albertville, **3** Aladar Gerevich, **4** Matti Nykanen, **5** Doves, **6** Katarina Witt, **7** Fred Lorz, **8** Miriam Blasco, **9** Amsterdam, **10** Ann Packer, **11** Andre Agassi, **12** Nadia Comaneci, **13** 1936, **14** Lasse Viren, **15** South Africa.

# RUGBY LEAGUE

# • RUGBY LEAGUE - QUIZ 1 •

*Answers on page 322*

1. In which year was the Northern Rugby Football Union (later to become the Rugby Football League) formed - 1885 or 1895?
2. In 1897, who won the first Northern Union - later Rugby League - Challenge Cup final?
3. Name the first team to retain the Challenge Cup?
4. When did Wembley stage its first Challenge Cup final?
5. Which player was voted 1998 Man of Steel?
6. What nationality is Laurie Daley?
7. From which club did Bradford Bulls sign Shaun Edwards in May 1997?
8. Where do Featherstone Rovers play?
9. Which Wigan player was voted 1995 Man of Steel?
10. Tony Mestrov made his debut for London Broncos during the 1995-96 season When was he born - 1970 or 1973?
11. Which club paid Hull £150,000 for Lee Crooks in June 1987?
12. Which Hull player won the Harry Sunderland Trophy for Man of the Match in the 1991 Premiership final?
13. In which year did Wigan's Cliff Hill become the first substitute to play in a Challenge Cup final - 1970 or 1974?
14. In which decade was Chris Hesketh awarded the MBE?
15. Which Reg captained Widnes in the 1979 Challenge Cup final?

## *Answers to page 322*

**1** St. Helens, **2** Joyner, **3** Graham Rees, **4** Wigan, **5** Widnes, **6** 1968, **7** 1997, **8** 12, **9** 1940's, **10**Tommy Martyn , **11** Castleford, **12** Martin Offiah, **13** Leeds, **14** Australia, **15** Featherstone Rovers.

# • RUGBY LEAGUE - QUIZ 2 •

*Answers on page 323*

**1** For which club did Richard Price score 308 points during the 1997 season?

**2** Which club paid Widnes £150,000 for Andy Currier in August 1993?

**3** From which club did Craig Makin join Salford Reds?

**4** Who scored three tries for Great Britain v New Zealand on 12 November, 1955?

**5** Which club sold Andy Gregory to Wigan for £130,000 during the 1986-87 season?

**6** Which club plays its home matches at the Odsal Stadium?

**7** Wigan won their first Challenge Cup in 1924 True or false?

**8** When was Jeff Grayshon awarded the MBE - 1982 or 1992?

**9** Which Australian team beat Hunter Mariners 36-12 in the final of the 1997 World Club Championship?

**10** Who beat Bradford Bulls 62-14 in the quarter-finals of the 1997 World Club Championship?

**11** Which Wigan player was voted 1993 Man of Steel?

**12** When was Great Britain international Adrian Morley born - 1972 or 1977?

**13** Which two teams were given record fines following a brawl during a televised Challenge Cup tie in February 1997?

**14** In which year did Barrow beat Workington Town in the Challenge Cup final - 1955 or 1958?

**15** Which club signed Kelvin Skerrett from Wigan Warriors in 1997?

---

### *Answers to page 323*

**1** 1991, **2** Shaun Edwards, **3** 1960's, **4** Leeds Rhinos, **5** 1920's, **6** Joynt, **7** Widnes, **8** Central Park, **9** Australia, **10** Jonathan Davies, **11** Australia, **12** 1970's, **13** Bradford Northern, **14** Ellery Hanley, **15** Swinton Lions.

# • RUGBY LEAGUE - QUIZ 3 •

*Answers on page 320*

1 Which club won the Premiership Trophy in 1976 and 1977?

2 Which John captained Castleford in the 1986 Challenge Cup final?

3 Which player scored a try for St Helens in the first minute of the 1972 Challenge Cup final?

4 Which club beat Salford 70-6 on 14 March, 1993?

5 Which team beat Warrington 14-7 to win the 1975 Challenge Cup final?

6 In which year did Leeds and Wakefield Trinity contest the 'Watersplash final'?

7 In which year did Shaun Edwards score the 300th try of his career?

8 How many goals did Roy Rafferty kick for Sheffield Eagles v Fulham on 21 September, 1986 - 8, 10 or 12?

9 In which decade did King George VI become the first reigning monarch to attend a Rugby League match?

10 Which St Helens player won the Lance Todd Trophy for Man of the Match in the 1997 Challenge Cup final?

11 Who did Wigan beat 28-12 to win the 1992 Challenge Cup?

12 Which Wigan player won the Lance Todd Trophy at the 1992 and 1994 Challenge Cup finals?

13 Which team beat Barrow 90-0 on 11 February, 1990?

14 In which country do Parramatta play?

15 For which club did Don Fox score 162 tries between 1953 and 1966?

---

## *Answers to page 320*

**1** 1895, **2** Batley, **3** Batley, **4** 1929, **5** Iestyn Harris, **6** Australian, **7** London Broncos, **8** Post Office Road, **9** Denis Betts, **10** 1970, **11** Leeds, **12** Greg Mackey, **13** 1970, **14** 1970's, **15** Bowden.

# • RUGBY LEAGUE - QUIZ 4 •

*Answers on page 321*

**1** When was the blood bin introduced - 1985 or 1991?

**2** Which 21-year-old captained Wigan in the 1988 Challenge Cup final?

**3** In which decade did the BBC2 Floodlit Trophy competition begin?

**4** Which club knocked St Helens out of the 1999 Challenge Cup?

**5** In which decade was John Wilson appointed Rugby League Secretary?

**6** Which Chris won the Harry Sunderland Trophy in 1993?

**7** Who beat Wigan 19-6 in the 1984 Challenge Cup final?

**8** At which ground do Wigan play?

**9** Who did Great Britain beat 8-4 at Wembley on 22 October, 1994?

**10** Who scored Great Britain's only try in this Test?

**11** For which country did Mal Meninga play?

**12** In which decade did Australia achieve their first-ever clean sweep in an Ashes series?

**13** Who won the Premiership Trophy in 1978?

**14** Who captained Leeds in the Challenge Cup finals of 1994 and 1995?

**15** Which team plays its home matches at Gigg Lane?

***Rugby League underwent the most dramatic facelift in its history in 1995 when its clubs took £87 million from TV and Newspaper mogul, Rupert Murdoch.***

---

*Answers to page 321*

**1** Batley Bulldogs, **2** Featherstone Rovers, **3** Widnes, **4** Mick Sullivan, **5** Warrington, **6** Bradford Bulls, **7** True, **8** 1992, **9** Brisbane Broncos, **10** Auckland Warriors, **11** Andy Platt, **12** 1977, **13** St Helens and Wigan Warriors, **14** 1955, **15** Halifax Blue Sox.

# • RUGBY LEAGUE - QUIZ 5 •

*Answers on page 326*

1 Which club beat Sheffield Eagles 68-2 on 18 August, 1996?

2 Who beat Australia SL 30-12 on 26 September, 1997?

3 Which club won the first Challenge Cup of the 1950's?

4 Name the first Wigan player to win the Lance Todd Trophy?

5 In which decade was the World Cup first staged?

6 Which English team beat Canberra Raiders 38-18 in the 1997 World Club Championship?

7 In which year did Shaun Edwards receive the OBE - 1992 or 1996?

8 Which Hull Sharks player scored 40 tries in 32 League and Cup matches during 1997?

9 Which club signed Tevita Vaikona from Hull Sharks in October 1997?

10 From which club did St Helens sign Paul Newlove in November 1995?

11 Name the first player to be sent off in a Challenge Cup final at Wembley?

12 Which Brisbane Broncos player scored 13 tries during the 1997 World Club Championship?

13 Which player made his senior debut for Hull in the 1960 Challenge Cup final?

14 Which Huddersfield player won the Lance Todd Trophy on his 19th birthday in 1953?

15 Who scored five tries for Wigan Warriors v Sheffield Eagles on 29 June, 1997?

## *Answers to page 326*

**1** Martin Offiah, **2** Odsal Stadium, Bradford, **3** True, **4** 1992, **5** Hunter Mariners, **6** Allan Langer, **7** Leeds, **8** Schofield, **9** Leigh, **10** Hull, **11** Eric Ashton, **12** Warrington, **13** 1920's, **14** Leeds, **15** Australia.

# • RUGBY LEAGUE - QUIZ 6 •

*Answers on page 327*

1 Which Shaun started the 1999 season as coach of Gateshead Thunder?

2 Which Sam won the Harry Sunderland Trophy in 1994?

3 Which Wakefield Trinity player scored 34 points v Highfield on 27 October, 1992?

4 Which 20-year old captained Bradford Bulls in the 1996 Challenge Cup final?

5 What nationality is Jonathan Davies?

6 At which ground did Great Britain beat Australia 20-12 in November 1997?

7 Name Great Britain's two try scorers in this Test?

8 Who captained Great Britain in this Test?

9 Who won the 1974 Challenge Cup final?

10 Which Brisbane Broncos player scored five tries v Halifax in the quarter-finals of the 1997 World Club Championship?

11 Who scored ten tries for Wigan v Leeds on 10 May, 1992?

12 When was Kris Radlinksi born - 1972 or 1976?

13 Who won the Silk Cut Plate final in 1997?

14 For which club did Mike Smith score six tries v Doncaster on 13 April, 1968?

15 Which Widnes forward was sent off in the 1993 Challenge Cup final?

---

## *Answers to page 327*

**1** Kris Radlinski, **2** 1970's, **3** 1993, **4** Wigan, **5** Andy Gregory, **6** Ellery Hanley, **7** Salford, **8** Newlove, **9** 1912, **10** Shane Cooper, **11** Batley, **12** Halifax Blue Sox, **13** Thrum Hall, **14** Rochdale Hornets, **15** 1940's.

# • RUGBY LEAGUE - QUIZ 7 •

*Answers on page 324*

1 Which Great Britain player scored five tries v France on 16 February, 1991?

2 Which ground hosted the 1954 Challenge Cup final replay?

3 Leeds won the Premiership Trophy in 1979 True or false?

4 In which year did Lee Crooks captain Castleford in the Challenge Cup final - 1989 or 1992?

5 Which Australian team knocked Wigan out of the 1997 World Club Championship?

6 Who captained Brisbane Broncos in the final of the 1997 World Club Championship?

7 Which club paid Wigan £250,000 for Ellery Hanley in September 1991?

8 Which Garry scored 38 tries during the 1983-84 season?

9 Which Division Two team scored 1,156 League points during the 1985-86 season?

10 Which club won all of their 26 Division Two matches during the 1978-79 season?

11 Which Wigan player was awarded the MBE in 1966?

12 For which club did Brian Bevan score seven tries v Bramley on 22 April, 1953?

13 In which decade was the Challenge Cup final first broadcast on radio?

14 In 1975, which team beat Halifax 26-11 in the Premiership Trophy final?

15 Who did Great Britain beat 18-14 on 5 November, 1978?

## *Answers to page 324*

**1** St. Helens, **2** New Zealand, **3** Warrington, **4** Cec Mountford, **5** 1950's, **6** London Broncos, **7** 1996, **8** Tevita Vaikona, **9** Bradford Bulls, **10** Bradford Northern, **11** Syd Hynes1, **12** Steve Renouf, **13** Mike Smith, **14** Peter Ramsden, **15** Tony Smith.

# • RUGBY LEAGUE - QUIZ 8 •

*Answers on page 325*

1 Which Wigan player won the Harry Sunderland Trophy in 1995?

2 In which decade was the hooter system to signal the end of a match introduced?

3 In which year did Jason Robinson make his Great Britain debut - 1991 or 1993?

4 Which team won the 1988 Challenge Cup final?

5 Who won the first of his two Lance Todd Trophies at this final?

6 Which Bradford Northern player was voted 1985 Man of Steel?

7 Which club won the Division One Championship in the 1973-74 season?

8 Which Paul scored a hat-trick of tries for Great Britain v France on 2 April, 1993?

9 When did Dewsbury first win the Challenge Cup - 1912 or 1932?

10 Who captained St Helens in the 1991 Challenge Cup final?

11 For which club did Simon Wilson kick 13 goals v Leigh on 26 March, 1995?

12 Which club plays its home matches at The Shay?

13 What was the name of their previous ground?

14 For which club did Jack Williams score 103 tries between 1931 and 1937?

15 In which decade was the Welsh League formed?

***To take on a new face Rugby League was brought out of the winter into the summer and each team picked a new animal friendly name.***

---

## *Answers to page 325*

**1** McRae, **2** Panapa, **3** Mark Conway, **4** Robbie Paul, **5** Welsh, **6** Old Trafford, **7** Jason Robinson and Andrew Farrell, **8** Andrew Farrell, **9** Warrington, **10** Steve Renouf, **11** Martin Offiah, **12** 1976, **13** Hull Kingston Rovers, **14** Featherstone Rovers, **15** Richard Eyres.

# • RUGBY LEAGUE - QUIZ 9 •

*Answers on page 330*

1 1n 1973, who became the first substitute to score a try in the Challenge Cup final?

2 Which team won the Challenge Cup in 1977 and 1978?

3 Which Castleford player scored 158 goals during the 1976-77 season?

4 Who captained Wigan in three successive Challenge Cup finals, 1992-94?

5 James Lowes joined Bradford Bulls from which club in 1996?

6 In which decade was Bill Fallowfield appointed Rugby League Secretary?

7 Which Great Britain player scored three tries v New Zealand on 8 June, 1968?

8 How many tries did Great Britain's Keith Fielding score v France on 20 January, 1974?

9 Who lost to Wigan in the 1991 Challenge Cup final?

10 Which Dennis won the Lance Todd Award at the 1991 Challenge Cup final?

11 Where do Huddersfield Giants play?

12 Which club won the 1966 Challenge Cup?

13 Who signed Robbie Paul from New Zealand club Waitakere in July 1994?

14 Which Bobbie scored three tries for Great Britain v Fiji on 5 October, 1996?

15 From which club did Bradford Bulls sign Steve McNamara?

## *Answers to page 330*

**1** Wigan, **2** Leeds, **3** Derwent Park, **4** St Helens, **5** Widnes, **6** Bradford Bulls, **7** Runcorn Highfield, **8** Leigh, **9** Wigan Warriors, **10** Steve Hesford, **11** 1980's, **12** Keighley Cougars, **13** Sheffield Eagles, **14** 1965, **15** Warrington.

# •RUGBY LEAGUE - QUIZ 10•

*Answers on page 331*

1 Which team beat Carlisle 112-0 on 14 September, 1986?

2 For which club did Frano Botica score 423 points during the 1992-93 season?

3 Who won the Regal Trophy in 1991?

4 In which year did Alan Hunte score the 200th try of his career - 1994 or 1997?

5 Points for a try were increased from three to four in 1985 True or false?

6 What nationality is Iestyn Harris?

7 Which Great Britain player was sent off in their 8-4 win over Australia on 22 October, 1994?

8 In which decade did Mick Burke make his Great Britain debut?

9 Who won the Challenge Cup in 1997?

10 How old was Jeff Grayshon when he played in his last Great Britain match - 36, 41 or 46?

11 From which club did Iestyn Harris join Leeds Rhinos in 1997?

12 Who did Wigan beat 8-2 in the 1987 World Club Challenge?

13 Name the first player to be transferred for £100,000?

14 Where do Hunslet Hawks play?

15 How many tries did Wigan's Martin Offiah score in the 1992 Challenge Cup final?

## *Answers to page 331*

**1** Workington Town, **2** Halifax, **3** Wembley, **4** Andy Goodway, **5** Jason Robinson, **6** Davies, **7** Leigh, **8** Leeds, **9** Widnes, **10** Eric Ashton, **11** 1950's, **12** Don Fox, **13** Kear, **14** St. Helens, **15** Widnes.

# •RUGBY LEAGUE - QUIZ 11•

*Answers on page 328*

1 For which club did Jim Sullivan make 774 appearances between 1921-46?

2 Which team beat Wigan 58-3 on 14 October, 1972?

3 At which ground do Workington Town play?

4 Gary Connolly made his Wigan debut during the 1993-94 season What was his previous club?

5 From which club did Bobby Goulding join St Helens in July 1994?

6 Which club won the 1997 Super League?

7 Which team lost 61 consecutive League and Cup matches from January 1989 to February 1991?

8 Which team lost 78-22 to Batley on 26 March, 1995?

9 Henry Paul made his debut for Bradford Bulls in 1999 From which club did he join them?

10 Which player scored 2,416 points for Warrington between 1975 and 1985?

11 In which decade was the first Charity Shield match contested?

12 Which team plays its home matches at Cougar Park?

13 Daryl Powell made his debut for Keighley Cougars during the 1994-95 season From which club did he join them?

14 In which year was Daryl Powell born - 1965 or 1970?

15 Who beat Halifax 38-10 in the 1986 Premiership Trophy final?

***London Broncos were the unhappy victims of a spot of Super League history making when they were swept aside 58-6 for St. Helens' biggest win of the season. It was also their biggest ever defeat.***

---

## *Answers to page 328*

**1** David Hartley, **2** Leeds, **3** Geoff 'Sammy' Lloyd, **4** Dean Bell, **5** Leeds, **6** 1940's, **7** Clive Sullivan, **8** Three, **9** St. Helens, **10** Betts, **11** Alfred McAlpine Stadium, **12** St. Helens, **13** Bradford Northern, **14** Goulding, **15** Hull.

# •RUGBY LEAGUE - QUIZ 12•

*Answers on page 329*

**1** For which club did Lyn Hopkins score 438 points during the 1981-82 season?

**2** For which club did Stan Kielty make 482 appearances between 1946 and 1958?

**3** At which stadium did Australia SL beat Great Britain 38-14 in November 1997?

**4** Who was Great Britain's coach for the 1997 Test Series with Australia?

**5** Which Great Britain player scored a try in each of the three 1997 matches with Australia?

**6** Which Jonathan was voted 1994 Man of Steel?

**7** For which club did Steve Halliwell score 49 tries during the 1985-86 season?

**8** Who knocked Wigan out of the 1999 Challenge Cup?

**9** Which club won the Premiership Trophy in 1980?

**10** Who captained Wigan in the Challenge Cup final six times between 1958 and 1966?

**11** During which decade did Featherstone Rovers first reach the Challenge Cup final?

**12** Which Wakefield Trinity player missed a crucial last-minute conversion in the 1968 Challenge Cup final?

**13** Which John started the 1999 season as coach of Sheffield Eagles?

**14** For which club did Kel Coslett make over 500 appearances between 1961 and 1976?

**15** Stuart Spruce made his debut for Bradford Bulls in 1996 From which club did he join them?

---

*Answers to page 329*

**1** St. Helens, **2** Wigan, **3** Warrington, **4** 1997, **5** False, **6** Welsh, **7** Shaun Edwards, **8** 1980's, **9** St Helens, **10** 36, **11** Warrington Wolves, **12** Manly, **13** Joe Lydon, **14** South Leeds Stadium, **15** 2.

# •RUGBY LEAGUE - QUIZ 13•

*Answers on page 334*

1 Who beat Great Britain 40-4 on 30 October, 1982?

2 Which stadium held the replay of the 1982 Challenge Cup final?

3 In 1992, who succeeded David Oxley as Rugby League Chief Executive?

4 Who captained Widnes in the 1984 Challenge Cup final?

5 In which year did Mike Forshaw make his debut for Bradford Bulls?

6 When was the official Rugby League Hall of Fame introduced - 1982 or 1988?

7 Simon Haughton made his Wigan debut during the 1993-94 season When was he born - 1970 or 1975?

8 Who did Wigan beat 20-14 in the 1994 World Club Challenge?

9 In which decade was the Rugby League Professional Players' Association formed?

10 Which Warrington Wolves player scored 17 tries during the 1997 Super League?

11 Who did St Helens beat 50-20 in the semi-final of the 1997 Challenge Cup?

12 Which player scored four tries for Great Britain v New Zealand on 2 November, 1985?

13 For which club did Mike Fletcher kick 199 goals during the 1989-90 season?

14 In 1976, which substitute became the first to score two tries in a Challenge Cup final?

15 Who captained Hull in the 1985 Challenge Cup final?

## *Answers to page 334*

**1** False, **2** Geoff 'Sammy' Lloyd, **3** Janette Smith, **4** 1960's, **5** 3, **6** Knowsley Road, **7** True, **8** France, **9** Widnes, **10** Hull, **11** Neil Fox, **12** Hull Kingston Rovers, **13** 1913, **14** Fulham, **15** London Broncos.

# •RUGBY LEAGUE - QUIZ 14•

*Answers on page 335*

**1** Which Chris skippered St Helens in the 1987 Challenge Cup final?

**2** Name the first player to win the Harry Sunderland Trophy in successive seasons?

**3** Who scored 2,082 points for Dewsbury in two spells at the club?

**4** St Helens beat Warrington 80-0 on 4 January, 1996 True or false?

**5** Who captained Widnes in the 1981 Challenge Cup final?

**6** At which ground do Batley Bulldogs play?

**7** For which club did Joe Ball score 135 goals during the 1956-57 season?

**8** Which Widnes player won the 1981 Lance Todd Trophy?

**9** Where do Hull Sharks play?

**10** Who skippered Wigan in the 1985 Challenge Cup final?

**11** For which club did Tom Van Vollenhoven score 62 tries during the 1958-59 season?

**12** Which Wigan player landed a 61-yard drop goal against Warrington on 25 March 1989?

**13** Which Warrington Wolves player scored six drop goals during the 1997 Super League?

**14** For which club did Albert Worrall make 503 appearances between 1921 and 1938?

**15** When was Andy Farrell born - 1972 or 1975?

## *Answers to page 335*

**1** Salford, **2** Widnes, **3** St Helens, **4** Castleford, **5** Canterbury Bulldogs, **6** John Duffy, **7** Belle Vue, **8** Auckland Warriors, **9** 1982, **10** Paris Saint Germain, **11** 173, **12** Bradford Northern, **13** Wakefield Trinity, **14** Headingley, **15** Davies.

# •RUGBY LEAGUE - QUIZ 15•

*Answers on page 332*

1 Hull Kingston Rovers beat Oldham 67-11 on 24 September, 1979 True or false?

2 Which player scored 369 points for Hull during the 1978-79 season?

3 Who was the first woman physiotherapist in a Challenge Cup final?

4 Danny Peacock made his debut for Bradford Bulls in 1997 In which decade was he born?

5 How many tries did Great Britain's Garry Schofield score v France on 7 March, 1993?

6 Where do St Helens play?

7 Neil Fox was awarded the MBE in 1983 True or false?

8 Against which country did Great Britain's Bill Burgess score three tries on 30 November, 1968?

9 Who won the Challenge Cup final in 1979?

10 Who lost 38-5 to Wakefield Trinity in the 1960 Challenge Cup final?

11 Which player scored twenty points in this final?

12 Who won the Premiership Trophy in 1981?

13 When did Huddersfield first win the Challenge Cup - 1913 or 1933?

14 Who beat Whitehaven 72-6 on 14 September, 1986?

15 For which club did Dan Staines start the 1999 season as coach?

***History was written again in 1998, when two non-league clubs reached the fifth round of the Challenge Cup for the first time since its records began.***

## *Answers to page 332*

**1** Australia, **2** Elland Road, Leeds, **3** Maurice Lindsay, **4** Eric Hughes, **5** 1997, **6** 1988, **7** 1975, **8** Brisbane Broncos, **9** 1980's, **10** Nigel Vagana, **11** Salford Reds, **12** Garry Schofield, **13** Hull Kingston Rovers, **14** Peter Glynn, **15** Lee Crooks.

# •RUGBY LEAGUE - QUIZ 16•

*Answers on page 333*

**1** For which club did David Watkins score points in 92 consecutive matches between 1972 and 1974?

**2** Which club won the Premiership Trophy in 1988, 1989 and 1990?

**3** In 1993, which club sold Gary Connolly to Wigan for £250,000?

**4** Which club paid Featherstone Rovers £170,000 for Graham Steadman in 1989?

**5** Which team beat Halifax Blue Sox 58-6 in the 1997 World Club Championship?

**6** Which 16-year-old made his debut for Warrington Wolves v London Broncos on 21 March, 1997?

**7** At which ground do Wakefield Trinity play?

**8** Who did Brisbane Broncos beat 22-16 in the semi-finals of the 1997 World Club Championship?

**9** When was the County Championship scrapped - 1982 or 1987?

**10** For which club did Phil Bergman score sixteen tries during the 1997 season?

**11** How many tries did Alan Davies score for Oldham between 1950 and 1961 - 73, 173 or 273?

**12** For which team did Keith Mumby score 1,828 points between 1973 and 1993?

**13** Which club did Leeds beat 11-10 in the 1968 Challenge Cup final?

**14** Where do Leeds Rhinos play?

**15** Which Jonathan scored 34 points for Widnes v Whitehaven on 26 August, 1990?

---

*Answers to page 333*

**1** Arkwright, **2** Alan Tait, **3** Nigel Stephenson, **4** True, **5** Mick Adams, **6** Mount Pleasant, **7** Barrow, **8** Mick Burke, **9** The Boulevard, **10** Graeme West, **11** St. Helens, **12** Joe Lydon, **13** Lee Briers, **14** Leigh, **15** 1975.

# •RUGBY LEAGUE - QUIZ 17•

*Answers on page 338*

1 For which club did Andy Currier score five tries v Featherstone Rovers on 25 September, 1988?

2 Who won the Regal Trophy in 1990?

3 Who did Hull Kingston Rovers beat 10-5 in the 1980 Challenge Cup final?

4 For which team did Mike Stacey kick 15 goals v Doncaster on 28 March, 1976?

5 Where do Sheffield Eagles play?

6 In which decade was the John Player Trophy competition launched?

7 How many times did Hull reach the Challenge Cup final during the 1980's?

8 In which country do Manly play?

9 At which ground do Doncaster Dragons play?

10 Who scored six tries for Canberra Raiders v Halifax in the 1997 World Club Championship?

11 For which club did Bernard Ganley kick 200 goals during the 1957-58 season?

12 Which former Castleford star was awarded the OBE in June 1991?

13 Which club were Super League champions in 1996?

14 Who scored 346 points for Rochdale Hornets during the 1994-95 season?

15 At which ground do Castleford Tigers play?

---

## *Answers to page 338*

**1** Halifax, **2** St. John Ellis, **3** Australian, **4** Keighley, **5** Bradford Northern, **6** Australian, **7** The Willows, **8** Gold Coast, **9** Castleford, **10** Widnes, **11** 1940's, **12** St. Helens, **13** 8, **14** Wigan, **15** Jonathan Davies.

# •RUGBY LEAGUE - QUIZ 18•

*Answers on page 339*

**1** In 1996, which club ended Wigan's record Challenge Cup run of 43 successive ties unbeaten?

**2** Which club won their first Challenge Cup in 1967?

**3** In which year did Andy Farrell become England's youngest ever captain, aged 20?

**4** From which club did Henry Paul join Wigan in August 1994?

**5** Who beat St Helens 19-18 to win the Challenge Cup in 1987?

**6** Which Graham won the Lance Todd Award in the 1987 Challenge Cup final?

**7** Which club won the Regal Trophy in 1992?

**8** Who captained Leeds in the Challenge Cup finals of 1994 and 1995?

**9** Where do Whitehaven Warriors play?

**10** For which club did Jack Walkington make 572 appearances between 1927 and 1948?

**11** Which club plays at Hilton Park?

**12** Which club did Leigh beat 92-2 on 30 April, 1986?

**13** Which club beat Leigh 94-4 on 26 February, 1995?

**14** In which decade did St Helens win their first Challenge Cup final?

**15** In 1995, which club sold Paul Newlove to St Helens for £250,000?

---

## *Answers to page 339*

**1** Tony Smith, **2** Hull K R, **3** Gary Prohm, **4** Davies, **5** Wilderspool, **6** Hunslet Hawks, **7** Castleford, **8** Leeds, **9** Hull Sharks, **10** 1970's, **11** Batley, **12** Leeds, **13** Elland Road, **14** Prescot Panthers, **15** 1950's.

# •RUGBY LEAGUE - QUIZ 19•

*Answers on page 336*

**1** Which team thrashed Hunslet 76-8 on 27 August, 1972?

**2** Which Castleford Tigers player scored 40 tries during the 1993-94 season?

**3** What nationality is Wendell Sailor?

**4** Who did Featherstone Rovers beat 86-18 on 17 September, 1989?

**5** Who did Featherstone Rovers beat 33-14 in the 1973 Challenge Cup final?

**6** What nationality is international centre Andrew Ettingshausen?

**7** Where do Salford Reds play?

**8** From which club did David Boughton join Huddersfield Giants?

**9** Who won the Challenge Cup in 1969 and 1970?

**10** From which club did Joe Lydon join Wigan in 1986?

**11** In which decade was the first all-ticket match?

**12** For which club did Shane Cooper score six tries v Hull in February 1988?

**13** How many Wigan players made the Great Britain starting line-up v Papua New Guinea on 24 October, 1978 - 4, 8 or 12?

**14** Who won the Regal Trophy in 1995?

**15** Which player scored 342 points for Widnes during the 1990-91 season?

---

## *Answers to page 336*

**1** Widnes, **2** Wigan, **3** Hull, **4** Leigh, **5** Don Valley Stadium, **6** 1970's, **7** 4, **8** Australia, **9** Meadow Court, **10** Ken Nagas, **11** Oldham, **12** Mal Reilly, **13** St. Helens, **14** Martin Strett, **15** Wheldon Road.

# •RUGBY LEAGUE - QUIZ 20•

*Answers on page 337*

1 Who scored five tries for Wigan v Sheffield Eagles on 29 June, 1997?

2 Anthony Sullivan made his debut for St Helens during the 1991-92 season From which club did he join them?

3 Which Hull Kingston Rovers player scored 45 tries during the 1984-85 season?

4 Which Jonathan was awarded the MBE in January 1995?

5 Where do Warrington Wolves play?

6 Which club won the 1997 Division Two Championship?

7 Which club signed Lee Crooks from Leeds in January 1990?

8 Who did Leigh beat in the final of the 1971 Challenge Cup?

9 Which club won the 1997 Division One Championship?

10 In which decade was David Oxley appointed Rugby League Secretary?

11 For which team did Simon Wilson kick 127 goals during the 1994-95 season?

12 Which club did Wigan beat in the 1994 and 1995 Challenge Cup finals?

13 At which stadium did Australia beat Great Britain 37-20 in November 1997?

14 Des Drummond made his debut for Barrow Braves in 1997 From which club did he join them?

15 In which decade was Des Drummond born?

---

*Answers to page 337*

**1** Salford Reds, **2** Featherstone Rovers, **3** 1996, **4** Auckland Warriors, **5** Halifax, **6** Eadie, **7** Widnes, **8**Ellery Hanley , **9** Recreation Ground, **10** Hunslet, **11** Leigh Centurions, **12** Keighley, **13** Workington Town, **14** 1950's, **15** Bradford.

# •RUGBY LEAGUE - QUIZ 21•

*Answers on page 342*

1 Who did Hunter Mariners beat 22-18 in the semi-finals of the 1997 World Club Championship?

2 In which decade was the Premiership Trophy competition launched?

3 Which Henderson scored 3 tries for Great Britain against France on 6 December, 1981?

4 Which team plays its home matches at Spotland?

5 Which Bradford Bulls player was voted 1997 Man of Steel?

6 In which position does James Lowes play?

7 Which player scored 478 tries for Wigan between 1953 and 1968?

8 When was Barrie-Jon Mather born - 1969 or 1973?

9 Who became coach of Huddersfield Giants in November 1997?

10 Who beat Hunslet 20-16 in the 1965 Challenge Cup final?

11 Who lost to Wigan in the 1990 Challenge Cup final?

12 When was David Watkins awarded the MBE - 1976 or 1986?

13 Who was Great Britain's scrum half for the 1997 Test series with Australia SL?

14 For which club did Joe Ferguson make 626 appearances between 1899 and 1923?

15 Which team plays its home matches at New Craven Park?

## *Answers to page 342*

**1** The Stoop, **2** Shaun Edwards, **3** 1960's, **4** Wigan, **5** St. Helens, **6** Dewsbury Rams, **7** Daryl Powell, **8** Geoff Gunney, **9** Brian McDermott, **10** Featherstone Rovers, **11** True, **12** Tea Ropati, **13** Garry Schofield, **14** Chris Joynt, **15** False.

# •RUGBY LEAGUE - QUIZ 22•

*Answers on page 343*

1 Who scored four tries for Great Britain v France on 14th March, 1959?

2 For which club did Alan Hardisty score 206 tries between 1958 and 1971?

3 Kelvin Skerrett joined Wigan in August 1990 From which club?

4 Which team won the Challenge Cup in successive seasons during the 1950's?

5 Where do Bramley play?

6 Who won the Premiership Trophy in 1982 and 1983?

7 Which Shaun scored ten tries for Wigan v Swinton on 29 September, 1992?

8 Who kicked 12 goals for Auckland Warriors v Bradford Bulls on 20 July, 1997?

9 Jim Lewthwaite scored 50 tries for which club during the 1956-57 season?

10 Which Castleford Tigers player scored five drop goals during the 1997 season?

11 From which club did Paul Sculthorpe join St Helens in 1997?

12 At which ground Lancashire Lynx play?

13 When did Hull Kingston Rovers reach their first Challenge Cup final - 1905 or 1935?

14 Which Clive scored seven tries for Hull v Doncaster on 15 April, 1968?

15 How many Challenge Cup finals did Leeds reach during the 1970's?

---

*Answers to page 343*

**1** Newlove, **2** Martin Pearson, **3** Featherstone Rovers, **4** David Topliss, **5** Andy Farrell, **6** Dewsbury, **7** 1994, **8** Wigan, **9** Widnes Vikings, **10** Bobbie Goulding, **11** Hull, **12** Bradford Bulls, **13** Hull Kingston Rovers, **14** Leeds, **15** Wigan.

# •RUGBY LEAGUE - QUIZ 23•

*Answers on page 340*

1 Where do London Broncos play?

2 Which Shaun scored 40 tries in the 1991-92 season?

3 In which decade was Martin Offiah born ?

4 From which club did Stephen Holgate join Hull Sharks?

5 For which club did Tom Van Vollenhoven score 392 tries between 1957 and 1968?

6 Which team plays at New Crown Flatt?

7 Which Sheffield Eagles player won the Tom Bergin Trophy in 1992?

8 Which Hunslet player received the MBE in June 1970?

9 In 1997, which Bradford Bulls player was sent off in the Challenge Cup semi-final clash with Leeds Rhinos?

10 For which club did Jim Denton make 440 appearances between 1921 and 1934?

11 Roger Millward captained Hull KR in the 1980 Challenge Cup final True or false?

12 Which Auckland Warriors player scored 4 tries v Warrington Wolves on 22 June, 1997?

13 Which Great Britain international was awarded the OBE in 1994?

14 Who captained St Helens in the 1997 Premiership Trophy final?

15 Oldham beat Bramley 70-0 on 12 February, 1995 True or false?

---

## *Answers to page 340*

**1** Cronulla Sharks, **2** 1970's, **3** Gill, **4** Rochdale Hornets, **5** James Lowes, **6** Hooker, **7** Billy Boston, **8** 1973, **9** Garry Schofield, **10** Wigan, **11** Warrington, **12** 1986, **13** Bobbie Goulding, **14** Oldham, **15** .Hull Kingston Rovers

# •RUGBY LEAGUE - QUIZ 24•

*Answers on page 341*

1. Which Paul won the Tom Bergin Trophy in 1993?
2. Who scored 40 points for Featherstone Rovers v Whitehaven on 26 November, 1995?
3. From which club did Bradford Northern sign Paul Newlove in July 1993?
4. Who captained Hull in the 1982 Challenge Cup final and subsequent replay?
5. Name the second player to win the Harry Sunderland Trophy twice?
6. For which team did Les Holliday score 32 points v Barrow on 11 September, 1994?
7. In which year did Va'aiga Tuigamala first play in a Challenge Cup final?
8. Which club won the Regal Trophy in 1993?
9. Which team plays its home matches at Naughton Park?
10. Who captained St Helens in the 1997 Challenge Cup final?
11. Which club lost in the Challenge Cup finals of 1908, 1909 and 1910?
12. Which club won 20 successive Super League matches from the start of the 1997 season?
13. Who won the Premiership Trophy in 1984?
14. For which club did John Holmes make over 600 appearances between 1968 and 1989?
15. Who beat Leeds 74-6 on 10 May, 1992?

***For the first time ever a female referee was picked, Julia Lee, a day-nursery teacher was appointed for the 17th Varsity clash between Oxford and Cambridge.***

---

*Answers to page 341*

**1** Alex Murphy, **2** Castleford, **3** Bradford Northern, **4** Wigan, **5** Headingley, **6** Widnes, **7** Edwards, **8** Gene Ngamu, **9** Barrow, **10** Brad Davis, **11** Warrington Wolves, **12** Deepdale, **13** 1905, **14** Sullivan, **15** 4.

# •RUGBY LEAGUE - QUIZ 25•

*Answers on page 346*

1 In which decade did Clive Sullivan receive the MBE?

2 For which country did former Wigan star Brett Kenny play?

3 For which club did Keith Elwell make 239 consecutive appearances between 1977 and 1982?

4 For which club did Chris Johnson score 173 goals during the 1985-86 season?

5 In which year did Richard Branson take over London Broncos and become chairman?

6 Which player skippered Warrington in the 1990 Challenge Cup final?

7 Which John started the 1999 season as coach of Halifax Blue Sox?

8 Which Bob scored 334 points for Castleford during the 1983-84 season?

9 In which year was Ellery Hanley awarded the MBE - 1985 or 1990?

10 From which club did Leeds Rhinos sign Iestyn Harris for £350,000?

11 In the 1983 Challenge Cup final, Featherstone Rovers fielded a team without any English players True or false?

12 For which club did Edward Rogers make 501 appearances from 1906-25?

13 Which team beat Hull 66-16 on 23 April, 1995?

14 For which country did Kevin Iro play?

15 Who lost 15-14 to Castleford in the 1986 Challenge Cup final?

## *Answers to page 346*

**1** Wakefield Trinity, **2** Ellery Hanley, **3** Castleford, **4** 1983, **5** New Zealand, **6** 13, **7** Widnes, **8** Bramley, **9** St Helens, Leigh and Warrington, **10** Widnes, **11** 1980, **12** 4, **13** Castleford Tigers, **14** Brian Bevan, **15** Mike Fletcher.

# •RUGBY LEAGUE - QUIZ 26•

*Answers on page 347*

**1** Who scored six tries for Featherstone Rovers v Keighley on 17 September, 1989?

**2** In which decade did Castleford first win the Challenge Cup?

**3** Which country did Great Britain beat 37-0 on 6 December, 1981?

**4** Who did Wigan beat 27-0 in the 1989 Challenge Cup final?

**5** Which club scored 1,735 points from 45 matches in the 1994-95 season?

**6** How many appearances for Great Britain did Ellery Hanley make as a player - 26, 36 or 46?

**7** For which club did Albert Lunn score 1,870 points between 1951 and 1963?

**8** In January 1996, who succeeded Eric Hughes as coach of St Helens?

**9** Who won the Premiership Trophy in 1987?

**10** From which club did Wigan Warriors sign prop Lee Hansen in April 1997?

**11** During which decade was Mick Sullivan transferred from Huddersfield to Wigan for £9,500?

**12** For which club did Walter Gowers make 456 appearances between 1922 and 1946?

**13** For which club did Steve Hesford kick 170 goals during the 1978-79 season?

**14** Paul Vautin was captain of St Helens in the 1989 Challenge Cup final True or false?

**15** In 1997, which club paid Castleford Tigers £150,000 for scrum half Tony Smith?

---

## *Answers to page 347*

**1** True, **2** 4, **3** False, **4** Roger Millward, **5** Widnes, **6** David Ward, **7** Huddersfield, **8** Graham Eadie, **9** Hudson, **10** Mike Umaga, **11** Huddersfield, **12** True, **13** Widnes, **14** False, **15** Widnes.

# •RUGBY LEAGUE - QUIZ 27•

*Answers on page 344*

**1** Who lost 86-0 to Castleford on 17 April, 1995?

**2** Who captained Wigan in the Challenge Cup finals of 1989, 1990 and 1991?

**3** Who won the Regal Trophy in 1994?

**4** In which year was the Sin Bin introduced - 1983 or 1987?

**5** Which country beat Great Britain 32-16 on 28 July, 1984?

**6** How many successive League matches did Widnes win at the start of the 1981-82 season - 9, 13 or 17?

**7** Which team thrashed Dewsbury 82-0 on 30 November, 1986?

**8** For which club did John Wolford make over 400 appearances between 1962 and 1976?

**9** Which three clubs did Alex Murphy captain in Challenge Cup finals?

**10** For which club did Mick Burke kick 140 goals during the 1978-79 season?

**11** In which year did Lee Crooks make his senior debut for Hull - 1980 or 1983?

**12** How many times did Castleford win the BBC2 Floodlit Trophy - 4, 5 or 6?

**13** From which club, in 1997, did Wigan Warriors sign Tony Smith for £150,000?

**14** Which Hall of Fame player scored 740 tries for Warrington between 1945 and 1962?

**15** Who kicked 14 goals for Hull Kingston Rovers v Whitehaven on 18 March, 1990?

---

## *Answers to page 344*

**1** 1970's, **2** Australia, **3** Widnes, **4** Leigh, **5** 1997, **6** Mike Gregory, **7** Pendlebury, **8** Beardmore, **9** 1990, **10** Warrington Wolves, **11** False, **12** Hull, **13** Wigan, **14** New Zealand, **15** Hull K R.

# •RUGBY LEAGUE - QUIZ 28•

*Answers on page 345*

**1** Andy Farrell played in every Super League game during the 1996, 97 and 98 seasons True or false?

**2** How many points did St Helens drop during the inaugural 1996 Super League season?

**3** Paul Loughlin kicked 17 goals for St Helens v Carlisle on 14 September, 1986 True or false?

**4** Which former Great Britain, Castleford and Hull KR player was awarded the MBE in 1983?

**5** Who lost 20-14 to Wigan in the 1993 Challenge Cup final?

**6** Name Leeds' captain in the 1978 Challenge Cup final?

**7** Which team did Castleford thrash 94-12 on 18 September, 1988?

**8** Who captained Halifax in the 1988 Challenge Cup final?

**9** Which Terry captained Featherstone Rovers in the 1983 Challenge Cup final?

**10** Who scored five tries for Halifax Blue Sox v Workington Town on 21 July, 1996?

**11** For which club did Doug Clark make 485 appearances between 1909 and 1929?

**12** Hull won the Premiership Trophy in 1991 True or false?

**13** From which club did St Helens sign Bobbie Goulding in July 1994?

**14** Martin Offiah won the Harry Sunderland Trophy in 1992 True or false?

**15** From which club did Martin Offiah join Wigan in January 1992?

***History was written in July 1998 when the BARLA team beat Australia Aboriginals 18-16 in Sydney, thanks to a second try five minutes from time.***

---

## *Answers to page 345*

**1** Chris Bibb, **2** 1930's, **3** France, **4** St. Helens, **5** Wigan, **6** 36, **7** Castleford, **8** Shaun McRae, **9** Wigan, **10** Widnes Vikings, **11** 1950's, **12** Rochdale Hornets, **13** Warrington, **14** True, **15** Wigan Warriors.

# •RUGBY LEAGUE - QUIZ 29•

*Answers on page 349*

1 Who scored 48 tries for Featherstone Rovers during the 1992-93 season?

2 Which Super League opponent did Bradford Bulls beat 68-0 in August 1997?

3 Against which country did Britain's Garry Schofield score three tries on 16 February, 1991?

4 For which club did Joe Lyman make 454 appearances between 1913 and 1931?

5 Which Australian team beat Warrington Wolves 40-12 on 8 June, 1997?

6 Who did Great Britain beat 42-0 in October 1987?

7 Which player scored two tries for St Helens in the 1997 Challenge Cup final?

8 Which club lost in the 1996 and 1997 Challenge Cup finals?

9 How many points did Bradford Bulls drop during the 1997 Super League season - 4, 6 or 8?

10 Who skippered Widnes in the 1993 Challenge Cup final?

11 Which club signed Garry Schofield for £155,000 in October 1987?

12 Who beat Salford Reds 50-8 during the 1997 World Club Championship?

13 Who did Great Britain beat 36-0 on 7 March, 1992?

14 For which club did Jack McLean score 261 tries between 1950 and 1956?

15 Who scored five tries for Widnes v Warrington on 15 March, 1989?

---

## *Answers to page 349*

**1** Paul Newlove, **2** Paris Saint Germain, **3** France, **4** Dewsbury, **5** Cronulla Sharks, **6** Papua New Guinea, **7** Tommy Martyn, **8** Bradford Bulls, **9** 4, **10** Paul Hulme, **11** Leeds, **12** Adelaide Rams, **13** France, **14** Bradford Northern, **15** Martin Offiah.

# •RUGBY LEAGUE - QUIZ 30•

*Answers on page 348*

**1** For which club did John McKeown kick 1,050 goals between 1948 and 1961?

**2** What nationality is Gorden Tallis?

**3** Which club signed Kelvin Skerrett from Wigan Wanderers in January 1997?

**4** Which Wigan winger scored five tries v Leeds on 9 August, 1996?

**5** Which Frano kicked 186 goals for Wigan during the 1994-95 season?

**6** In which year did Lee Crooks retire?

**7** Martin Offiah was awarded the MBE in 1995 True or false?

**8** Which club paid Featherstone Rovers £170,000 for Graham Steadman in June 1989?

**9** When did Shaun Edwards make his debut for Wigan - 1983 or 1986?

**10** Willie Horne scored 741 goals for which club between 1943 and 1958?

**11** In which year was Jason Robinson born - 1971 or 1974?

**12** Which Australian scored three tries v England at Wembley in November 1997?

**13** For which country did scrum half Peter Sterling play?

**14** Who lost 28-24 to Wigan in the 1985 Challenge Cup final?

**15** Who won the Premiership Trophy in 1993?

---

*Answers to page 348*

**1** Whitehaven, **2** Australian, **3** Halifax Blue Sox, **4** Jason Robinson, **5** Botica, **6** 1997, **7** False, **8** Castleford, **9** 1983, **10** Barrow, **11** 1974, **12** Laurie Daley, **13** Australia, **14** Hull, **15** St. Helens.

# RUGBY UNION

# • RUGBY UNION - QUIZ 1 •

*Answers on page 354*

1 What is the oldest international fixture in rugby union?

2 Which country won the 1987 World Cup?

3 Which country did Gareth Edwards play for?

4 In which decade was Gareth Edwards born?

5 Who did England beat 51-0 at Twickenham in 1990?

6 How many England caps did Bill Beaumont win - 24, 34 or 44?

7 How many times did England achieve the Grand Slam during the 1920s?

8 Who did Scotland beat 89-0 at the 1995 World Cup?

9 When was Bath founded -1865 or 1885?

10 Which country did Wales beat 102-11 in 1994?

11 In which year was Bill Beaumont born - 1952 or 1956?

12 Which country beat Scotland 51-15 at Murrayfield in 1993?

13 Which English city is home to Moseley?

14 How many times did Andy Irvine play for Scotland - 41, 51 or 61?

15 Which Irish player captained the British Lions in 1974?

## *Answers to page 354*

**1** England, **2** Scott Gibbs, **3** 1996, **4** 1968, **5** Romania, **6** 1993, **7** Andy Robinson, **8** Rory Underwood, **9** Fifty five, **10** South Africa, **11** Willie John McBride, **12** Zinzan Brooke, **13** New Zealand, **14** Coventry, **15** True.

# • RUGBY UNION - QUIZ 2 •

*Answers on page 355*

**1** Which Welsh player scored 20 tries in 46 internationals from 1966-78?

**2** Which country beat England 40-15 in 1991?

**3** Who captained the Welsh Grand Slam team of 1978?

**4** When did Gavin Hastings win his first senior Scotland cap - 1984 or 1986?

**5** Who announced that he was standing down as England captain in 1996?

**6** Which club won the Welsh Cup from 1973 to 1976?

**7** Which country did the British Lions beat 31-0 in 1966?

**8** Name the Welsh player sent off againstEngland at Twickenham in 1980?

**9** Which club won the Courage League Championship in the 1994-95 season?

**10** Who captained England at the 1995 World Cup?

**11** In which country was England international Adedayo Adebayo born?

**12** Which Bath flanker was sent off against Newcastle during the 1997-98 season?

**13** England lost seven consecutive internationals between 1971 and 1972 True or false?

**14** When did Willie John McBride win his first Irish cap - 1962 or 1964?

**15** Which club won the John Player Cup in 1972?

---

*Answers to page 355*

**1** Gavin and Scott Hastings, **2** Bath, **3** David Humphreys, **4** Australia, **5** Fourteen, **6** 1995, **7** Sandy Carmichael, **8** Philippe Saint-Andre, **9** Canada, **10** Neath, **11** Ieuan Evans, **12** Llanelli, **13** Argentina, **14** Australia, **15** Thirty six.

# • RUGBY UNION - QUIZ 3 •

*Answers on page 352*

1 Which country lost in the final of the 1991 World Cup?

2 In 1994, who left Swansea to join St Helens Rugby League club in a £150 000 deal?

3 In which year did he rejoin Swansea in a deal worth £250,000?

4 When was England international Phil de Glanville born - 1968 or 1972?

5 Which country did Ireland beat 60-0 at Dublin in 1986?

6 In which year did Peter Winterbottom win his last England cap?

7 Who was Bath's head coach at the start of the 1997-98 season?

8 Who is England's record try-scorer?

9 How many times did JPR Williams play for Wales - 45, 55 or 65?

10 Which country did the British Lions beat 28-9 in 1974?

11 Who played in 52 consecutive internationals for Ireland between 1964 and 1975?

12 Which New Zealand back-row forward landed a drop goal from 40 yards against England in the 1995 World Cup?

13 Against which country did Jonathan Callard make his England debut?

14 Name the winners of the 1973 John Player Cup?

15 Wales won 11 consecutive matches between 1907 and 1910 True or false?

***As we move into World Cup year, 18 countries have made it through to the finals leaving seven nations (Tonga, Morocco, Uruguay, South Korea, Holland, Portugal and Georgia) to fight it out for the remaining two places.***

## *Answers to page 352*

**1** England v Scotland, **2** New Zealand, **3** Wales, **4** 1940s, **5** Argentina, **6** Thirty four, **7** Four, **8** Ivory Coast, **9** 1865, **10** Portugal, **11** 1952, **12** New Zealand, **13** Birmingham, **14** Fifty one, **15** Willie John McBride.

# • RUGBY UNION - QUIZ 4 •

*Answers on page 353*

**1** Which two brothers made their senior Scottish debuts against France in 1986?

**2** From which club did Gloucester sign England international Steve Ojomoh?

**3** Who landed two drop goals for Ireland against Wales at Wembley in February 1999?

**4** Which southern hemisphere country did Wales beat 28-3 at Cardiff in 1975?

**5** How many penalties did Gavin Hastings convert for Scotland in the 1986 Five Nations Championship - 7, 14 or 21?

**6** In which year did South Africa first play in the World Cup?

**7** Who played in 49 consecutive internationals for Scotland between 1967 and 1978?

**8** In 1994, who became the first wing to captain France since Christian Darrouy in 1967?

**9** Who did England crush 60-19 at Twickenham in 1994?

**10** From which Welsh club did Harlequins sign Gareth Llewellyn in 1996?

**11** Which player has scored most tries for Wales?

**12** From which Welsh club did Bath sign Ieuan Evans during the 1997-98 season?

**13** Which country did Scotland beat 49-3 at Murrayfield in 1990?

**14** Which southern hemisphere nation lost 27-12 to Ireland in 1979?

**15** How many England caps did David Duckham win - 36, 56 or 76?

---

## *Answers to page 353*

**1** Gerald Davies, **2** Australia, **3** Phil Bennett, **4** 1986, **5** Will Carling, **6** Llanelli, **7** Australia, **8** Paul Ringer, **9** Leicester, **10** Will Carling, **11** Nigeria, **12** Nathan Thomas, **13** True, **14** 1962, **15** Gloucester.

# • RUGBY UNION - QUIZ 5 •

*Answers on page 358*

1. Which club side won the John Player Cup in 1975?
2. In which decade was JPR Williams born?
3. Who played in 44 consecutive internationals for England between 1989 and 1995?
4. For which country did Tim Horan win his first senior cap in 1989?
5. Which country did the British Lions beat 20-7 in 1993?
6. Which player scored 24 individual points for Wales against Italy at Cardiff in 1994?
7. From which club did Harlequins sign Garrett Halpin in 1998?
8. Garrett Halpin represented Ireland in the shot put at the 1987 World Championships in Rome True or false?
9. Which club won the Courage League Championship in the 1988-89 season?
10. How many tries did South Africa score in their 25-9 win over the British Lions in 1955 - 3 or 7?
11. How many Grand Slams did Wales achieve during the 1950s?
12. In which position does Ireland's Keith Wood play?
13. Who started the 1998-99 season as team manager of Leicester?
14. Who beat Wales 63-6 in 1991?
15. In which decade was England international Jason Leonard born?

## *Answers to page 358*

**1** Wilson, **2** 1990, **3** Melrose, **4** Jonathan Webb, **5** Coventry, **6** Fifty three, **7** Tonga, **8** 1967, **9** New Zealand, **10** Jonathan Wilkinson, **11** Phil de Glanville, **12** Three, **13** 1960s, **14** Australia, **15** Richmond.

# • RUGBY UNION - QUIZ 6 •

*Answers on page 359*

**1** In which year did Phil Bennett win his first Welsh cap - 1969 or 1971?

**2** Where do Leicester play home matches?

**3** In which year did Neil Back win his first England cap - 1994 or 1996?

**4** Which country won the Hong Kong Sevens four times during the 1980s?

**5** Which position does Richard Cockerill play?

**6** From which club did Newcastle sign Rob Andrew?

**7** When was Rob Andrew born - 1961 or 1963?

**8** Which European country beat England 37-12 in 1972?

**9** When were Gloucester founded - 1873 or 1893?

**10** Who captained Scotland 25 times between 1989 and 1992?

**11** England international Tony Underwood was born in Bedfordshire True or false?

**12** What nationality is scrum-half Gary Armstrong?

**13** Which country lost 15-12 in the final of the 1995 World Cup?

**14** Who did England beat 58-23 at Twickenham in 1989?

**15** Which country beat the British Lions 38-6 in 1983?

---

## *Answers to page 359*

**1** Scott Quinnell, **2** Kingsholm, **3** Dusty, **4** Bath, **5** Gavin Hastings, **6** New Zealand, **7** Orrell, **8** Western Samoa, **9**1970s , **10** Argentina, **11**Neil Back , **12** 667, **13** Andre Joubert, **14** 3, **15** South Africa.

# • RUGBY UNION - QUIZ 7 •

*Answers on page 356*

1 Which Jeff made his New Zealand debut against Scotland at Murrayfield in 1993?

2 When did Doddie Weir win his first senior Scotland cap - 1990 or 1992?

3 From which Scottish club did Newcastle sign Doddie Weir?

4 Who scored 67 points for England in the 1992 Five Nations Championship?

5 Who won the John Player Cup in 1974?

6 How many caps did Gareth Edwards win for Wales - 53, 63 or 73?

7 Who did Ireland beat 32-9 at Brisbane in the 1987 World Cup?

8 When was French international Philippe Saint-Andre born - 1967 or 1970?

9 Against which southern hemisphere country did Kyran Bracken make his England debut in 1993?

10 Who became England's youngest capped international for 71 years when he came on as a replacement against Ireland in 1988, aged 18 years 301 days?

11 Who captained Bath in the 1995 Pilkington Cup final?

12 How many League games did Newcastle lose during the 1997-98 season?

13 In which decade was Tim Rodber born?

14 For which country does winger Joe Roff play?

15 Which club plays its home matches at the Madejski Stadium?

---

## *Answers to page 356*

**1** Bedford, **2** 1940s, **3** Will Carling, **4** Australia, **5** New Zealand, **6** Neil Jenkins, **7** London Irish, **8** False - he represented Ireland in the hammer, **9** Bath, **10** Seven, **11** Two, **12** Hooker, **13** Dean Richards, **14** Australia, **15** 1960s.

# • RUGBY UNION - QUIZ 8 •

*Answers on page 357*

**1** Which nephew of Barry John won his first Welsh cap against Canada in 1993?

**2** Where do Gloucester play?

**3** William Hare made his England debut in 1974 What was his nickname?

**4** From which club did Northampton sign Jonathan Sleightholme?

**5** Who won 61 caps for Scotland between 1986 and1995?

**6** Who beat South Africa 55-35 in August 1997?

**7** From which club did Leicester sign Austin Healey ?

**8** Who did Australia beat 73-3 at Sydney in 1994?

**9** In which decade was England international Martin Johnson born?

**10** Against which country did Nick Beal make his senior England debut in December 1996?

**11** Rearrange NICK BEAL to form the name of another England international of the 1990's.

**12** How many points Gavin Hastings score for Scotland between 1986 and 1995 - 445, 556, or 667?

**13** Who scored 38 individual points for South Africa against Swansea in 1994?

**14** How many Grand Slams did Wales complete during the 1970s?

**15** Who beat England 18-0 in July 1998?

---

## *Answers to page 357*

**1** 1969, **2** Welford Road, **3** 1994, **4** Australia, **5** Hooker, **6** Wasps, **7** 1963, **8** France, **9** 1873, **10** David Sole, **11** False - Malaysia, **12** Scottish, **13** New Zealand, **14** Fiji, **15** New Zealand.

# • RUGBY UNION - QUIZ 9 •

*Answers on page 362*

1 Which Five Nations opponents beat England 26-21 at Twickenham in 1974?

2 Which club plays its home matches at Vicarage Road?

3 How many tries did Scotland score in their 89-0 win over the Ivory Coast in 1995?

4 Which New Zealand player scored four tries against England at the 1995 World Cup?

5 Which club won the John Player Cup in 1976?

6 Which southern hemisphere nation lost 34-6 in Paris in 1976?

7 For which country did fly-half Hugo Porta play?

8 How many Australian caps did David Campese win - 72, 82 or 92?

9 Who beat the British Lions 34-14 in 1962?

10 Which club won the Welsh Premier Division in the 1997-98 season?

11 Between 1980 and 1988, Roy Laidlaw won 47 caps for Scotland In which position did he play?

12 Name the player who scored in all four Tests of Australia's 1984 tour of the British Isles?

13 Who scored four tries for Wales in their 40-9 win over Canada at the 1987 World Cup?

14 How many penalty goals did Gavin Hastings convert for Scotland between 1986 and 1995 - 120, 130 or 140?

15 Who scored four tries for Australia against United States in Sydney in 1983?

---

## *Answers to page 362*

**1** England and Scotland, **2** 1960s, **3** Phil Bennett, **4** Craig Chalmers, **5** Argentina, **6** New Zealand, **7** Phil Bennett, **8** Nick Farr-Jones, **9** New Zealand, **10** Tom Kiernan, **11** Thierry Lacroix, **12** Bristol, **13** Four, **14** Five, **15** South Africa.

# •RUGBY UNION - QUIZ 10•

*Answers on page 363*

1. How many conversions did Michael Lynagh score for Australia between 1984 and 1995 - 120, 140 or 160?
2. In which year did Jim Staples make a try-scoring international debut for Ireland?
3. Which England player scored five tries against Fiji at Twickenham in 1989?
4. In which year was Gareth Llewellyn born - 1966 or 1969?
5. Which player was sent off against Eastern Province during England's 1994 tour of South Africa?
6. Where do Harlequins play?
7. Which European country did England beat 41-13 at Richmond in 1907?
8. Which player scored 52 points for Wales in the 1986 Five Nations Championship?
9. Where do Bath play?
10. Which Five Nations opponents beat Wales 36-3 in 1991?
11. In which year was the World Cup first staged?
12. Who knocked Australia out of the 1995 World Cup?
13. Which player won the game with a late drop goal?
14. When were Harlequins founded - 1866 or 1896?
15. How many Grand Slams did France achieve in the 1980s?

---

## *Answers to page 363*

**1** Australia and New Zealand, **2** Australia, **3** England, **4** Canada, **5** Two, **6** Wales, **7** Japan, **8** Nine, **9** Seventy two, **10** Edge Hall Road, **11** Thirty eight , **12** Australia, **13** Ben Clarke, **14** Japan, **15** Sixteen.

# • RUGBY UNION - QUIZ 11 •

*Answers on page 360*

1 Which two countries compete for the Calcutta Cup?

2 In which decade was Zinzan Brooke born?

3 Which Welsh player captained the British Lions in 1977?

4 Which player scored two drop goals for Scotland against England at Twickenham in 1995?

5 Which national side is known as the Pumas?

6 Who beat England 40-10 in June 1998?

7 Which Welsh player converted ten penalty goals for the British Lions between 1974 and 1977?

8 Who captained Australia 36 times between 1988 and 1992?

9 Which country was unbeaten in 17 internationals between 1965 and 1969?

10 Which Irish player captained the 1968 British Lions team?

11 Which French player scored eight penalties against Ireland at Dublin in 1995?

12 From which club did Bath sign England hooker Mark Regan?

13 How many matches did England's Tony Underwood play in the 1995 World Cup?

14 How many overseas tours did Willie John McBride make, as a player, with the British Lions?

15 Which country went unbeaten in 14 matches between 1994 and1995?

---

## *Answers to page 360*

**1** Ireland, **2** Saracens, **3** Thirteen, **4** Jonah Lomu, **5** Newcastle Gosforth, **6** Australia, **7** Argentina, **8** Ninety two, **9** South Africa, **10** Swansea, **11** Scrum-half, **12** Mark Ella, **13** Ieuan Evans, **14** 140, **15** David Campese.

# • RUGBY UNION - QUIZ 12 •

*Answers on page 361*

1 Which two countries contest the Bledisloe Cup?

2 Which country beat the British Lions 30-12 in 1989?

3 Which Five Nations opponents did France beat 37-12 at Colombes in 1972?

4 Which country did Ireland beat 46-19 at the 1987 World Cup?

5 How many Grand Slams did France win during the 1980s?

6 Against which country did Scotland's John Rutherford score two drop goals atMurrayfield in 1985?

7 Who did England beat 60-7 at Sydney in the 1987 World Cup?

8 When South Africa beat Scotland 44-0 at Murrayfield in 1951, how many tries did the Springboks score - 5, 7 or 9?

9 How many caps did Michael Lynagh win for Australia - 52, 72 or 92?

10 Where do Orrell play?

11 How many tries did Serge Blanco score for France between 1980 and 1991 - 28, 38 or 48?

12 Which southern hemisphere nation beat Scotland 37-12 at Murrayfield in 1984?

13 Who captained Richmond during the 1997-98 season?

14 Who did Scotland beat 47-9 at Murrayfield in 1991?

15 How many tries did Wales score in their 102-11 win over Portugal in 1994 - 12, 14 or 16?

***The 1999 World Cup in Britain, Ireland and France promises to the biggest and best tournament yet with gate receipts alone expected to be around £70 million.***

---

*Answers to page 361*

**1** 140, **2** 1991, **3** Rory Underwood, **4** 1969, **5** Tim Rodber, **6** Stoop Memorial Ground, **7** France, **8** Paul Thorburn, **9** The Recreation Ground, **10** France, **11** 1987, **12** England, **13** Rob Andrew, **14** 1866, **15** Two.

# • RUGBY UNION - QUIZ 13 •

*Answers on page 366*

**1** Which country was thrashed by South Africa 96-13 in June 1998?

**2** How many tries did South Africa score during this match?

**3** Which player scored nine conversions in this match?

**4** Name the two New Zealand players to score six tries apiece at the 1987 World Cup?

**5** Which southern hemisphere country beat Ireland 42-17 at Dublin in 1992?

**6** How many New Zealand caps did Grant Fox win - 36, 46 or 56?

**7** In which decade did South Africa lose seven consecutive Test matches?

**8** What nationality is Allan Bateman?

**9** Who converted 177 penalties for Australia between 1984 and 1995?

**10** Who captained the British Lions in 1997?

**11** From which French club did Damian Cronin join Wasps in July 1996?

**12** When was Lawrence Dallaglio born - 1970 or 1972?

**13** Name the Australian player who scored six tries at the 1991 World Cup?

**14** Against which southern hemisphere country did Ben Clarke make his England debut in 1992?

**15** Which French player scored six tries at the 1991 World Cup?

## *Answers to page 366*

**1** Brendan Mullin, **2** Francois Pienaar, **3** Ireland, **4** New Zealand, **5** New Zealand, **6** Rob Andrew, **7** False - only 69 of them, **8** South Africa, **9** Canada, **10** Australia, **11** Neil Jenkins, **12** Bristol, **13** The Springboks, **14** Tom Kiernan, **15** Australia.

# • RUGBY UNION - QUIZ 14 •

*Answers on page 367*

1 Which Sean played in seventeen World Cup matches for New Zealand between 1987 and 1995?

2 Who scored four tries for Wales against Portugal in Lisbon in 1994?

3 Name the winners of the 1977 John Player Cup?

4 Who knocked Scotland out of the 1995 World Cup?

5 How many times was Willie John McBride capped by the British Lions - 13, 15 or 17?

6 In which decade was Joel Stransky born?

7 Which Five Nations opponent did Ireland beat 22-0 at Dublin in 1947?

8 Who captained Bath in the 1995 Pilkington Cup final?

9 Which Scottish player scored 56 points in the 1995 Five Nations Championship?

10 From which club did Northampton sign Patrick Lam in July 1998?

11 Who did France beat 45-10 in Paris in the 1996 Five Nations?

12 In which year did Phil Bennett win his last Welsh cap?

13 England international Kyran Bracken was born in Dublin True or false?

14 Who beat Scotland 48-30 during the 1995 World Cup?

15 How many points did Scotland score in the 1995 Five Nations Championship - 47, 67 or 87?

---

*Answers to page 367*

**1** England and France, **2** Serge Blanco, **3** Rob Andrew, **4** South Africa, **5** Welsh, **6** Italy, **7** Jeremy Guscott, **8** New Zealand, **9** Simon Culhane, **10** Eleven, **11** 102, **12** Romania, **13** Australia, **14** Harlequins, **15** Cardiff.

# •RUGBY UNION - QUIZ 15•

*Answers on page 364*

1 Who scored 17 tries for Ireland between 1984 and 1995?

2 Name South Africa's captain at the 1995 World Cup?

3 Which country won their first Grand Slam in 1948?

4 Which country did the British Lions tour in 1968?

5 Which country lost in the final of the 1995 World Cup?

6 Who scored 24 points on his England debut against Romania in 1985?

7 Rob Andrew played all of his 71 England games at fly-half True or false?

8 Which southern hemisphere country beat Ireland 38-0 in 1912?

9 Which country did Wales beat 40-9 at the 1987 World Cup?

10 Which national side is known as the Wallabies?

11 Which player scored 24 points for Wales against Canada at Cardiff in 1993?

12 From which club did Gareth Archer rejoin Newcastle at the end of the 1995-96 season?

13 What is the nickname of the South African rugby union team?

14 Who captained Ireland 24 times between 1963 and 1973?

15 Which southern hemisphere country beat Scotland 33-11 in June 1998?

## *Answers to page 364*

**1** Wales, **2** Fifteen, **3** Percy Montgomery, **4** Craig Green and John Kirwan, **5** Australia, **6** Forty six, **7** 1960s, **8** Welsh, **9** Michael Lynagh, **10** Martin Johnson, **11** Bourges, **12** 1972, **13** David Campese, **14** South Africa, **15** Jean-Baptiste Lafond.

# • RUGBY UNION - QUIZ 16 •

*Answers on page 365*

**1** Name the two losing semi-finalists at the 1995 World Cup?

**2** Which French legend was known as the 'Biarritz Bombshell'?

**3** Who scored two drop goals for England against Argentina at the 1995 World Cup?

**4** Which southern hemisphere country beat Italy 62-31 in Bologna in November 1997?

**5** What nationality is top referee and TV pundit Clive Norling?

**6** Who beat Ireland 22-12 at Treviso in 1995?

**7** The British Lions beat South Africa 18-15 at Durban in June 1997 Who won the game with a drop goal?

**8** Which country scored 21 tries in one game against Japan at the 1995 World Cup?

**9** Which player scored 45 individual points in this match?

**10** How many successive internationals did Ireland lose between 1991 and 1993 - 7, 11 or 15?

**11** How many points did Wales score during the 1976 Five Nations Championship - 82, 102 or 122?

**12** Who did Scotland beat 55-28 at the 1987 World Cup?

**13** Which southern hemisphere nation lost to Argentina in Buenos Aires in November 1997?

**14** From which English club did Richmond sign French flanker Laurent Cabannes?

**15** Which club won the Welsh Cup in 1986 and 1987?

---

## *Answers to page 365*

**1** Fitzpatrick, **2** Nigel Walker, **3** Newcastle Gosforth, **4** New Zealand, **5** Seventeen, **6** 1960s, **7** England, **8** Phil de Glanville, **9** Gavin Hastings, **10** Newcastle, **11** Ireland, **12** 1978, **13** True, **14** New Zealand, **15** Eighty seven.

# • RUGBY UNION - QUIZ 17 •

*Answers on page 370*

1. Which country did Scotland beat 51-12 at Murrayfield in 1991?
2. Who scored 52 individual points for Ireland in the 1983 Five Nations Championship?
3. In which decade was David Campese born?
4. Which player scored two tries for Scotland in their 24-21 defeat by England at Twickenham in 1999?
5. Who did England beat 58-3 in 1989?
6. Which national side is known as the All Blacks?
7. Who did Ireland beat 44-8 at Dublin in 1995?
8. How many times did Jean-Pierre Rives captain France - 14, 24 or 34?
9. Which South African scored the winning drop goal in the 1995 World Cup final?
10. Who scored the only try for the British Lions in the 20-7 win over New Zealand in 1993?
11. Who is England's most-capped prop?
12. Who did Ireland beat 49-22 at Dublin in 1988?
13. Who won the John Player Cup in 1978?
14. When were Leicester founded - 1860 or 1880?
15. Which Welsh player converted eight penalties against Canada at Cardiff in 1993?

## *Answers to page 370*

**1** True, **2** Francois Pienaar, **3** England, **4** Cardiff, **5** Romania, **6** Eighty five, **7** Ciaran Fitzgerald, **8** Sixty three, **9** Eden Park, **10** United States, **11** Llanelli, **12** Bath, **13** Two, **14** Jean-Patrick Lescarboura, **15** Zimbabwe.

# • RUGBY UNION - QUIZ 18 •

*Answers on page 371*

1. How many caps did Gareth Edwards win for the British Lions?
2. Scrum-half Dickie Jeeps won 13 caps for the British Lions between 1955 and 1962 True or false?
3. Which French player scored nine conversions against Zimbabwe in 1987?
4. Which country won the 1991 World Cup?
5. Who beat South Africa 25-16 in Cape Town on 21 June, 1997?
6. Which two Lions players scored a try apiece in this match?
7. Which player scored most points at the 1995 World Cup?
8. Who scored 35 tries for New Zealand between 1984 and 1994?
9. Which southern hemisphere country beat England 35-9 in 1984?
10. Who beat Scotland 34-10 at Murrayfield in 1994?
11. Rory Underwood was born in Newcastle True or false?
12. How many consecutive internationals did England lose between 1971 and 1972 - 5, 7 or 9?
13. Which Welsh forward was known as 'Merv the Swerve'?
14. Which country did Wales beat 49-14 at Swansea in 1910?
15. In which decade was Hugo Porta born?

### Answers to page 371

**1** 1930s, **2** 1995, **3** Simon Hodgkinson, **4** New Zealand, **5** Tonga, **6** 1978, **7** Ireland, **8** Ireland, **9** 1970s, **10** England, **11** Sean Fitzpatrick, **12** South Africa, **13** Leicester, **14** Fifty five, **15** Barry John.

# • RUGBY UNION - QUIZ 19 •

*Answers on page 368*

1 Namibia beat Ireland 26-15 in 1991 True or false?

2 Who captained South Africa 24 times between 1993 and 1995?

3 Who did New Zealand trounce 64-22 in June 1998?

4 With which club side did Gareth Edwards spend his entire career?

5 Who did Scotland beat 49-16 at Murrayfield in 1995?

6 How many caps did Rory Underwood win for England - 65, 85 or 105?

7 Which Irish international captained the 1983 British Lions?

8 How many times did Willie John McBride play for Ireland - 53, 63 or 73?

9 In which stadium was the 1987 World Cup final held?

10 Who did England beat 37-9 at Twickenham in 1991?

11 Which Welsh club side beat New Zealand 9-3 in 1973?

12 Which club were Courage League Champions in the 1992-93 season?

13 How many drop goals did Ollie Campbell score for Ireland against Australia in Sydney in 1979?

14 Name the French player who scored 54 points during the 1984 Five Nations Championship?

15 Which country did Ireland beat 55-11 at Dublin in 1991?

---

## *Answers to page 368*

**1** Zimbabwe, **2** Ollie Campbell, **3** 1960s, **4** Alan Tait, **5** Romania, **6** New Zealand, **7** Fiji, **8** Thirty four, **9** Joel Stransky, **10** Rory Underwood, **11** Jason Leonard, **12** Western Samoa, **13** Gloucester, **14** 1880, **15** Neil Jenkins.

# • RUGBY UNION - QUIZ 20 •

*Answers on page 369*

1 In which decade was Australian scrum-half Ken Catchpole born?

2 When did Graham Rowntree win his first England cap - 1993 or 1995?

3 Which England player scored 60 points in the 1991 Five Nations Championship?

4 Which country did the British Lions tour in 1983?

5 Who did Scotland beat 41-5 at the 1995 World Cup?

6 In which year did Gareth Edwards play his last games for Wales?

7 Who beat Scotland 26-8 at Murrayfield in 1953?

8 Which northern hemisphere country did New Zealand beat 59-6 in 1992?

9 In which decade did Mike Burton become the first England player to be sent off in an international?

10 Which Five Nations opponents did Wales beat 34-21 in 1967?

11 Which Sean won 73 New Zealand caps between 1986 and 1995?

12 Who beat Ireland 33-0 in June 1998?

13 Which club won the John Player Cup in 1979?

14 How many caps did Wade Dooley win for England between 1985 and 1993 - 45, 55 or 65?

15 Which player scored two drop goals for Wales against England at Cardiff in 1971?

***With an estimated television audience of three and a half billion viewers in 150 countries the Rugby World Cup will have the fourth largest audience in sport.***

---

## *Answers to page 369*

**1** Ten, **2** True, **3** Didier Camberabero, **4** Australia, **5** British Lions, **6** Matt Dawson and John Tait, **7** Thierry Lacroix, **8** John Kirwan, **9** South Africa, **10** South Africa, **11** False - Middlesbrough, **12** Seven, **13** Mervyn Davies, **14** France, **15** 1950s.

# • RUGBY UNION - QUIZ 21 •

*Answers on page 374*

1 When was Moseley formed -1873 or 1893?

2 Which Scottish player captained the 1989 British Lions?

3 Scottish international player Damian Cronin was born in Germany True or false?

4 Which country plays at Murrayfield?

5 How many times was Welsh international Graham Price capped by the British Lions - 10, 12 or 14?

6 Which country plays at Twickenham?

7 In 1974, the British Lions became the first side to win a major series in South Africa True or false?

8 In which decade was Serge Blanco born?

9 Which country did the British Lions tour in 1989?

10 How many times did Bill Beaumont captain England - 15, 21 or 27?

11 Which Scottish scrum-half, born in 1966, made his international debut against Australia in 1988?

12 In which decade did Scotland lose seventeen consecutive matches?

13 In which stadium was the 1991 World Cup final held?

14 Who scored six tries for New Zealand against Japan at the 1995 World Cup?

15 Who did Wales beat 29-6 at Cardiff in 1994?

---

## *Answers to page 374*

**1** 1981, **2** Six, **3** Prop (Tight-head), **4** Rory Underwood, **5** 1993, **6** Wales, **7** Waterloo, **8** Martin Johnson, **9** 1993, **10** Brendan Venter, **11** Nineteen, **12** Stoop Memorial Ground, **13** Gavin Hastings, **14** Lawrence Dallagio, **15** England.

# • RUGBY UNION - QUIZ 22 •

*Answers on page 375*

**1** How many Grand Slams did Wales achieve during the 1970s?

**2** Robert Paparemborde won 56 caps for France between 1975 and 1983 In which position did he play?

**3** Which player scored 30 individual points for France against Zimbabwe in 1987?

**4** Who converted 140 penalty goals for Scotland between 1986 and 1995?

**5** Which country lost 64-12 to France in 1996?

**6** When was Matt Dawson born - 1970 or 1972?

**7** Who did France thrash 70-12 at the 1987 World Cup?

**8** Which country won the Hong Kong Sevens from 1994 and 1996?

**9** Who beat Scotland 51-26 at Suva in May 1998?

**10** Which Australian scored six penalties against France at Sydney in 1986?

**11** In which year was the first Hong Kong Sevens tournament?

**12** Who won it?

**13** Who did England beat 34-6 at Twickenham in 1990?

**14** Who played in 46 consecutive internationals for France between 1973 and 1979?

**15** Who beat Scotland 44-0 at Murrayfield in 1951?

## *Answers to page 375*

**1** Leicester, **2** Simon Culhane, **3** Wasps, **4** True, **5** 1989, **6** Victoria Park, **7** Simon Fenn, **8** 1997, **9** Brive, **10** Leicester, **11** Alain Penaud, **12** Leicester, **13** 93, **14** True, **15** 1880.

# • RUGBY UNION - QUIZ 23 •

*Answers on page 372*

**1** In which year did Fran Cotton play his last England international?

**2** How many times did Ronnie Dawson captain the British Lions 4, 6 or 8?

**3** In which position does Darren Garforth play?

**4** Who is England's all-time leading try-scorer?

**5** In which year did Martin Johnson win his first England cap - 1991 or 1993?

**6** Who did Scotland beat 35-10 at Inverleith in 1924?

**7** From which club did Harlequins sign Will Greenwood in June 1996?

**8** Who captained the 1997 British Lions?

**9** When did Conor O'Shea win his first Irish cap -1993 or 1995?

**10** Which member of the South African World Cup-winning squad joined London Irish during the 1997-98 season?

**11** How old was Scott Gibbs when he made his debut for Wales in 1991?

**12** At which ground do London Scottish play?

**13** Which Scottish player captained the 1993 British Lions?

**14** Who captained Wasps during the 1997-98 season?

**15** Which country lost 12-6 in the 1991 World Cup final?

## *Answers to page 372*

**1** 1873, **2** Finlay Calder, **3** True, **4** Scotland, **5** Twelve, **6** England, **7** True, **8** 1950s, **9** Australia, **10** Twenty one, **11** Gary Armstrong, **12** 1950s, **13** Twickenham, **14** Marc Ellis, **15** Scotland.

# •RUGBY UNION - QUIZ 24•

*Answers on page 373*

**1** From which club did Bedford sign Rory Underwood?

**2** Which New Zealander scored 20 conversions in a single game against Japan in 1995?

**3** Which club were Courage League champions in the 1996-97 season?

**4** Western Samoa reached the quarter-finals of both the 1991 and 1995 World Cups True or false?

**5** When did Andrew Burnell win his first Scotland cap -1989 or 1992?

**6** Where do West Hartlepool play?

**7** Which London Scottish flanker required over 20 stitches in a ripped ear after an incident against Bath in the 1997-98 season?

**8** In which year did Eric Miller win his first Irish cap -1995 or 1997?

**9** Which French team won the 1997 European Cup?

**10** Which English club lost 28-9 in the 1997 European Cup final?

**11** Who captained Brive in the 1996-97 season?

**12** Which club won the John Player Cup in 1980?

**13** How many French caps did Serge Blanco win -73, 83 or 93?

**14** Jeremy Guscott was born in Bath in 1965 True or false?

**15** When was Northampton formed -1880 or 1900?

## *Answers to page 373*

**1** Three, **2** Hooker, **3** Didier Camberabero, **4** Gavin Hastings, **5** Romania, **6** 1972, **7** Zimbabwe, **8** New Zealand, **9** Fiji, **10** Michael Lynagh, **11** 1976, **12** Cantabrians, **13** Wales, **14** Roland Bertranne, **15** South Africa.

# •RUGBY UNION - QUIZ 25•

*Answers on page 378*

**1** Which country drew 15-15 with Scotland at Murrayfield in 1995?

**2** JPR Williams won 54 Welsh caps at full-back and one as a flanker True or false?

**3** Who did Wales beat 40-3 at Cardiff in 1985?

**4** Which country beat Wales 52-3 in 1988?

**5** Who captained France 34 times between 1978 and 1984?

**6** Which university did Will Carling go to?

**7** Who scored two tries on his debut for England against Canada in 1992?

**8** How many conversions did England's Jonathan Webb score between 1987 and 1993 - 41, 61 or 81?

**9** Which Scottish international prop was nicknamed 'Mighty Mouse'?

**10** Which player scored 12 drop goals for Scotland between 1979 and 1987?

**11** For which country did Simon Poidevin play?

**12** In which decade was Jean-Pierre Rives born?

**13** At which club did Mike Brewer begin the 1998-99 season as Director of Rugby?

**14** Which Welsh player scored five tries for the British Lions between 1974 and 1977?

**15** Who did England beat 44-22 at the 1995 World Cup?

---

## *Answers to page 378*

**1** True, **2** 1997, **3** Newcastle, **4** John Rutherford, **5** Ireland, **6** Scotland, **7** Canada, **8** Rob Andrew, **9** France, **10** Newcastle, **11** Paul Grayson, **12** France, **13** Gavin Hastings, **14** 140, **15** Harlequins.

# • RUGBY UNION - QUIZ 26 •

*Answers on page 379*

1 Which country knocked New Zealand out of the 1991 World Cup?

2 From which club did Northampton sign Patrick Lam for £100,000 in July 1998?

3 Which English player captained the 1980 British Lions?

4 What nationality was fly-half Barry John?

5 In which decade was Scottish international Andy Irvine born?

6 Which Irish hooker scored his fourth try in twenty internationals against Wales at Wembley in February 1999?

7 Which French club won the 1996 European Cup?

8 Which country thrashed England 76-0 in 1998?

9 How many tries did Australia score in this game?

10 When did John Devereux win his first Welsh cap -1986 or 1990?

11 When did Philippe Sella make his debut for France - 1982 or 1984?

12 In which year did Peter Wheeler win his last England cap?

13 Which country did Fergus Slattery play for between 1970 and 1984?

14 Which French player scored five tries during the 1983 Five Nations Championship?

15 Who won the John Player Cup in 1981?

## *Answers to page 379*

**1** Cardiff, **2** Wales, **3** Twenty one, **4** Mike Gibson, **5** Bill Beaumont, **6** Newcastle, **7** Phil Bennett, **8** Australia, **9** 1991, **10** Wasps, **11** New Zealand, **12** 1927, **13** England, **14** True, **15** Italy.

# • RUGBY UNION - QUIZ 27 •

*Answers on page 376*

1 England won ten consecutive matches between 1994 and 1995 True or false?

2 In which year did David Rees make his England debut -1995 or 1997?

3 Which club were English Premiership champions in the 1997-98 season?

4 Which Scottish player scored two drop goals against Ireland at Murrayfield in 1987?

5 Which Five Nations opponents did Wales beat 34-9 in 1976?

6 Against which country did England's Rob Andrew score seven penalties at Twickenham in 1995?

7 Who did England beat 60-19 at Twickenham in 1994?

8 Which player scored 30 points during this match?

9 Which European country lost 18 successive matches between 1911 and 1920?

10 Which English club team is known as the 'Falcons'?

11 Who scored 58 points for England in the 1995-96 Five Nations Championship?

12 Who did Ireland beat 24-0 at Cork in 1913?

13 Which player scored 44 points for Scotland against Ivory Coast in 1995?

14 How many conversions did Michael Lynagh score for Australia between 1984 and 1995 -120, 140 or 160?

15 Which club side won the John Player Cup in 1988?

---

## *Answers to page 376*

**1** Western Samoa, **2** True, **3** Fiji, **4** New Zealand, **5** Jean-Pierre Rives, **6** Durham, **7** Ian Hunter, **8** 41, **9** Ian McLauchlan, **10** John Rutherford, **11** Australia, **12** 1950s, **13** West Hartlepool, **14** JJ Williams, **15** Western Samoa.

# • RUGBY UNION - QUIZ 28 •

*Answers on page 377*

1 Which Welsh club side lost in the final of the 1996 European Cup?

2 Who knocked England out of the 1987 World Cup?

3 How many drop goals did Rob Andrew score in England internationals between 1985 and 1995 - 11, 21 or 31?

4 Who won 69 caps for Ireland between 1964 and 1979?

5 Who captained England's 1980 Grand Slam team?

6 From which club did Leicester sign Tim Stimpson?

7 Which Welsh player scored 44 points for the British Lions between 1974 and 1977?

8 Who beat England 25-6 in July 1997?

9 When did John Eales make his debut for Australia - 1987 or 1991?

10 From which club did Newcastle sign Nigel Popplewell?

11 Who knocked England out of the 1995 World Cup?

12 When was Orrell formed - 1907 or 1927?

13 Who knocked Scotland out of the 1991 World Cup?

14 Wales lost 71-8 to New South Wales in 1991 True or false?

15 Who did Ireland beat 31-15 at Dublin in 1988?

***The first World Cup in New Zealand and Australia in 1987 made a paltry profit of £1.5 million. Eight years later, and the organisers of the 1995 World Cup in South Africa, were laughing all the way to the bank with a £250 million gross profit.***

---

*Answers to page 377*

**1** Australia, **2** Newcastle, **3** Bill Beaumont, **4** Welsh, **5** 1950s, **6** Keith Wood, **7** Toulouse, **8** Australia, **9** Eleven, **10** 1986, **11** 1982, **12** 1984, **13** Ireland, **14** Patrick Esteve, **15** Leicester.

# • RUGBY UNION - QUIZ 29 •

*Answers on page 382*

1 Which England player scored 66 points in the 1998 Five Nations Championship?

2 Which two clubs shared the John Player Cup in 1982?

3 Which player scored two drop goals for Wales against Ireland at Wellington in 1987?

4 Who played in 63 consecutive internationals for New Zealand between 1986 and 1995?

5 Who did Wales beat 57-10 at Bloemfontein in 1995?

6 In which year did Gary Whetton win his first cap for New Zealand - 1981 or 1983?

7 How many penalties did Gavin Hastings score in the British Lions' 1993 Test series with New Zealand - 8, 12 or 16?

8 Which country hosted the 1995 World Cup?

9 In which country was England international Victor Ubogu born?

10 How many Ireland caps did Brendan Mullin win between 1984 and 1995 - 35, 55 or 75?

11 Which country beat Japan 106-4 in Tokyo on 1 November, 1987?

12 Which country did scrum-half Sid Going play for between 1967 and 1976?

13 Who did Wales beat 46-0 at Cardiff in 1987?

14 How many tries did the British Lions score in the 1974 Test series with South Africa - 8, 10 or 12?

15 From which club did Harlequins sign England international Dan Luger in 1996?

---

## *Answers to page 382*

**1** One, **2** South Africa, **3** France, **4** 111, **5** Argentina, **6** Nigeria, **7** France, **8** Rory Underwood, **9** 1970s, **10** Jeremy Guscott, **11** John Carleton, **12** Bath, **13** Saracens, **14** Nine, **15** True.

# • RUGBY UNION - QUIZ 30 •

*Answers on page 383*

**1** Who won the Middlesex Sevens from 1986 and 1990?

**2** How many penalties did Scotland's Gavin Hastings convert against Tonga at Pretoria in 1995?

**3** Which South African flanker captained Transvaal to successive Currie Cup wins in 1993 and 1994?

**4** In which decade was Welsh legend Barry John born?

**5** Which club won the John Player Cup in 1983?

**6** Who scored 48 conversions for France between 1982 and 1993?

**7** Which Welsh player scored two drop goals for the British Lions between 1974 and 1977?

**8** Which northern hemisphere country did Western Samoa beat 34-9 in 1994?

**9** In which year did Scott Gibbs join Swansea from Neath?

**10** Who did Ireland beat 50-28 at the 1995 World Cup?

**11** Who scored the only British Lions try in the 35-16 defeat by South Africa at Ellis Park in July 1997?

**12** Which English club won the 1998 European Cup?

**13** Which French club did they beat in the final?

**14** Which New Zealand player scored seventeen points in the 1987 World Cup final?

**15** How many Scotland caps did John Rutherford win - 42, 52 or 62?

---

## *Answers to page 383*

**1** Tony Diprose, **2** Saracens, **3** Francois Pienaar, **4** Seventy nine, **5** Loftus Road, **6** 1876, **7** Grant Fox, **8** Namibia, **9** Andrew Mehrtens, **10** South Africa, **11** Australia, **12** Danie Gerber, **13** Gavin Hastings, **14** Harlequins, **15** Eighty six.

# • RUGBY UNION - QUIZ 31 •

*Answers on page 380*

1 How many Grand Slams did France achieve during the 1970s?

2 Which country won the 1995 World Cup?

3 Who lost 29-9 in the 1987 World Cup final?

4 How many times did Philippe Sella play for France between 1982 and 1995 - 91, 101 or 111?

5 With which country did England draw 13-13 at Twickenham in 1978?

6 In which African country was Steve Ojomoh born?

7 Who did Scotland beat 31-3 at Inverleith in 1912?

8 Which England player scored five tries against Fiji at Twickenham in 1989?

9 In which decade did fly-half Tony Ward win his first cap for Ireland?

10 Who scored three tries on his England debut against Romania in Bucharest in 1989?

11 When England beat Scotland 30-18 in 1980, who became the first Englishman for 56 years to score three tries in one Test?

12 Which club won the John Player Cup from 1984 to 1987?

13 From which club did Harlequins sign Jason Leonard in 1990?

14 How many conversions did Gavin Hastings score against v the Ivory Coast in Rustenburg in 1995?

15 Romania beat Wales 24-6 in 1983 True or false?

## *Answers to page 380*

**1** Paul Grayson, **2** Gloucester and Moseley, **3** Jonathan Davies, **4** Sean Fitzpatrick, **5** Japan, **6** 1981, **7** Twelve, **8** South Africa, **9** Nigeria, **10** Fifty five, **11** New Zealand, **12** New Zealand, **13** United States, **14** Ten, **15** Orrell.

# • RUGBY UNION - QUIZ 32 •

*Answers on page 381*

1 Who was captain of Saracens during the 1997-98 season?

2 Which club beat Wasps to win the Tetley's Bitter Cup in 1998?

3 Who was player-coach of Saracens during the 1997-98 season?

4 How many points did the British Lions score in four Test matches during the 1974 tour of South Africa - 59, 79 or 99?

5 Where do Wasps play?

6 When were Saracens formed -1876 or 1896?

7 Which New Zealand player scored 645 points between 1985 and 1993?

8 Who did Wales beat 38-23 at Windhoek in 1993?

9 Which New Zealand player scored 2 drop goals against Australia in Auckland in 1995?

10 Which southern hemisphere country lost 9-6 at Dublin in 1965?

11 Who beat Scotland 45-3 in June 1998?

12 Who scored 19 tries in internationals for South Africa between 1980 and 1992?

13 Which player scored 66 points for the British Lions between 1989 and 1993?

14 Who won the Pilkington Cup in 1991?

15 How many conversions did Gavin Hastings score for Scotland between 1986 and 1995 - 66, 86 or 106?

---

*Answers to page 381*

**1** Harlequins, **2** Eight, **3** Francois Pienaar, **4** 1940s, **5** Bristol, **6** Didier Camberabero, **7** Phil Bennett, **8** Wales, **9** 1991, **10** Japan, **11** Matt Dawson, **12** Bath, **13** Brive, **14** Grant Fox, **15** Forty two.

# • RUGBY UNION - QUIZ 33 •

*Answers on page 385*

1 In 1978, which Australian became the first forward in history to score four tries in a Test?

2 Who played 53 consecutive internationals for Wales between 1967 and 1978?

3 Who captained Newcastle during the 1997-98 season?

4 How many conversions did Michael Kiernan score for Ireland between 1982 and 1991 - 20, 40 or 60?

5 Which New Zealand player scored seven penalties against Western Samoa at Auckland in 1993?

6 Which player scored two drop goals for Wales against Scotland at Cardiff in 1988?

7 Which Five Nations opponents did Scotland beat 33-6 at Murrayfield in 1986?

8 Who converted 128 penalty goals for New Zealand between 1985 and 1993?

9 Which Five Nations opponents did Wales beat 35-12 at Cardiff in 1972?

10 Which England player scored two dropped goals against France in Paris in 1996?

11 Who did Scotland beat 60-21 at the 1987 World Cup?

12 In which decade did Munster become the first-ever Irish team to beat New Zealand?

13 Against which country did Tim Rodber make his England debut in 1992?

14 Who won the Pilkington Cup in 1989 and 1990?

15 Who beat France 52-10 at the Parc des Princes in November 1997?

---

## *Answers to page 386*

**1** Zimbabwe, **2** Barry John, **3** Western Samoa, **4** Barbarians, **5** Ireland, **6** Sixteen, **7** Bath, **8** South Africa, **9** Gavin Hastings, **10** Wasps, **11** Fiji, **12** John Rutherford, **13** Spain, **14** 1867, **15** 1973.

# • RUGBY UNION - QUIZ 34 •

*Answers on page 386*

**1** What nationality is Joel Stransky?

**2** Who did Scotland beat 37-21 at Murrayfield in 1989?

**3** When did Richard Hill make his England debut - 1993 or 1997?

**4** Who did South Africa beat 40-11 at Johannesburg in 1995?

**5** Who scored 63 tries for Australia between 1982 and 1995?

**6** Which Five Nations opponents did Ireland beat 21-0 at Dublin in 1950?

**7** How many caps did Mervyn Davies win for Wales - 18, 38 or 58?

**8** When did Brian Moore win his first England cap - 1987 or 1989?

**9** Colin Deans won 52 caps for Scotland between 1978 and 1987 In which position did he play?

**10** Which club won the Pilkington Cup in 1993?

**11** Who scored 911 points for Australia between 1984 and 1995?

**12** In which decade was England's David Duckham born?

**13** Which country was trounced by South Africa 61-22 in August 1997?

**14** How many tries did South Africa score in this match?

**15** What nationality is Philippe Sella?

***President Nelson Mandela is a great supporter of South African rugby and he was given the ideal present on his 80th birthday when the Springboks beat the Aussies.***

---

*Answers to page 385*

**1** Greg Cornelsen, **2** Gareth Edwards, **3** Dean Ryan, **4** Forty, **5** Grant Fox, **6** Jonathan Davies, **7** Scotland, **8** Grant Fox, **9** Scotland, **10** Paul Grayson, **11** Zimbabwe, **12** 1970s, **13** Scotland, **14** Bath, **15** South Africa.

# • RUGBY UNION - QUIZ 35 •

*Answers on page 384*

1 Who did Wales beat 42-13 in 1993?

2 Which Welshman scored two dropped goals for the British Lions between 1968 and 1971?

3 In which country was Va'aiga Tuigamala born?

4 Who won the Middlesex Sevens in 1997 and 1998?

5 Which country plays at Lansdowne Road?

6 How many penalties did Paul Thorburn score for Wales during the 1986 Five Nations Championship - 8, 12 or 16?

7 Which club won the Pilkington Cup in 1996?

8 Which country plays at Ellis Park?

9 Which player scored eighteen points for the British Lions against New Zealand in Christchurch in 1993?

10 From which club did Newcastle sign Dean Ryan?

11 Who won the Hong Kong Sevens from 1990 and 1992?

12 Which Scottish player scored two drop goals against New Zealand at Murrayfield in 1983?

13 Which European country lost 54-0 to Wales in 1994?

14 In which year were Wasps formed -1867 or 1887?

15 In which year did Gareth Edwards score 'The Try' for the Barbarians in the 23-11 win over New Zealand at Cardiff Arms Park?

## *Answers to page 385*

**1** South African, **2** Ireland, **3** 1997, **4** Wales, **5** David Campese, **6** Scotland, **7** Thirty eight, **8** 1987, **9** Hooker, **10** Leicester, **11** Michael Lynagh, **12** 1940s, **13** Australia, **14** Eight, **15** French.

# SNOOKER

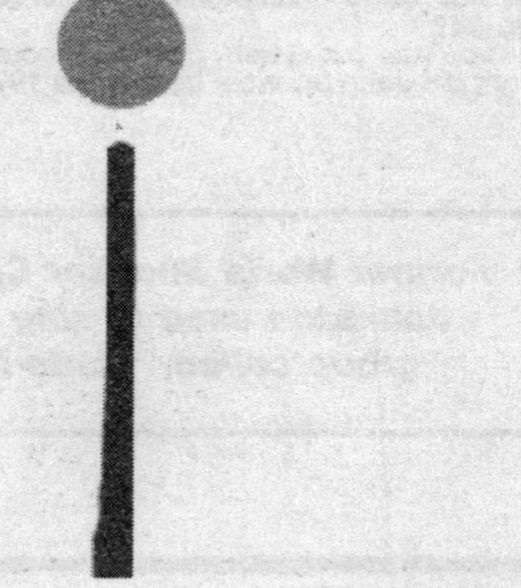

# SNOOKER - QUIZ 1

*Answers on page 390*

1 In which year was snooker invented?

2 Whose 1984 Rothmans Grand Prix title was his first major win?

3 What is the record for the longest senior frame, made during the Hofmeister World Doubles?

4 Which year saw the World Championship prize money exceed 100,000?

5 In which theatre has the World Championship been held since 1977?

6 Who won the 1977 Masters, his first professional event?

7 In which capacity is John Williams known to snooker fans?

8 Who successfully defended her Women's World Open Championship title in 1996?

9 Who lost to Rex Williams 9-8 after leading 8-2 in 1979, in his first professional event?

10 Who was British Open champion in 1996?

11 In which year did Joe Davis retire as World Champion?

12 Who was World Champion in 1964-68?

13 What is a snooker ball made of?

14 Who was World Championship runner-up for five consecutive years, 1990-94?

15 Whom did John Spencer beat in the 1971 World Championship final?

***Former World Snooker Champion Joe Johnston used to sing with a pop group called, 'Made In Japan'.***

---

## *Answers to page 390*

**1** Ronnie O'Sullivan, **2** Alex Higgins, **3** Seven, **4** England, **5** 1978, **6** Black pool, **7** Wembley Conference Centre, **8** Steve James, **9** Vera Selby, **10** John Street, **11** 1, **12** Willie Thorne, **13** European Open, **14** Slate, **15** Doug Mountjoy.

# SNOOKER - QUIZ 2

*Answers on page 391*

1 How are snooker's Mandy and Alison Fisher related?

2 What is snooker's longest-running sponsored event?

3 Whom did Steve Davis whitewash in the 1981 Jameson final?

4 Where is the British Open held?

5 Howmany minutes did Tony Drago take to win the fifth frame from Danny Fowler in the 1988 Fidelity Unit Trusts International?

6 In which year was Jimmy White World Amateur champion?

7 What is the diameter of the modern snooker ball?

8 Who was the first snooker player to appear on This Is Your Life?

9 In which year was the first set of world rankings published?

10 Who won the 1979 World Championship at the end of his debut season?

11 Where was the 1976 World Championship held?

12 Which nation successfully defended their World Cup title in 1989?

13 Who won the Scottish Masters in 1999?

14 How many red balls are used in a frame of snooker?

15 Which happens more often, snooker's maximum break or golf's hole in one?

---

### *Answers to page 391*

**1** 1975, **2** Jimmy White, **3** 250 - 1, **4** Steve Davis, **5** All-Ireland 'A', **6** Llanelli, **7** Fidelity Unit Trusts International, **8** 4, **9** Military cadets, **10** Cliff Thorburn, **11** 1997, **12** Alison Fisher, **13** Blackpool, **14** 147, **15** John Campbell.

# SNOOKER - QUIZ 3

*Answers on page 388*

**1** Who won his first UK Open in 1993?

**2** Which World Champion was once an apprentice jockey?

**3** How many attempts did Dennis Taylor need to sink the final black in the 1985 World Championship?

**4** Which nation won their first World Cup in 1981?

**5** In which year did Steve Davis turn professional?

**6** To which game were additional colours added to form snooker?

**7** Where have the Benson & Hedges Masters been held since 1979?

**8** Who scored the highest break of 140 in the 1988 World Championship before losing in the quarter-final?

**9** Who, in 1976, became the first women's World Champion?

**10** Who became the first secretary of the professional Referees' Association in 1979?

**11** How many points is a red ball worth?

**12** Who did Steve Davis beat in the final of the 1985 UK Open?

**13** Which competition's second champion was Tony Jones, in 1991?

**14** What is a snooker table made of?

**15** Whom did Steve Davis beat to win his first World Championship in 1981?

## *Answers to page 388*

**1** 1875, **2** Dennis Taylor, **3** 76 minutes, **4** 1989, **5** The Crucible, **6** Doug Mountjoy, **7** Referee, **8** Karen Corr, **9** Terry Griffiths, **10** Nigel Bond, **11** 1946, **12** John Pulman, **13** Crystallate, **14** Jimmy White, **15** Warren Simpson.

# SNOOKER - QUIZ 4

*Answers on page 389*

**1** When was the first Benson & Hedges Masters held?

**2** Who potted the last black on Pot Black?

**3** What were Joe Johnson's odds to win the 1986 World Championships?

**4** Who was World Championship runner-up 1985-6?

**5** Who successfully defended their World Cup title in 1987?

**6** In which Welsh town was Terry Griffiths born?

**7** What did the Jameson International become in 1987?

**8** How many points is the brown ball worth?

**9** Who were originally called 'snookers'?

**10** After his World Championship win the previous year, who was ranked No1 in 1981?

**11** In which year did Ken Doherty become World Champion for the first time?

**12** Who was Women's UK champion 1986 - 1990?

**13** Where was the UK Open first held in 1977?

**14** How many points are there in a maximum break?

**15** Who was Australian champion 1985 - 1988?

## *Answers to page 389*

**1** They're not, **2** Benson & Hedges Masters, **3** Dennis Taylor, **4** Assembly Rooms, Derby, **5** Three, **6** 1980, **7** 2 1/6 in, **8** Ray Reardon, **9** 1976, **10** Terry Griffiths, **11** Wythenshawe Forum, **12** England, **13** Stephen Hendry, **14** 15, **15** Hole in one.

# • SNOOKER - QUIZ 5 •

*Answers on page 394*

1 Where, in 1926, was the first Professional Championship of Snooker's Pool played?

2 In which year did Steve Davis win his first World Championship?

3 How many players were invited to play in the Masters 1981-83?

4 Who successfully defended her Women's UK title in 1992?

5 Who compiled the World Championships' first maximum break?

6 How many points is the green ball worth?

7 How many times was Joe Davis Word Champion?

8 Who did Stephen Hendry defeat in the 1995 World Championship final?

9 In which country were the 1996 World Cup Championships held?

10 Who, at 18 in 1987, became the youngest ranking tournament winner?

11 What nationality were brothers Silvino and Mannie Francisco?

12 Who took over from Rex Williams as WPBSA chairman?

13 Who won their second World Cup in 1983?

14 How many pots are needed to make a maximum break?

15 Who holds the record as the oldest Word Champion, at 45?

***In 1997, when Irishman Ken Doherty became World Champion, beating Stephen Hendry, not a single crime was reported to Dublin Police while the final match was played.***

## *Answers to page 394*

**1** Terry Griffiths,**2** Alex Higgins, **3** 1957, **4** Ray Reardon, **5** 3, **6** Australia, **7** Steve Davis, **8** 1940, **9** Winifred Atwell, **10** Deauville Casino, France, **11** A screw, **12** Whirlwind, **13** 1983, **14** Gary Owen, **15** Stephen Hendry.

# SNOOKER - QUIZ 6

*Answers on page 395*

1 Who became 1998 Irish Masters champion after Ronnie O'Sullivan was disqualified for failing a drugs test?

2 At which venue did Joe Davis collapse while watching brother Fred play?

3 In which year was Stacey Hillyard Women's World Open champion?

4 Who was Scotland's first Word Champion?

5 Who won the European Open title in 1997?

6 Who did John Spencer beat in the 1969 World Championship final?

7 Where is the Irish Masters held?

8 Who was the first unranked Word Champion?

9 How many countries took part in the 1996 World Cup?

10 Who was the first to appear in two World Championship finals at the Crucible?

11 What is the minimum penalty for a foul stroke?

12 Whom did Stephen Hendry beat in 1988 to win his first British Open title?

13 Which father and son have partnered each other in major tournaments?

14 Who won his second UK Open title in 1997?

15 Who, at 23 yrs and 1 month, became the youngest Word Champion in 1972?

---

*Answers to page 395*

**1** Mike Barrett, **2** Horace Lindrum, **3** 1983, **4** Jimmy White, **5** 16, **6** Steve Davis, **7** Stun shot, **8** James Wattana, **9** 1964, **10** Stephen Hendry, **11** Steve Davis, **12** 6, **13** Mercantile Credit Classsic, **14** Graham Miles, **15** Dennis Taylor.

# SNOOKER - QUIZ 7

*Answers on page 392*

1. Who won his third consecutive Irish Masters title in 1982?
2. Who appeared in every semi-final of the now discontinued Canadian Open?
3. In which year was the last Professional Matchplay championship held?
4. Who was top of the world rankings 1976-1980?
5. How many consecutive World Championships has Steve Davis won?
6. In which country were the 1975 World Championships held?
7. Who was the first to win twice at the Crucible?
8. Which year saw Joe and Fred Davis meet in the World Championship final?
9. Whose Black and White Rag was Pot Black's theme tune?
10. Where was the first European Open held?
11. What is a shot with backspin called?
12. What was Jimmy White's nickname?
13. In which year was Sue Foster Women's World Champion?
14. Who won the first two World Amateur titles?
15. Who won the European Open title in successive years, 1993-4?

## *Answers to page 392*

**1** Thurston's Hall, London, **2** 1981, **3** 12, **4** Tessa Davidson, **5** Cliff Thorburn, **6** 3, **7** 15, **8** Nigel Bond, **9** Scotland, **10** Stephen Hendry, **11** South African, **12** John Virgo, **13** England, **14** 36, **15** Ray Reardon.

# SNOOKER - QUIZ 8

*Answers on page 393*

**1** Which boxing promoter promoted the Dry Blackthorn Cup, which lasted a year, and the Champion of Champions, which lasted three years?

**2** Whom did Joe Davis defeat in his last World Championship final?

**3** Which year saw the first World Championship at the Crucible to end in the third session?

**4** Who successfully defended his World Matchplay title in 1990?

**5** How many contestants were invited to play in the Masters from 1983?

**6** Who compiled the first televised maximum break, in Oldham in 1982?

**7** Which shot stops the ball dead on impact with the object ball?

**8** Who was 1992 World Matchplay champion?

**9** In which year was the first World as apposed to World Matchplay Championship held?

**10** Who was the first player to achieve three maximum breaks in ranking tournaments?

**11** Who won his fourth consecutive UK Open title in 1987?

**12** How many points does a winner get for winning a ranking tournament?

**13** What did the Lada Classic become in 1985?

**14** Whom did Ray Reardon beat to win the 1974 World Championship?

**15** Who was 1987 Masters champion?

---

### *Answers to page 393*

**1** Ken Doherty, **2** The Crucible, **3** 1984, **4** Walter Donaldson, **5** John Higgins, **6** Gary Owen, **7** Goff's Sales Ring, Kill, **8** Terry Griffiths, **9** 39, **10** Cliff Thorburn, **11** 4 points, **12** Mike Hallett, **13** Geoff and Neal Foulds, **14** Ronnie O'Sullivan, **15** Alex Higgins.

# SNOOKER - QUIZ 9

*Answers on page 398*

1. How many years separate Alex Higgins's two world titles?
2. In which city is the Crucible Theatre?
3. Who beat David Taylor to win the 1982 Jamesons International?
4. In which year was the first UK Women's Championship held?
5. Who was the 1993 Grand Prix champion?
6. Who long was the Embassy World Championships longest frame, between Cliff Thorburnand Doug Mountjoy?
7. Whom did John Parrott beat to become the first European Open Champion?
8. Which year saw Willie Thorne win the Mercantile Credit Classic?
9. Which twice British Open winner comes from Tooting?
10. In which country was the first World Amateur Championship held?
11. Who made the first witnessed maximum break, in 1934?
12. Which Irishman was 1977 UK Open champion?
13. Who did Steve Davis beat to win his fourth UK Open title, in 1986?
14. Which player was fined for headbutting?
15. Where was the first Benson & Hedges Masters tournament held?

---

*Answers to page 398*

**1** Silvino Francisco, **2** Alison Fisher, **3** Jubbulpore, **4** Ray Edmonds, **5** 1969, **6** 2, **7** Cliff Thorburn, **8** Bob Chaperon, **9** 10, **10** John Higgins, **11** The Hexagon Theatre, Reading, **12** Steve Davis and Joe Johnson, **13** John Parrott, **14** 1980, **15** Warren King.

# • SNOOKER - QUIZ 10 •

*Answers on page 399*

**1** Which Welshman was 1989 Mercantile Credit Classic champion?

**2** Which year's championship saw Steve Davis's first ranking tournament final?

**3** Who won her eighth Women's Amateur Championship in 1968?

**4** In which Lancashire town was Tony Knowles born?

**5** Who won the European Open title in 1993?

**6** What connects the Forward Chemicals Tournament, the British Gold Cup and the Northern Ireland Classic?

**7** Who won his third and last World Championship in 1977?

**8** How many points is the blue ball worth?

**9** Where was the Benson & Hedges Masters held 1976-1978?

**10** Which year saw the last appearance of Pot Black?

**11** Who became, in 1989, the first to make two official maximum breaks?

**12** Which competition's 1985 final was the first ranking final without a British competitor?

**13** Which nation won their first World Cup in 1982?

**14** Whom did Alex Higgins beat to win his second World Championship?

**15** Who, at 18, was the youngest World Amateur champion in 1980?

***Terry Griffiths worked as an insurance agent until July 1978. In 1979 he became World Champion at his first attempt.***

---

*Answers to page 399*

**1** Wales, **2** 1916, **3** Kirk Stevens, **4** South African, **5** Chelsea, **6** Darren Morgan, **7** John Parrott, **8** 10, **9** Ann-Marie Farren, **10** Edinburgh, **11** Canadian Masters, **12** 6, **13** Jimmy White, **14** Eddie Charlton, **15** 1981.

# • SNOOKER - QUIZ 11 •

*Answers on page 396*

1 Who shared the winner's photograph for the 1985 British Open with the Dulux Dog?

2 Who won her seventh Women's World Championship title in 1994?

3 In which Indian city was snooker first played?

4 Who won World Amateur titles in 1972 and 1974?

5 In which year did Pot Black first appear?

6 How many points is the yellow ball worth?

7 Who was the losing finalist in the Crucible's first Word Championship?

8 Which Canadian was British Open champion in 1990?

9 How many players were invited to play in the Masters until 1981?

10 Who became World Champion in 1998?

11 Where is the Grand Prix held?

12 Which two players were the first to appear together twice in a final at the Crucible?

13 Who was 1996 European Open champion?

14 In which year did Terry Griffiths win his only Masters title?

15 Who was Australian champion in 1986 and 1987?

## *Answers to page 396*

**1** 10, **2** Sheffield, **3** Tony Knowles, **4** 1986, **5** Peter Ebdon, **6** 69 minutes, **7** Terry Griffiths, **8** 1985, **9** Jimmy White, **10** India, **11** Murt O'Donoghue, **12** Patsy Fagan, **13** Neal Foulds, **14** Alex Higgins, **15** West Centre Hotel, Fulham.

# SNOOKER - QUIZ 12

*Answers on page 397*

1 Which nation were the first World Cup champions?

2 Which year saw the inauguration of the English Amateur Snooker Championship?

3 Who scored a maximum break against Jimmy White in the 1984 Masters?

4 What nationality is Perrie Mans?

5 Which football team does Jimmy White support?

6 Who was 1996 Irish Masters champion?

7 Who successfully defended his European Open title in 1990?

8 How many players entered the first World Championship in 1926?

9 Who was 1987 Women's World Open champion?

10 In which city were Walter Donaldson and Stephen Hendry born?

11 What was the first ranking tournament to be held outside England?

12 How many points is the pink ball worth?

13 Who was the first Scottish Masters champion, in 1981?

14 Who had Pot Black's highest break with 110?

15 Which year saw Alex Higgins win his last Masters title?

## *Answers to page 397*

**1** Doug Mountjoy, **2** 1985, **3** Maureen Baynton, **4** Bolton, **5** Steve Davis, **6** They were only held once, **7** John Spencer, **8** 5, **9** The New London Theatre, **10** 1986, **11** Cliff Thorburn, **12** British Open, **13** Canada, **14** Ray Reardon, **15** Jimmy White.

# • SNOOKER - QUIZ 13 •

*Answers on page 401*

**1** Which snooker legend of the 1980s was born in Plumstead?

**2** Whom did Ray Reardon beat in 1978 to win his 6th World Championship?

**3** Who was Australia's Women's World Open champion in 1980?

**4** In which year did Joe Davis compile the first official maximum?

**5** With which song did The Matchroom Mob with Chas and Dave hit the TopTen in 1986?

**6** Who was the first Australian World Champion?

**7** Where was the World Championship held in 1972?

**8** Who was 1992 European Open champion?

**9** What is the line called of which the 'D' forms a part?

**10** Who, at 21 in 1990, became the youngest World Champion?

**11** Mike Hallett became Scottish Masters champion in 1993 True or false?

**12** Which Grimsby lad won the first Junior Pot Black title in 1981?

**13** What was Alex Higgins's nickname?

**14** In which year was the first World Amateur Championship held?

**15** Which Scot was the 1994 Masters champion?

***Joe Davis, the Billiards legend, reputedly created the game of Snooker and held its World title from 1927 to 1946.***

---

## *Answers to page 402*

**1** Stephen Hendry, **2** Ray Reardon, **3** Dennis Taylor, **4** 10, **5** Canada, **6** Silvino Francisco, **7** Belle Vue, Manchester, **8** Fred Davis, **9** 35, **10** 1969, **11** Mark Williams, **12** The Guildhall, Preston, **13** 5, **14** Steve Davis, **15** Hong Kong.

# • SNOOKER - QUIZ 14 •

*Answers on page 402*

1 Who was the first to win the European Open three times?

2 Whose Spitting Image puppet tried to make him 'interesting'?

3 What nationality is James Wattana?

4 How many points is the black ball worth?

5 In which year were Horace Lindrum and Clark McConachy the only World Championship contenders?

6 Which World Champion learned to play snooker as a miner?

7 How many snooker events, other than the snooker World Championship, does the Crucible host?

8 Which country was the first, other than England, to host the World Championships?

9 Who was 1991 World Matchplay champion?

10 Which snooker commentator's name is usually preceded by 'Whispering'?

11 Which British Open champion came from Hampstead?

12 In which year was Neal Foulds Scottish Masters champion?

13 Who won her fourth Women's UK title in 1998?

14 Who is the last World Amateur champion to go on to become Word Champion?

15 Who won consecutive Masters titles from 1985 to 1986?

---

*Answers to page 400*

**1** Steve Davis, **2** Perrie Mans, **3** Lesley McIlraith, **4** 1955, **5** Snooker Loopy, **6** Horace Lindrum, **7** Selly Park British Legion, **8** Jimmy White, **9** The baulk line, **10** Stephen Hendry, **11** False - 1991, **12** Dean Reynolds, **13** Hurricane, **14** 1963, **15** Alan McManus.

# • SNOOKER - QUIZ 15 •

*Answers on page 400*

**1** Who successfully defended his Grand Prix title in 1991?

**2** Who lost his seventh World Championship final to Alex Higgins in 1982?

**3** Which Word Champion comes from Coalisland?

**4** How many ranking points does a player get for winning the World Championship?

**5** Which nation were the 1990 World Cup champions?

**6** Which British Open champion was a former oil company executive?

**7** Where was the 1974 World Championship held?

**8** Which snooker champion captured the world professional billiards title in 1980?

**9** Over how many frames is the World Championship final fought?

**10** In which year did the World Championship become a knock-out event?

**11** Who was 1996 Grand Prix champion?

**12** Where has the UK Open been held since 1978?

**13** How many consecutive World Championships has Stephen Hendry won?

**14** Who won his third Masters title in 1997?

**15** Which former British colony does 1997 World Amateur champion Marco Fu come from?

---

## *Answers to page 401*

**1** John Parrott, **2** Steve Davis, **3** Thai, **4** 7, **5** 1952, **6** Ray Reardon, **7** None, **8** South Africa, **9** Gary Wilkinson, **10** Ted Lowe, **11** Tony Meo, **12** 1992, **13** Karen Corr, **14** Ken Doherty, **15** Cliff Thorburn.

# TENNIS

# TENNIS - QUIZ 1

*Answers on page 406*

**1** How many countries entered the Davis Cup in 1998 - 71, 101 or 131?

**2** Which tennis player was nicknamed 'the ice maiden'?

**3** Who won his third Wimbledon men's singles title in 1971?

**4** Where was the first lawn tennis court marked out by Majors Henry Gem and Walter Clopton Wingfield in 1858?

**5** Who was fined a (then) record $6,000 for verbal abuse in 1981?

**6** In which year did Steffi Graf win her first Wimbledon singles title?

**7** Which German aristocrat won the French Open in 1936?

**8** How many people does Wimbledon's Centre Court seat - 9,120, 11,120 or 13,120?

**9** Who, at Toulouse in 1986, won the title held previously by his father and grandfather?

**10** Who won his third consecutive US Open title in 1987?

**11** Who won the first of her six Wimbledon singles titles in 1966?

**12** Which country reintroduced tennis to the Olympics as a demonstration event in 1968?

**13** Who became, at 17 in 1989, the youngest winner of The French Open?

**14** Which British tennis player rose in the world rankings from 48 to 6 in 1995?

**15** In 1985, which 14-year-old became the youngest player to win a match at the US Open?

***Greg Rusedski turned down a million dollars from manufacturers Donnay to use their equipment in favour of his Wilson raquet for which he gets no sponsorship.***

## *Answers to page 406*

**1** Jean Borotra, **2** Wayne Ferreira, **3** Algerian, **4** Vitas Gerulaitis, **5** 1990, **6** Jack Kramer, **7** Roger Taylor, **8** Vijay Armitraj, **9** Chris Lewis, **10** Steffi Graf, **11** Manuel Santana, **12** Martina Navratilova, **13** Brian Tobin, **14** Arantxa Sanchez Vicario, **15** Marcel Bernard.

# TENNIS - QUIZ 2

*Answers on page 407*

1 What did the Men's Grand Prix change its name to?

2 Who retired in September 1996 after months trying to recover from a serious stomach muscle injury?

3 Which Mexican tennis legend died in a plane crash in 1969?

4 With whom did John Newcombe win five men's doubles titles at Wimbledon and four in Australia?

5 Who beat reigning champion Steffi Graf in the 1992 Olympic final?

6 Who did Martina Navratilova beat to win her second Wimbledon singles title in 1983?

7 Who restored French pride by winning the French Open women's singles in 1938 and 1939?

8 Professional tennis players Emilio and Javier are elder brothers of which top female player?

9 Who was Chris Evert's first husband?

10 In which town was the first lawn tennis club formed in 1872?

11 Whose record of eight Wimbledon singles titles did Martina Navratilova equal in 1987?

12 Who successfully defended her fourth consecutive US Open singles title in 1978?

13 Which 1960 Wimbledon champion was Australian Davis Cup team captain for 20 years?

14 Which 14th century French king is said to have died from a chill caught after a game of real tennis?

15 How are double Olympic doubles winners Gigi and Mary Joe Fernandez related?

---

*Answers to page 407*

**1** Ken Fletcher, **2** Yannick Noah, **3** Monica Seles, **4** John McEnroe, **5** 1905, **6** Chris Evert, **7** The US Open, **8** Boris Becker, **9** Henry V, **10** Stefan Edberg, **11** 1977, **12** Tom Okker, **13** Dark green and purple, **14** Zina Garrison, **15** Dick Savitt.

# TENNIS - QUIZ 3

*Answers on page 404*

1 Who is the only player to have taken part, as a veteran, in celebrations for Wimbledon's 50th, 75th and 100th anniversaries?

2 Who was the first South African to reach the top 10 rankings since they began in 1973?

3 What nationality is Tarik Benhabiles, who reached a world ranking of 22 in 1987?

4 Which 1977 Australian Open champion died in 1994?

5 Which year saw Martina Navratilova win a record ninth Wimbledon singles title?

6 The Grand Prix circuit was devised by which former Wimbledon champion?

7 With whom did John Newcombe win three US men's doubles titles?

8 Who led India to the 1974 Davis Cup final?

9 Who did John McEnroe beat in the final to win his second Wimbledon singles title?

10 Who became, in 1982, the youngest player to earn a WTA ranking?

11 Who was given the Medal of Isabella by General Franco for winning the 1965 US Championship?

12 Which former Wimbledon champion has three of the old No 1 Court's seats on her verandah?

13 Which Australian was elected president of the ITF in 1991?

14 Who was Australian Open women's runner-up in 1994 and 1995?

15 Who was the first post-war French Open men's champion?

## *Answers to page 404*

**1** 131, **2** Chris Evert, **3** John Newcombe, **4** Edgbaston, **5** John McEnroe, **6** 1988, **7** Baron Gottfried von Cramm, **8** 13,120, **9** Guy Forget, **10** Ivan Lendl, **11** Billie Jean King, **12** Mexico, **13** Michael Chang, **14** Greg Rusedski, **1 5** Mary Joe Fernandez.

# TENNIS - QUIZ 4

*Answers on page 405*

**1** With whom did Margaret Court win the Wimbledon mixed doubles four times?

**2** Who, in 1979, became the first Frenchman to win the French Open since 1946?

**3** Who won her third consecutive French Open title in 1993?

**4** Who was thrown out of the Davis Cup team in 1984 for 'outrageous behaviour?

**5** In which year did Australia enter the Davis Cup for the first time - 1905, 1915 or 1925?

**6** The father of which tennis legend won the Canadian men's singles title in 1947?

**7** Which was the only Grand Slam event to continue during WW2?

**8** Who was Wimbledon men's runner-up for two years after he last won there in 1989?

**9** Which English king received a gift of tennis balls "stuffed with good hide and wool wadding" from the French Dauphin?

**10** Who won the ATP Tour's Sportsmanship Award so many times they named it after him?

**11** In which year was the WCT Tour last held?

**12** Who was known as 'The Flying Dutchman'?

**13** What are the colours of the All England Lawn Tennis and Croquet club?

**14** Who did Martina Navratilova defeat in the final, to win her record ninth Wimbledon singles title?

**15** In 1951, who won the Wimbledon men's singles title at his first attempt?

---

## *Answers to page 405*

**1** The ATP Tour, **2** Gabriela Sabatini, **3** Rafael Osuna, **4** Tony Roche, **5** Jennifer Capriati, **6** Andrea Jaeger, **7** Simone Mathieu, **8** Arantxa Sanchez Vicario, **9** John Lloyd, **10** Leamington, **11** Helen Wills Moody, **12** Chris Evert, **13** Neale Fraser, **14** Louis X, **15** They're not.

# TENNIS - QUIZ 5

*Answers on page 410*

1 Who won the French Open in 1956 on her first visit, and was the first black woman to achieve major success in lawn tennis?

2 With whom did Yannick Noah win the men's doubles at the 1984 French Open?

3 Who ended Steffi Graf's run of five consecutive Grand Slam titles in Paris in 1989?

4 What little-known title have the Wimbledon Championships had since 1913?

5 Who won the French Open women's title for a record seventh time in 1986?

6 What nationality is Thomas Muster?

7 Who was Wimbledon women's runner-up for the third consecutive time in 1980?

8 Which US tennis player has been coached by his brother Carl since 1991?

9 In which city, in 1975, were Arthur Ashe and Ilie Nastase both disqualified from the same match?

10 Who, at 19 in 1988, became the youngest player to win the Grand Slam?

11 Who successfully defended his French Open title in 1994?

12 Which English king had four tennis courts at his Palace of Whitehall that he had taken from Cardinal Wolsey?

13 Who was the first British tennis player to win the BBC Sports Personality of the Year award?

14 Who lost the 1977 Wimbledon final to Virginia Wade?

15 Who became, in 1990, the first Ecuadorian to win a Grand Slam title?

## *Answers to page 410*

**1** Mary Joe Fernandez, **2** Tracy Austin, **3** Rod Laver, **4** Bangladesh, **5** Chris Evert, **6** English, French and Spanish, **7** Michael Stich, **8** Gabriela Sabatini, **9** New Zealand, **10** Clay, **11** Rosie Casals, **12** Yannick Noah, **13** Charles VIII, **14** John Newcombe, **15** Arthur Gore.

# TENNIS - QUIZ 6

*Answers on page 411*

1 Who became, in 1980, the first mother to win Wimbledon in 66 years?

2 What is the name of the women's end-of-the-year showpiece held in Madison Square Gardens?

3 Who was presented with one of the 1922 Centre Court benches by the cable network for which she commentates?

4 In which year did the Masters become the ATP Tour Championships?

5 How many courts does Wimbledon have?

6 Which Italian painter is said to have had to flee after killing his tennis opponent in a frenzy in 1606?

7 Who won Wimbledon the year after an emergency appendectomy had seen his world ranking slump to 413?

8 What nationality is Jan Kodes?

9 Who won her third consecutive Australian Open title in 1993?

10 Who was the first post-war Wimbledon men's singles champion?

11 During which year's US Open did Martina Navratilova defect?

12 Which Australian won the Wimbledon triple crown in 1952?

13 In which Caribbean country have the ITF based their registered office?

14 Who did Stan Smith beat in the final to win the 1972 Wimbledon title?

15 With whom did Raul Ramirez win 39 men's doubles titles?

***In 1997, when Irishman Ken Doherty became World Champion, beating Stephen Hendry, not a single crime was reported to Dublin Police while the final match was played.***

---

*Answers to page 411*

**1** Darlene Hard, **2** Yevgeny Kafelnikov, **3** Bill Johnson, **4** Table tennis, **5** Anthony Wilding, **6** Coupe des Mousquetaires, **7** Jennifer Capriati, **8** Sphairistike, **9** Monica Seles, **10** Roy Emerson, **11** 1986, **12** Jana Novotna, **13** 1989, **14** Belarus, **15** Frank Hadow.

# TENNIS - QUIZ 7

*Answers on page 408*

1. Who won the Australian women's doubles with Patty Fendick in 1991?
2. Who beat Martina Navratilova in the final of the 1981 US Open?
3. Who beat fellow Australian Roy Emerson in the final of the 1962 French Open?
4. Which country's National Tennis Centre is at Ramna Green?
5. Whose record 1,309 matches won was broken by Martina Navratilova in 1991?
6. What are tennis's three official languages?
7. Who is the only ATP Tour champion to have finished with a 5-0 record?
8. Which Argentinian was world junior champion at the age of 13?
9. Which country combined with Australia as Australasia in the Davis Cup until 1921?
10. What was Chris Evert's favoured surface?
11. With whom did Billie Jean King win five Wimbledon women's doubles titles between 1967 and 1973?
12. Who was the winning Davis Cup captain in Sweden in 1996?
13. Which French king died after hitting his head on the lintel of the door leading to his tennis court?
14. Who beat Wilhelm Bungert in the final of the 1967 Wimbledon men's singles championship?
15. At what age did Arthur Gore win the 1909 Wimbledon singles title - 37, 39 or 41?

## *Answers to page 408*

**1** Anthea Gibson, **2** Henri Leconte, **3** Arantxa Sanchez Vicario, **4** The World Championships, **5** Martina Navratilova, **6** Austrian, **7** Chris Evert (Lloyd), **8** Michael Chang, **9** Stockholm, **10** Steffi Graf, **11** Sergi Bruguera, **12** Henry VIII, **13** Greg Rusedski, **14** Betty Stove, **15** Andres Gomez.

# TENNIS - QUIZ 8

*Answers on page 409*

1 From 1958 to 1962, who won the US women's doubles for five consecutive years with different partners?

2 Who won the men's singles title at the 1999 Australian Open?

3 Whom did Bill Tilden beat in six successive US Championship finals?

4 Which sport did Fred Perry dominate before tennis?

5 Who remains New Zealand's most successful player with four Wimbledon titles?

6 What is the name of the trophy that the winner of the French men's title receives?

7 In 1980, which 14-year-old became the youngest to be ranked in the woman's top 10?

8 What did Major Wingfield officially call lawn tennis when he applied for its patent in 1874?

9 Who did Guenter Parche stab on court in Hamburg in 1993?

10 Which Australian won the last men's amateur French Championships in 1967?

11 In which post-war year has the Australian Open not been held?

12 Who beat Mary Pierce in the 1997 Chase Championships final to win her first major title?

13 In which year were Steffi Graf and Boris Becker both Wimbledon singles champions?

14 Which country does Natasha Zvereva come from?

15 Who remains the only player never to have lost a set at Wimbledon?

## *Answers to page 409*

**1** Evonne Cawley, **2** The Chase Championships, **3** Billie Jean King, **4** 1990, **5** 18, **6** Caravaggio, **7** Pat Cash, **8** Czech, **9** Monica Seles, **10** Yvon Petra, **11** 1975, **12** Frank Sedgman, **13** The Bahamas, **14** Ilie Nastase, **15** Brian Gottfried.

# TENNIS - QUIZ 9

*Answers on page 414*

1 Which British No 1 broke his leg in three places in 1994?

2 On whose royal shoulder did Jana Novotna cry after losing the 1993 Wimbledon final?

3 Which 21-year-old Harvard graduate donated an international competition trophy in 1900?

4 Which year saw the Battle of the Sexes?

5 Which Wimbledon champion was prevented from playing in 1961 by an attack of jaundice?

6 Who did Andre Agassi beat in the final of the 1992 Wimbledon men's singles championship?

7 Who still holds the record of being, at 15, Wimbledon's youngest champion?

8 Who was the 1998 French Open men's singles champion?

9 With whom did Martina Navratilova win 20 major women's doubles titles between 1981 and 1990?

10 In 1933, who became the first British player for 30 years to win the US championship?

11 Which popular national game did tennis surpass on vicarage lawns at the end of the nineteenth century?

12 Whose 1924 women's Olympic gold medal stood until 1988?

13 What is the height of the net-posts?

14 Which New Zealander made the Wimbledon final in 1983?

15 Who took up tennis as a remedial exercise for a crippling illness and went on to become 1951 Wimbledon triple crown winner?

## *Answers to page 414*

**1** Lew Hoad, **2** Steffi Graf, **3** Harry Hopman, **4** Brazil, **5** Don Budge, **6** Pat Cash, **7** The Wimbledon Championships, **8** Tom Okker, **9** Paraguay, **10** Fred Perry's, **11** Coupe Suzanne Lenglen, **12** Stan Smith, **13** John McEnroe, **14** 2, **15** 131.

# TENNIS - QUIZ 10

*Answers on page 415*

**1** Whose 1997 victory in Key Biscayne made her the youngest world No 1?

**2** Who was known as 'The Hustler'?

**3** Whose record 279 Wimbledon matches is 14 more than Billie Jean King?

**4** Which French champion was known for wearing a beret?

**5** In which year were Jimmy Connors and Chris Evert engaged when they both won Wimbledon?

**6** Who won her first Grand Slam title at Wimbledon in 1998?

**7** Which Atlantic island is credited with being the launching pad for the establishment of tennis in the US?

**8** Which Italian holds the record for winning the most consecutive Davis Cup rubbers and ties?

**9** With whom did Pam Shriver win the women's doubles Olympic gold in 1988?

**10** Who did Ivan Lendl beat in the final of the 1986 French Open?

**11** Whose 374 weeks at the No 1 spot overtook Martina Navratilova's 331?

**12** In which year did the All England Croquet Club vote to include lawn tennis?

**13** Which is the youngest of the Grand Slam competitions?

**14** Which country did Olympic bronze medallist Molla Mallery represent?

**15** With whom did Bob Hewitt win the 1962 and 1964 Wimbledon men's doubles?

***By the end of 1998 Pete Sampras had won ten Grand Slam titles and four Wimbledon championships.***

---

*Answers to page415*

**1** Helen Jacobs, **2** Flushing Meadows, **3** The Fed Cup, **4** Jacques Brugnon, **5** 3ft, **6** Bob Lutz, **7** Alex Olmedo, **8** 1936, **9** Martina Hingis, **10** Chris Evert, **11** 22, **12** Fred Perry, **13** Jim Courier, **14** Qatar, **15** Goran Ivanisevic.

# TENNIS - QUIZ 11

*Answers on page 412*

1 Who was the first player in the post-war era to win the Wimbledon men's singles title two years in succession?

2 Who successfully defended her Wimbledon singles title in 1989?

3 Which Australian coach guided Ken Rosewall, Rod Laver and John Newcombe, among others?

4 Which nation reached the semi-finals in the Fed Cup in their debut appearance in 1965?

5 Who is the only player to win Wimbledon's triple crown in two successive years?

6 Who did Mats Wilander beat to win the 1988 Australian Open?

7 Which tennis competition came into existence on Monday, July 9, 1877?

8 Who won the 1976 US Open men's doubles with Marty Riessen?

9 In which country was Olympic gold medallist Gigi Fernandez born?

10 Whose statue is immediately opposite Wimbledon's Members' Enclosure?

11 What is the name of the trophy that the winner of the French women's title receives?

12 Who was nicknamed 'The Leaning Tower of Pasadena'?

13 Who became, in 1990, the first player to be disqualified from a Grand Slam event for foul language?

14 How many countries took part in the first Davis Cup in 1900?

15 How many countries took part in the 1998 Davis Cup - 111, 121 or 131?

## *Answers to page 412*

**1** Tim Henman, **2** The Duchess of Kent's, **3** Dwight Filley Davis, **4** 1973, **5** Maria Bueno, **6** Goran Ivanisevic, **7** Lottie Dod, **8** Carlos Moya, **9** Pam Shriver, **10** Fred Perry, **11** Croquet, **12** Helen Wills Moody, **13** 3ft 6ins, **14** Chris Lewis, **15** Doris Hart.

# TENNIS - QUIZ 12

*Answers on page 413*

**1** Who beat Hilde Spirling to become the 1936 Wimbledon champion?

**2** Which Grand Slam venue was opened on 1978?

**3** Which competition was first held in 1963 to celebrate the 50th anniversary of the ITF?

**4** Which one of the 'Musketeers', known as 'Toto', was the doubles specialist?

**5** What is the height of the middle of the net, in feet?

**6** With whom did Stan Smith win four US men's doubles titles?

**7** Who, in 1959, won both the Australian and Wimbledon finals, but lost in the US final to Neale Fraser?

**8** In which year did Fred Perry become men's Wimbledon champion for the last time?

**9** Who successfully defended her Australian Open title in 1998?

**10** Whose 157 singles titles puts her second only to Martina Navratilova?

**11** How many players paid the £105 to enter the first Wimbledon tournament in 1877 - 22, 44 or 66?

**12** In 1934, who became the first British player in 25 years to win Wimbledon?

**13** Who won his second consecutive French Open title in 1992?

**14** In which country did Tim Henman reach his first ATP Tour final, only to finish as runner-up?

**15** Who reached the men's doubles final at the 1990 French Open with Petr Korda?

---

*Answers to page 413*

**1** Martina Hingis, **2** Bobby Riggs, **3** Martina Navratilova, **4** Jean Borotra, **5** 1974, **6** Jana Novotna, **7** Bermuda, **8** Nicola Pietrangeli, **9** Zina Garrison, **10** M Pernfors, **11** Steffi Graf, **12** 1875, **13** Australian Open, **14** Norway, **15** Fred Stolle.

# TENNIS - QUIZ 13

*Answers on page 418*

**1** Which Swede reached 5 in the world rankings No 5 in 1985 but never won a major title?

**2** Which tournament did Hazel Hotchkiss win for the third consecutive time in 1911?

**3** Which nation were the losing Davis Cup finalists in 1969, 1971 and 1972?

**4** Which male tennis player spent a record 270 weeks as the world's No 1?

**5** Who got his big toe stuck in a hotel tap the day before winning the 1975 US Open?

**6** How many times did Ken Rosewall win the Wimbledon men's singles title?

**7** Who did not defend his Wimbledon men's singles title in 1973?

**8** Who, in 1909, was the last British men's singles Wimbledon champion until Fred Perry in 1934?

**9** Which year of the 1990s saw an all-German Wimbledon men's final?

**10** What tennis technique did A T Myers reputedly introduce to the game at the second Wimbledon tournament in 1878?

**11** With whom did Louise Brough win 12 US doubles titles?

**12** Which World Trade Fair site used to serve as the US Open centre court?

**13** Which Brazilian's Wimbledon successes resulted in a postage stamp being issued in her honour?

**14** If Bill Tilden was 'Big Bill', which frail stockbroker was 'Little Bill'?

**15** At which venue was the first Fed Cup staged?

---

## *Answers to page 418*

**1** Bill Knight, **2** Romanian, **3** George Hillyard, **4** Hard courts, **5** Spain, **6** Pete Sampras, **7** Anke Huber, **8** Ireland, **9** Dick Stockton, **10** Trafalgar Square, **11** Billie Jean King, **12** 1927, **13** Germany, **14** Jan Kodes, **15** Cameroon.

# TENNIS - QUIZ 14

*Answers on page 419*

**1** Who was the first left-hander to win the Wimbledon women's singles title?

**2** In which city can Flushing Meadows be found?

**3** Who became, in 1907, the first overseas player to win the Wimbledon men's singles title?

**4** In which year did the first recorded doubles competition take place - 1878, 1888 or 1898?

**5** Who was French Open runner-up in 1990 and 1991?

**6** Who was the first player to win each of the Grand Slam titles at least four times?

**7** Which nation were the first Fed Cup champions?

**8** In which country was the Manifesto on the All-Round Development of Lawn Tennis published in 1878?

**9** Who became, in 1996, the first player since John McEnroe to finish in the top 5 rankings in both men's singles and doubles?

**10** With whom did John McEnroe win the 1992 Wimbledon men's doubles title?

**11** Which Brazilian sprang to fame after his surprise 1997 French Open victory?

**12** Which Wimbledon women's champion did not to defend her title in 1974?

**13** Who hit 17 consecutive aces to turn the match and win a 1927 Wimbledon men's semi-final?

**14** What did the Men's Grand Prix Masters change its name to in 1990?

**15** Whose tournament wins span from 1953 to 1978?

***Martina Hingis, among her many firsts, is the youngest of either sex to win a million dollars in prize money.***

---

*Answers to page 419*

**1** Jean Borotra, **2** 1973, **3** Ken Fletcher, **4** Russian, **5** Ann Smith, **6** Wimbledon, **7** Spencer Gore, **8** Reebound Ace, **9** The Wightman Cup, **10** Michael Chang, **11** Petr Korda, **12** Canada, **13** Peter Fleming, **14** Fred Perry, **15** Bill Tilden.

# TENNIS - QUIZ 15

*Answers on page 416*

1 Who won singles and mixed doubles at the 1959 German Championships and went on to become manager of British men's tennis?

2 What nationality were Ion Tiriac and Ilie Nastase?

3 Which RN Commander married Wimbledon champion Blanche Bingley and became secretary of the All England Club from 1907 to 1924?

4 What type of courts are currently used at the US Open?

5 Which nation won the Fed Cup in 1995?

6 Who is known as 'Pistol Pete'?

7 Who did Monica Seles beat in the final to win her fourth Australian Title?

8 In which country were the first championships for women held in 1879?

9 With whom did Rosie Casals win the 1976 US mixed doubles title?

10 At which London landmark did Pete Sampras and Andre Agassi play to film a commercial?

11 Which tennis legend's maiden name was Moffit?

12 In which year was seeding first used in all five Wimbledon events?

13 In which country is the ATP Tour Championships Final held each year?

14 Who insisted, though only before his 1973 Wimbledon victory, that "grass is only for cows"?

15 In which country was former French No 1 Yannick Noah born?

## *Answers to page 416*

**1** Andres Jarryd, **2** US Championships, **3** Romania, **4** Ivan Lendl, **5** Manuel Orantes, **6** None, **7** Stan Smith, **8** Arthur Gore, **9** 1991, **10** Overarm serving, **11** Margaret du Pont, **12** The Louis Armstrong Stadium, **13** Maria Bueno, **14** Bill Johnson, **15** Queen's Club.

# TENNIS - QUIZ 16

*Answers on page 417*

**1** Who was known as the 'Bounding Basque'?

**2** Which year saw 93 players obey a call from the ATP to boycott Wimbledon?

**3** Whose partnership with Margaret Court was the first to achieve the Grand Slam in mixed doubles?

**4** What nationality is Yevgeny Kafelnikov?

**5** With whom did Dick Stockton win the 1984 French mixed doubles title?

**6** What is the only professional event without advertising boards around the courts?

**7** Who was the first Wimbledon men's singles champion?

**8** What is the name of the hard court surface used at Melbourne Park?

**9** Which women's competition was exclusively between America and Great Britain?

**10** Who won the French Open men's singles title in 1989?

**11** Which Australian Open champion used to be Ivan Lendl's ballboy in Davis Cup matches in Prague?

**12** What is British No 1 Greg Rusedski's country of origin?

**13** With whom did John McEnroe win a record 7 ATP Tour World Championship doubles titles?

**14** Who successfully defended his US title in 1934?

**15** Whose sudden defeat in a 1927 Wimbledon men's semi-final was reportedly due to being hypnotised?

---

## *Answers to page 417*

**1** Ann Jones, **2** New York, **3** Sir Norman Brookes, **4** 1878, **5** Andre Agassi, **6** Steffi Graf, **7** USA, **8** Russia, **9** Yevgeny Kafelnikov, **10** Michael Stich, **11** Gustavo Kuerten, **12** Billie Jean King, **13** Henri Cochet, **14** ATP Tour World Championship, **15** Ken Rosewall's.

# • TENNIS - QUIZ 17 •

*Answers on page 422*

1. Who was the first Dutchman to win the men's singles title at Wimbledon?
2. Who qualified for the ATP Tour World Championship play-offs for a record 14 years, from 1972 and 1985?
3. What nationality is Marcelo Rios?
4. Who became, at 14, the youngest player to compete in and win a Fed Cup match?
5. What shape court did Major Wingfield design for his new version of tennis?
6. Who was the first post-war French Open women's champion?
7. Who was the first woman to reach career prize money of $1m?
8. In which year did the US National Lawn Tennis Association drop the National?
9. Who was known in Australia as 'Fiery Fred'?
10. Which Russian was the 1973 Wimbledon men's singles runner-up?
11. On which surface is the French Open played?
12. Which second Wimbledon champion returned to Ceylon to continue his career as a tea planter rather than defend his title?
13. In which year was the Wightman Cup first held - 1903, 1913 or 1923?
14. Who was French junior champion in 1952 and French men's champion in 1953?
15. Who repeated that feat exactly 30 years later?

***Wimbledon residents can earn upto £10,000 during the Wimbledon fortnight by renting their homes to tennis stars who prefer not to stay in hotels.***

## *Answers to page 422*

**1** Bill Larned, **2** 9, **3** Vera and Helena Sukova, **4** Costa Rica, **5** Boris Becker, **6** 27ft, **7** Stan Smith, **8** The Philadelphia Cricket Club, **9** Elizabeth 'Bunny' Ryan, **10** The Maureen Connolly Trophy, **11** 1891, **12** Andre Agassi, **13** John McEnroe, **14** South Africa, **15** Roscoe Tanner.

# TENNIS - QUIZ 18

*Answers on page 423*

**1** Who entered Wimbledon in 1994 ranked 1130, and finished ranked 213, the biggest one-tournament rise since official rankings began?

**2** In which year did Jimmy Connors win his only Australian singles title?

**3** At which major tournament were Pauline Betz, Lottie Dod, Suzanne Lenglen and Maureen Connolly the only champions never to lose at singles?

**4** Which country won the Davis Cup for the first time in 1927?

**5** Which Wimbledon champion was beaten in its first round in 1989 and 1990?

**6** In which year were the first Australian National Championships held - 1900,1905 or 1910?

**7** What is a tennis court's length, in feet?

**8** With whom did Richard Sears win five out of six US men's doubles titles?

**9** Who lost all three Wimbledon finals in 1977?

**10** On which surface is Wimbledon played?

**11** Which nation lost to Italy in the 1976 Davis Cup final?

**12** Whose time over 400m put her third among German woman athletes hoping to win selection to the Seoul Olympic Games?

**13** Which Spaniard was the 1976 Masters champion?

**14** Which year saw the last Wightman Cup?

**15** Which South African Australian Open champion took American citizenship?

---

## *Answers to page 423*

**1** Henri Laconte, **2** 1987, **3** Ken Rosewall, **4** Paris, **5** Helena Sukova and Cyril Suk, **6** Margaret Court, **7** Bjorn Borg, **8** 1975, **9** Margaret du Pont, **10** Olga Morozova, **11** Elizabeth Ryan, **12** Evert and Navratilova, **13** New York, **14** Pete Sampras, **15** Art Larsen.

# • TENNIS - QUIZ 19 •

*Answers on page 420*

1. Whose 1911 win, at the age of 38, makes him still the oldest US men's singles champion?
2. How many years separate Arantxa Sanchez Vicario's first and third French Open wins?
3. Who are the only mother and daughter to have both been in Grand Slam finals?
4. Which country holds the Coffee Bowl, one of the best junior events in the world?
5. Who was the first unseeded Wimbledon champion since seeding began in 1922?
6. What is a tennis court's width, in feet?
7. Who, in 1970, was the first Masters champion?
8. At which club did the US women's singles and doubles championships begin in 1887?
9. Which tennis legend died the night before Billie Jean King broke her record of 19 Wimbledon titles?
10. What is the 21-and-under version of the Wightman Cup called?
11. Which year saw the first official South African Championships - 1888, 1891 or 1894?
12. Which US tennis player's father Mike boxed for Iran in the 1952 Olympics?
13. Who did Bjorn Borg beat in the final to win his fifth consecutive Wimbledon singles title?
14. What nationality is Wayne Ferreira?
15. Which US tennis player was nicknamed the 'Cannonball Kid'?

## *Answers to page 420*

**1** Richard Krajicek, **2** Jimmy Connors, **3** Chilean, **4** Anna Kournikova, **5** Hourglass, **6** Margaret Osborne, **7** Chris Evert, **8** 1920, **9** Fred Stolle, **10** Alex Metreveli, **11** Clay, **12** R F 'Frank' Hadow, **13** 1923, **14** Ken Rosewall, **15** Mats Wilander.

# • TENNIS - QUIZ 20 •

*Answers on page 421*

**1** Who beat Pete Sampras in straight sets in the 1991 Davis Cup final?

**2** In which year were yellow balls first seen at Wimbledon?

**3** Who was nicknamed 'Muscles'?

**4** In which city was the Decimel Club, France's oldest, formed in 1877?

**5** Who were the first brother and sister team to win the French mixed doubles title?

**6** Who won a record 62 Grand Slam titles?

**7** Who won 6 French Open men's singles titles between 1974 and 1981?

**8** In which year did the US Lawn Tennis Association drop the Lawn?

**9** With whom did Neale Fraser win the 1962 Wimbledon mixed doubles title?

**10** Which Russian was the 1974 Wimbledon women's runner-up?

**11** Who won 19 Wimbledon titles, none of them in the singles?

**12** Which great rivalry first appeared on court at Akron, Ohio on March 22, 1973?

**13** In which city was Vitas Gerulaitis born?

**14** Who was the first player to win more than $5m in a year?

**15** Who was known as 'Tappy' and became the first left-handed US champion?

---

## *Answers to page 421*

**1** Guy Forget, **2** 1974, **3** Wimbledon, **4** France, **5** Pete Sampras, **6** 1905, **7** 78ft, **8** James Dwight, **9** Betty Stove, **10** Grass, **11** Chile., **12** Steffi Graf, **13** Manuel Orantes, **14** 1989, **15** Johan Kriek.

# TENNIS - QUIZ 21

*Answers on page 426*

1 Which country's 1991 Davis Cup victory was its first since 1932?

2 Who won the Grand Slam and Olympic gold in 1988?

3 In which year did Margaret Court and Billie Jean King beat the record for the longest Wimbledon women's singles final on record?

4 Whose doubles triumph with Dennis Ralston in 1960 made him the first Mexican to win a Wimbledon title?

5 Who denied Martina Navratilova a record tenth Wimbledon singles title in 1994?

6 Who won the 1962 Wimbledon women's singles title?

7 In which year were men's and women's tennis in America united in one event at Forest Hills?

8 With which Sunday school teacher did Fred Perry win Wimbledon mixed doubles in 1935 and 1936?

9 How many times did Chris Evert win the French Open women's singles titles?

10 What nationality is Goran Ivanisevic?

11 Who won Australian singles and doubles, French doubles, Wimbledon singles and US singles and doubles in 1958?

12 What have 'jumbo' and 'spaghetti' varieties?

13 With whom did John Lloyd win the Wimbledon mixed doubles title twice?

14 Which year saw the first French National Championships - 1925, 1935 or 1945?

15 Which Czech was in the top 10 world rankings for 13 consecutive years, 1980-92?

## *Answers to page 426*

**1** Fred Perry, **2** Roger Taylor, **3** Martina Navratilova, **4** Thelma Long, **5** Ecuadorian, **6** Wimbledon, **7** Hans Redl, **8** May Sutton, **9** Yarra, **10** Tim Henman, **11** 1893, **12** Rod Laver, **13** Swedish, **14** Pete Sampras, **15** Gerald Patterson.

# TENNIS - QUIZ 22

*Answers on page 427*

**1** Whose partnership with Stan Smith was the only one to win the US doubles on four different surfaces?

**2** With whom did Ken Flach win consecutive Wimbledon men's doubles in 1987-88?

**3** Who was US women's champion at 16 in 1904?

**4** Who won his only Grand Slam title in Australia in 1977?

**5** Until which year were there absolutely no rules governing rackets?

**6** Who won a record 20 Wimbledon titles?

**7** Whose record of 17 years in the US Top 10 from 1933 to 1949 stood until 1988?

**8** Until which year was the event now known as the French Open limited to French citizens?

**9** Who was the first man to earn $1m in prize money?

**10** In which city was Andre Agassi born?

**11** Which Swedish king, known as 'Mr G', introduced tennis to his country in 1878?

**12** Who played in his eighth consecutive US Open singles final in 1989?

**13** Which twice Australian Open winner won the Orange Bowl in 1986 and 1987?

**14** Which is the only Grand Slam competition that Virginia Wade failed to win?

**15** Who became, in Australia in 1977, the first British man to reach a Grand Slam singles final since Fred Perry in 1936?

***Wimbledon gateman Ted Edwards once refused entry to Martina Navratilova and Bing Crosby because he didn't recognise them.***

---

*Answers to page 427*

**1** Chuck McKinley, **2** Budge Patty, **3** America, **4** Kevin Curren, **5** Jack Kramer, **6** Deuce, **7** Jack Crawford, **8** 1971, **9** The Australian Open, **10** Stefan Edberg, **11** Jack Crawford, **12** 1964, **13** Manuel Santana, **14** Bjorn Borg, **15** Kathleen McKane.

# • TENNIS - QUIZ 23 •

*Answers on page 424*

**1** Who was the first player to win all four Grand Slam singles titles?

**2** Which British man reached the Wimbledon singles semi-finals in 1967, 1970 and 1973?

**3** Who played in her ninth consecutive Wimbledon singles final in 1990?

**4** Who won the Australian women's doubles 12 times, 10 of them with Nancy Bolton?

**5** What nationality is 1990 French Open champion Andres Gomez?

**6** Which tournament's original home was in Worple Road?

**7** Which Austrian Davis Cup player had lost an arm in WW2?

**8** Who became, in 1905, despite being born in England, the first American to win a Wimbledon title?

**9** In which river did Jim Courier celebrate, still in his tennis kit, after both his Australian Open victories?

**10** Which British tennis player's first ATP Tour win was in Sydney in 1997?

**11** Which year saw the first German Championships - 1893, 1903 or 1913?

**12** With whom did Darlene Hard successfully defend the Wimbledon mixed doubles title in 1960?

**13** What nationality is Bjorn Borg?

**14** Who set up 'Aces for Charity' in 1997, donating $100 for every ace he serves, amounting to $62,700 in the first year?

**15** Which twice Wimbledon champion was awarded the Military Cross in World War 1?

---

## *Answers to page 424*

**1** France, **2** Steffi Graf, **3** 1970, **4** Rafael Osuna, **5** Conchita Martinez, **6** Karen Susman, **7** 1935, **8** Dorothy Round, **9** Seven, **10** Croatian, **11** Ashley Cooper, **12** Rackets, **13** Wendy Turnbull, **14** 1925, **15** Ivan Lendl.

# • TENNIS - QUIZ 24 •

*Answers on page 425*

1 Who won the 1963 Wimbledon title after getting special permission to take part from his San Antonio college?

2 Which American won the French and Wimbledon men's singles titles in 1950?

3 Which country had the first national governing body for tennis?

4 With whom did Anne Smith successfully defend the US mixed doubles title in 1982?

5 Who was the first to win Wimbledon wearing shorts?

6 What is a score of 40-40 called?

7 Which Australian Wimbledon champion usually played in a long-sleeved cricket shirt?

8 In which year did Margaret Court lose in all three Wimbledon finals?

9 Which tennis competition was originally staged at Kooyong?

10 Who won his second successive US Open singles title in 1992?

11 Which defending champion did Fred Perry defeat in the 1934 Wimbledon final?

12 Which year saw the formation of the Asian Tennis Federation - 1954, 1964 or 1974?

13 Who was Wimbledon's first Spanish champion?

14 Who was 17 when he won his first major title, the Italian Open in 1974?

15 Whose marriage to Leslie Godfree made them the only married couple to win the Wimbledon mixed doubles title?

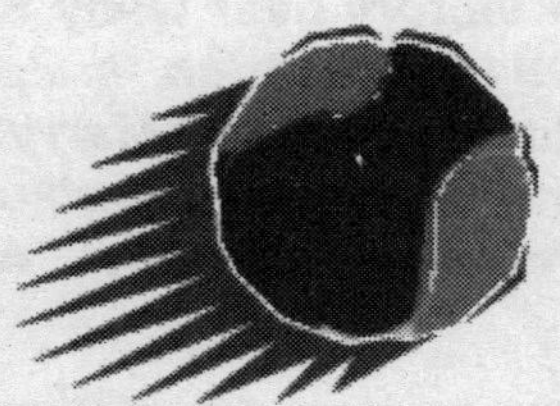

---

## *Answers to page 425*

**1** Bob Lutz, **2** Robert Seguso, **3** May Sutton, **4** Roscoe Tanner, **5** 1976, **6** Billie Jean King, **7** Frank Parker, **8** 1925, **9** Rod Laver, **10** Las Vegas, **11** Gustav V, **12** Ivan Lendl, **13** Jim Courier, **14** French Open, **15** John Lloyd.

# • TENNIS - QUIZ 25 •

*Answers on page 430*

**1** Who is coached by her mother, Melanie Molitor?

**2** Who won the US Open men's singles title in 1994?

**3** Who was US women's singles champion in 1968, the first Open year?

**4** Which is the only Grand Slam event to allow tie-breaks in the final set?

**5** Who was Bjorn Borg's coach for 12 years?

**6** Which tennis legend became a recluse after a conviction for homosexuality?

**7** Who beat Helena Sukova to win the 1993 US singles title?

**8** Who was ranked women's world No 1 1975-82?

**9** Which year saw the formation of the US Tennis Association - 1871, 1881 or 1891?

**10** What nationality is Amanda Coetzer?

**11** Whose 1996 knee injury ended his run of playing in 30 consecutive Grand Slam tournaments?

**12** Who, in 1946, was the last to win the Wimbledon title still wearing long flannels?

**13** What is the second leg of the Grand Slam?

**14** With whom did Ken Rosewall win all four Grand Slam men's doubles titles?

**15** Which doubles expert held the racket with both hands on both sides?

***During her victory over Gaby Sabatini in the 1991 Wimbledon final, a fan called to Steffi Graf: "Marry me, Steffi." And the imperturbable Steffi checked her serve to reply: "Are you rich?"***

## *Answers to page 430*

**1** Cedric Pioline, **2** Billie Jean King, **3** Joakim Nystrom, **4** Davis Cup, **5** Rod Laver, **6** First Lieutenant, **7** Maureen Connolly, **8** Jeff Tarango, **9** Wendy Turnbull, **10** Petr Korda, **11** Boris Becker, **12** 1913, **13** Mark Woodforde and Todd Woodridge, **14** Marcelo Rios, **15** Lindsay Davenport.

# TENNIS - QUIZ 26

*Answers on page 431*

1 Whose French Open title in 1997 made her the first Croatian to win a Grand Slam touranament?

2 For which country does Canadian-born Mary Pierce play?

3 Whose defeat in the 1981 Wimbledon final ended a record winning run of 41 consecutive rubbers?

4 With whom did Martina Navratilova win the 1995 Wimbledon mixed doubles?

5 To whom is Brooke Shields married?

6 What was Australian Open venue Melbourne Park called until 1996?

7 Which tennis player publicly accused Thomas Muster of drug-taking in 1995?

8 Who did Steffi Graf whitewash in the 1988 French Open final?

9 What nationality is Ivan Lendl?

10 Who partnered Billie Jean King in the mixed doubles win that made her Wimbledon's last triple champion?

11 Which Romanian was the 1978 French women's singles champion?

12 Who, in 1938, became the first tennis player to achieve the Grand Slam?

13 Who led the US Davis Cup team to victory in 1978 and 1979?

14 Which year saw the formation of the first governing body for tennis in England, Scotland and Wales - 1880, 1884 or 1888?

15 Which famous partnership won the Wimbledon men's doubles in 1980 and 1982?

---

*Answers to page 431*

**1** Maleeva, **2** Bjorn Borg, **3** Philippe Chatrier, **4** Patrick Rafter, **5** 1970, **6** Ken Rosewall, **7** Claudia Kohde-Kilsch, **8** Eddie Dibbs, **9** Arantxa Sanchez Vicario, **10** Martina Hingis, **11** 1981, **12** Rod Laver, **13** Georgian, **14** 1951, **15** Fred Stolle

# TENNIS - QUIZ 27

*Answers on page 428*

1 Who, at Wimbledon in 1997, was the first French finalist there since Yvon Petra in 1946?

2 Who was the last player to win the triple crown at Wimbledon?

3 With whom did Mats Wilander win the 1986 Wimbledon men's doubles title?

4 What was originally called 'Dwight's Pot'?

5 Who is the only man to have achieved the Grand Slam twice?

6 Which US Army rank did Arthur Ashe hold when he became US champion in 1968?

7 Who was known as 'Little Mo'?

8 Whose wife slapped an umpire at Wimbledon in 1995?

9 Which winner of 9 Grand Slam women's doubles titles was nicknamed 'Rabbit'?

10 Whose 1998 Australian Open win was his first Grand Slam tournament victory?

11 Who was Australian men's singles champion in 1991 and 1996?

12 When was the International Tennis Federation formed - 1903, 1913 or 1923?

13 Who won the 1996 Olympic men's doubles title?

14 Who displaced Pete Sampras as the world No 1 by defeating Andre Agassi in the 1998 Lipton Championship?

15 With whom did Mary Joe Fernandez win the French Open women's doubles in 1996?

## *Answers to page 428*

**1** Martina Hingis, **2** Andre Agassi, **3** Virginia Wade, **4** US Open, **5** Lennart Bergelin, **6** Bill Tilden, **7** Steffi Graf, **8** Chris Evert, **9** 1881, **10** South African, **11** Jim Courier, **12** Yvon Petra, **13** The French Open, **14** Lew Hoad, **15** Frew McMillan.

# TENNIS - QUIZ 28

*Answers on page 429*

**1** What is the surname of the three sisters who were all seeded in the 1993 Australian Open?

**2** Who won his fourth consecutive French Open singles title in 1981?

**3** Which Frenchman was elected president of the ITF in 1977?

**4** Whose 1997 victory made him the first Australian to win the US Open since 1976?

**5** Which year saw the introduction of tie-breaks to the US Open?

**6** Who reached his career best ranking of two in 1975?

**7** With whom did Helena Sukova win the 1987 Wimbledon women's doubles title?

**8** Who was the highest prize money-earner on the circuit in 1984, winning 84 of 111 matches?

**9** Who is known as 'The Barcelona Bumblebee'?

**10** Who became, in 1998, the youngest person to successfully defend a Grand Slam tournament?

**11** Which year saw a fight break out between a US radio reporter and a Daily Mirror reporter at a Wimbledon press conference?

**12** Who was Wimbledon men's runner-up in successive years in 1959 and 1960?

**13** What nationality was 1973 Wimbledon finalist Alex Metreveli?

**14** In which year did Maureen Connolly, at 16, beat Shirley Fry to become US champion?

**15** With whom did Ann Jones win the mixed doubles the day after winning the singles title at Wimbledon in 1969?

---

*Answers to page 429*

**1** Iva Majoli, **2** France, **3** Bjorn Borg, **4** Jonathan Stark, **5** Andre Agassi, **6** Flinders Park, **7** Boris Becker, **8** Natasha Zvereva, **9** Czech, **10** Owen Davidson, **11** Virginia Ruzici, **12** Don Budge, **13** Tony Trabert, **14** 1888, **15** Peter McNamara and Paul McNamee.

# TENNIS - QUIZ 29

*Answers on page 434*

1 To whom is former WTA Tour player Regina Rajchrtova married?

2 Who was the first French woman to win the Australian Open?

3 Who, at 15, was the youngest singles champion ever, and was never beaten at Wimbledon?

4 Who apologised to a ballgirl for accidentally striking her with a ball at Wimbledon?

5 Which German was the first president of the ITF?

6 With whom did Raul Ramirez win the 1976 Wimbledon men's doubles title?

7 In which year was equal prize money for men and women introduced to the US Open?

8 Which nation won the Davis Cup for the seventh consecutive time in 1926?

9 Who won the Wimbledon triple crown in 1920, 1922 and 1925?

10 How were Jean Borotra, Toto Brugnon, Henri Cochet and Rene Lacoste collectively known?

11 In which year did Maureen Connolly win her first Wimbledon championship?

12 Which Scandinavian tennis player won 11 men's titles in only two Grand Slam events?

13 In which year did the Australian Open move from late January to the Christmas-New Year holiday?

14 Who won his third consecutive Wimbledon men's title in 1995?

15 Who won the last of her record eight US singles wins at the age of 42?

---

## *Answers to page 434*

**1** Dorothea Douglass Chambers, **2** Anne Smith, **3** Cliff Richey, **4** 1962, **5** France, **6** Australia, **7** Vijay Armitraj, **8** Barcelona, **9** Alice Marble, **10** Swedish, **11** 1976, **12** Arthur Ashe, **13** Arantxa Sanchez Vicario, **14** 1974, **15** Evonne Goolagong.

# TENNIS - QUIZ 30

*Answers on page 435*

1 Which brothers were the first overseas pair to win the US doubles?

2 Who was the referee who was told in 1981 "You cannot be serious"?

3 Who won a record 24 Grand Slam singles titles?

4 In which year was the first tounament to include both amateurs and professionals held in Bournemouth?

5 Which Wimbledon runner-up was coach to another, Hana Mandlikova?

6 Which Wimbledon runner-up was, in turn, coached by Hana Mandlikova?

7 Who won his fifth US singles title in 1983?

8 At which venue has the US Open been held since 1978?

9 Who was the first American to win the Australian men's singles title?

10 Which Swedish tennis player was French Open men's singles champion in 1982?

11 Which nation won their sixth consecutive Davis Cup in 1932?

12 What is the surname of Cliff and Nancy, the first brother and sister to be ranked in the world top 10 in the same year?

13 How many junior singles titles did John McEnroe win?

14 In which country was Martina Navratilova born?

15 Whose grandfather-in-law Frank Shields had to concede the 1931 Wimbledon final due to injury?

***Czech Jana Novotna will be remembered for breaking down and crying on the shoulder of the Duchess of Kent after losing to Steffi Graf in the Wimbledon 1993 singles final.***

---

*Answers to page 435*

**1** 20, **2** Billie Jean King, **3** South Africa, **4** Conchita Martinez, **5** MaliVai Washington, **6** Gabriela Sabatini, **7** None, **8** Tim Mayotte, **9** USA, **10** 1977, **11** Ann Jones, **12** Hungary, **13** Jimmy Connors, **14** 1996, **15** Jaroslav Drobny.

# TENNIS - QUIZ 31

*Answers on page 432*

1. Which seven times Wimbledon singles champion was the 1903 women's badminton champion?
2. Which US tennis player was nicknamed 'Pepper'?
3. Who led the US Davis Cup team to victory against Germany in 1970?
4. Which year saw Rod Laver win the Grand Slam for the first time?
5. Which nation's 1997 victory made them only the sixth country to win the Fed Cup?
6. Whom did the USA beat in four consecutive Davis Cups, 1946-49?
7. Which Davis Cup captain appeared with Roger Moore in Octopussy?
8. In which city was Manuel Orantes born?
9. Who won the US singles title after having been told that TB would end her career?
10. What nationality is Mats Wilander?
11. Which year saw the arrival of the over-size racket?
12. Which American tennis player discovered Yannick Noah?
13. Who was the first Spaniard to win the French women's singles title?
14. Which was the first year for the US Open not to be held on grass?
15. Which part-aborigine won the French Open in 1971 on her first visit?

---

## *Answers to page 432*

**1** Petr Korda, **2** Mary Pierce, **3** Lottie Dod, **4** Tim Henman, **5** Dr Hans Otto Behrens, **6** Brian Gottfried, **7** 1973, **8** USA, **9** Suzanne Lenglen, **10** The Musketeers, **11** 1952, **12** Bjorn Borg, **13** 1972, **14** Pete Sampras, **15** Molla Mallory-Bjurstedt.

# • TENNIS - QUIZ 32 •

*Answers on page 433*

1 How many years separate Ken Rosewall's first and last Wimbledon finals?

2 Which tennis legend had so many knee operations that she joked you could play noughts and crosses between the scars?

3 Which country's Frew McMillan and Bob Hewitt dominated the doubles scene in the 1960s?

4 Who led Spain to a third successive Fed Cup victory in 1995?

5 Who did Richard Krajicek beat to win his Wimbledon singles title?

6 Which tennis star has a rose and two perfumes named after her?

7 How many times did Great Britain won the Fed Cup in the 1980s?

8 Who was known as 'Gentleman Tim'?

9 Who did Australia beat for four consecutive Davis Cups, 1950-53?

10 In which year's US Open did 17-year-old John McEnroe and 14-year-old Tracy Austin first appear?

11 Who did Nancy Richey beat in the 1968 French Open final?

12 Which country's most famous recent player is Balaz Taroczy?

13 Which male tennis player won a record 109 singles titles in the Open era?

14 Which year's Wimbledon men's final was visited by a male streaker?

15 Who first played at Wimbledon as a Czech, then won it in 1954 as an Egyptian?

---

## *Answers to page 433*

**1** Laurence and Reggie Doherty, **2** Fred Hoyles, **3** Margaret Court, **4** 1968, **5** Betty Stove, **6** Jana Novotna, **7** Jimmy Connors, **8** Flushing Meadow, **9** Dick Savitt, **10** Mats Wilander, **11** France, **12** Richey, **13** None, **14** Czechoslovakia, **15** Andre Agassi.

# TENNIS - QUIZ 33

*Answers on page 438*

1. Who is famous for wearing a white baseball cap?
2. With whom did Marty Riessen win the US mixed doubles title in 1969, 1970 and 1972?
3. What was the European Cup originally called?
4. Who did Iva Majoli beat to win the 1997 French Open singles title?
5. Who sued the ATP after they banned him from entering the French Open for signing a contract to play in World Team Tennis?
6. Who wore the all-white leotard when it made its one-and-only appearance at Wimbledon?
7. Whose nickname is 'The Big Cat'?
8. Which year's Australian Open quarter-final between Chanda Rubin and Arantxa Sanchez Vicario lasted over three and a half hours?
9. After whom is the main stadium at Flushing Meadows named?
10. Which nation won their fifth consecutive Davis Cup in 1972?
11. Who won the Wimbledon triple crown and Olympic gold in 1920?
12. Which nation hosted the Fed cup in 1969 in only their second appearance?
13. Who was the first woman to be elected to the All England Club committee?
14. Which trans-sexual reached the US Open doubles final with Bettyann Stuart in 1977?
15. Who broke his hand on a punchbag while training for the 1997 Australian Open?

***Steffi Graf was 14 when she played at Wimbledon for the first time. This time she was not successful vowing never to play on grass again!***

---

## *Answers to page 438*

**1** Jan Kodes, **2** Houston, **3** Germany, **4** Owen Davidson, **5** Aviator, **6** Forest Hills, **7** Tracy Austin, **8** 1978, **9** India, **10** Mats Wilander, **11** Margaret Court (nee Smith), **12** Jeff Tarango, **13** Iran, **14** Arthur Ashe, **15** Olga Morozova.

# TENNIS - QUIZ 34

*Answers on page 439*

1 Which Ukrainian won the German Open three years in succession, 1995-97?

2 Who won his third consecutive US Championships title in 1900?

3 Whose suspension led to a Wimbledon boycott by some men players?

4 Who was the first player to win the US Open on three different surfaces?

5 Who is the only man to achieve the Wimbledon triple crown on his one and only appearance there?

6 Which nation won the European Cup in 1976?

7 Who equalled Bjorn Borg's record of 11 Grand Slam titles by winning at Wimbledon in 1998?

8 Which tennis player displayed a 'No poll tax' sign at the 1990 National Championships in Telford?

9 Who beat Bessie Moore's 1892 record of youngest US championship finalist in 1978?

10 What nationality is Hana Mandlikova?

11 Who was ranked men's No 1 from 1981 to 1984?

12 For how many weeks was Jimmy Connors ranked No 1 in the world - 168, 218 or 268?

13 Which nation won consecutive Davis Cups in 1984 and 1985?

14 Who was the first Russian to win a Grand Slam event?

15 Which cup donator won the US men's doubles 1899-1901 with Holcombe Ward?

---

## *Answers to page 439*

**1** Francoise Durr, **2** 1936, **3** Pete Sampras, **4** Monica Seles, **5** Cilly Aussem, **6** Israel, **7** John McEnroe, **8** Arthur Ashe, **9** Great Britain, **10** Virginia Wade, **11** Jimmy Connors, **12** Italy, **13** Krishnan, **14** Tony Wilding, **15** Ken Fletcher.

# TENNIS - QUIZ 35

*Answers on page 436*

1 Who took Czechoslovakia's Davis Cup team to their first final in 1975?

2 In which US city was 1973's Battle of the Sexes held?

3 In which country was John McEnroe born?

4 Who won the Australian men's doubles with Ken Rosewall in 1972 and the US doubles with John Newcombe in 1973?

5 What was Roland Garros's profession?

6 From which venue did the US Open move in 1978?

7 Who, in 1979, became the youngest US women's champion?

8 Which year saw the French Open golden jubilee?

9 Which country conceded to South Africa in the 1974 Davis Cup final as an anti-apartheid protest?

10 Who won three of the four Grand Slam men's titles in 1988?

11 Who beat Maria Bueno in 1960 to win the first of her 11 Australian championships?

12 Which US tennis player mooned at the audience in Tokyo in 1994?

13 Which Middle East country entered the Davis Cup only once, in 1972?

14 Which tennis legend died of AIDS in 1993 after a blood transfusion?

15 Who, in 1974, became the first Soviet woman to reach the Wimbledon singles final?

## *Answers to page 436*

**1** Jim Courier, **2** Margaret Court, **3** The King's Cup, **4** Martina Hingis, **5** Jimmy Connors, **6** Anne White, **7** Miloslav Mecir, **8** 1996, **9** Arthur Ashe, **10** USA, **11** Suzanne Lenglen, **12** Greece, **13** Virginia Wade, **14** Renee Richards, **15** Yevgeny Kafelnikov.

# TENNIS - QUIZ 36

*Answers on page 437*

1 Who, in 1967, became the first French national to win the French Open for 19 years?

2 Which year saw Britain's last Davis Cup victory?

3 Who, in 1990, became the youngest US Open men's champion?

4 Who set a record in 1991 for prize money earned in a year, with $24m?

5 Which 1931 Wimbledon champion went on to become Contessa della Corta Brae?

6 In which country were the first courts laid by the Menorah Society?

7 Which tennis legend was previously a ball-boy for Bjorn Borg against Niki Pilic at the US Open?

8 With whom did Marty Riessen win the 1971 French Open men's doubles title?

9 Which nation won the Roland Garros Stadium's inaugural women's challenge match?

10 With whom did Olga Morozova win the Italian Open women's doubles in 1973?

11 Whose refusal to participate in the parade of former champions at Wimbledon's centenery celebrations led to him being booed the following day?

12 Which nation were consecutive Davis Cup runners-up, 1979-80?

13 What is the surname of Indian father and son Ramathan and Ramesh?

14 Who won the Wimbledon men's title four years in succession and was killed in action in France in 1915?

15 Who won the French men's doubles with Roy Emerson in 1964 and the Wimbledon doubles with John Newcombe in 1966?

---

*Answers to page 437*

**1** Andrei Medvedev, **2** Mal Whitman, **3** Niki Pilic, **4** Jimmy Connors, **5** Bobby Riggs, **6** Hungary, **7** Pete Sampras, **8** Andrew Castle, **9** Pam Shriver, **10** Czech, **11** John McEnroe, **12** 268, **13** Sweden, **14** Yevgeny Kafelnikov, **15** Dwight E Davis.

# • TENNIS - QUIZ 37 •

*Answers on page 442*

1. With what did the Swedish Tennis Association present Stefan Edberg on his retirement?
2. Who became, in 1955, the first British player to win the French Open since Peggy Scrivens in 1934?
3. Which nation were Davis Cup runners-up in 1994 and 1995?
4. At which venue were Helen Wills and Henri Cochet the first French Open singles champions?
5. What is the surname of tennis professionals Jeff, John, Pam and Tracy?
6. Who beat Jan Kodes in the first US Open final decided by a tie-break?
7. At which venue is Rome's Italian Open held?
8. Which pair won their second consecutive Wimbledon doubles title in 1990, each then going on to win it with Martina Hingis?
9. Which Australian Champion is now addressed as Reverend?
10. Who was Ivan Lendl's coach?
11. Which year saw Iraq's first appearance in the Davis Cup?
12. With whom are the phrases 'Pits of the world' and 'You cannot be serious' associated?
13. Who was on the winning Czech Davis Cup team in 1975 and on the winning US team in 1986?
14. What was the name of Pete Sampras's coach who died in 1996?
15. Who is the most recent example of a Wimbledon champion who was named after a previous Wimbledon champion?

---

## *Answers to page 442*

**1** Thomas Enqvist, **2** Roger Taylor, **3** Dan Maskell, **4** Slovakian, **5** They were twins, **6** Dorothy Round, **7** Margaret Court, **8** Bournemouth, **9** David Wheaton, **10** Dorothea Lambert Chambers, **11** 1949, **12** John Barrett, **13** Tim Henman, **14** The Wightman Cup, **15** Stan Smith.

# • TENNIS - QUIZ 38 •

*Answers on page 443*

**1** Who became, in 1996, the first left-hander to be ranked No 1 since John McEnroe?

**2** What phenomenon delayed the 1960 US Championships by a week?

**3** Which Wimbledon champion was also a golf champion, a hockey international and an archery Olympic silver medallist?

**4** Which nation won the Davis Cup in 1976?

**5** Which BBC sports presenter won the French Open in 1976?

**6** What nationality is the 1994 Olympic champion Mark Rosset?

**7** Who won 125 consecutive matches on clay between 1973 and 1979?

**8** Which December tournament has the sport's biggest prize money?

**9** Who became, in 1980, the only brother and sister team to win the Wimbledon mixed doubles?

**10** Which Swiss Olympic tennis gold medallist is 6ft 7in?

**11** Which year saw Japan's Davis Cup debut?

**12** Who did Billie Jean King beat in the 'Battle of the Sexes' in 1973?

**13** In which year did Wimbledon introduce its 'predominately white' dress code?

**14** Who won 19 Grand Slam singles titles and was known as 'Little Miss Poker Face'?

**15** Who did Angela Mortimer play in 1961 in the first all-British Wimbledon final in 47 years?

***British No 1 and No 2 tennis players, Greg Rusedski and Tim Henman, share the same birthday - September 6.***

---

*Answers to page 443*

**1** Marcello Rios, **2** 7, **3** Roy Emerson, **4** Magnus Larsson, **5** Ilie Nastase, **6** The Lipton Championships, **7** Martina Navratilova, **8** 1940, **9** Greg Rusedski, **10** Wilfred Baddeley, **11** Tracy Austin, **12** Armitraj, **13** Stefan Edberg, **14** Steffi Graf, **15** Kenya.

# TENNIS - QUIZ 39

*Answers on page 440*

1 Which Swede won the junior titles in Australia and Wimbledon in 1991?

2 Who beat Wieslaw Gasiorek in 1966 in the longest major tournament singles match on record?

3 Who was the voice of tennis on British television for 40 years?

4 What nationality is Miloslav Mecir?

5 What connects tennis pioneers Wilfred and Herbert Baddeley and Willie and Ernest Renshaw?

6 Who is the only British woman to have won Wimbledon twice since 1921, famous for refusing to play on Sundays?

7 Who won a record 17 titles in 1971?

8 In which English resort, in 1968, was the first tournament involving professionals and amateurs staged?

9 Which American won the Grand Slam Cup in 1991?

10 Who whitewashed Dora Boothby in the 1911 Wimbledon final?

11 Which year saw Israel's Davis Cup debut, a year after the establishment of the State of Israel?

12 Which British Davis Cup captain was married to Angela Mortimer?

13 Who was the first British player to be disqualified at Wimbledon?

14 Which annual women's competition between Britain and the USA was discontinued in 1990?

15 Who was the winner in the first Wimbledon singles final to be held on a Sunday?

## *Answers to page 440*

**1** A telescope, **2** Angela Mortimer, **3** Russia, **4** The Roland Garros Stadium, **5** Austin, **6** Stan Smith, **7** Foro Italico, **8** Jana Novotna and Helena Sukova, **9** Margaret Court, **10** Tony Roche, **11** 1983, **12** John McEnroe, **13** Martina Navratilova, **14** Tim Gullikson, **15** Martina Hingis.

# TENNIS - QUIZ 40

*Answers on page 441*

1 Who did Petr Korda defeat in a 1998 final to win his first Grand Slam title?

2 After how many games are the balls first changed?

3 Who failed to win his third consecutive Wimbledon singles win due to injury after crashing into the net post?

4 Which Swede won the Grand Slam Cup in 1994?

5 Who led the Davis Cup team that lost in three successive finals, 1970-72?

6 Which tournament is played at Key Biscayne?

7 Who won 74 consecutive matches between January and December 1984?

8 Which year saw five 500lb bombs destroy 1,200 Centre Court seats?

9 Who was the record fastest server in 1997?

10 Whose record of youngest Wimbledon men's singles champion was broken by Boris Becker?

11 Whose attempted comeback in 1989 ended after she broke a leg in a car accident?

12 What is the surname of the Indian brothers Vijay, Anand and Ashok?

13 Who, in 1983, became the first person to win a junior Grand Slam?

14 Whose 1996 Wimbledon title was her 100th career singles win?

15 Which nation have been Davis Cup regulars since 1986 despite having no public courts at home?

## *Answers to page 441*

**1** Thomas Muster, **2** A hurricane, **3** Lottie Dod, **4** Italy, **5** Sue Barker, **6** Swiss, **7** Chris Evert, **8** Grand Slam Cup, **9** John and Tracy Austin, **10** Marc Rosset, **11** 1921, **12** Bobby Riggs, **13** 1963, **14** Helen Wills Moody, **15** Christine Truman.

# LUCKY DIP

# • LUCKY DIP - QUIZ 1 •

*Answers on page 448*

**1** At which sport was Sidney Smith the first All-England champion, in 1900?

**2** Which year saw the Boat Race postponed until Sunday, Cambridge's boat having been damaged 20 minutes before the race?

**3** How old was Alice Blanche Leigh when she won her record 23rd British ladies' archery title?

**4** Who won his fourth World Professional billiards title in 1983?

**5** Who beat Laurent Fignon to win the 1989 Tour de France with the record narrowest margin of 8 seconds?

**6** What colour does a greyhound wear in lane three?

**7** Which sport was revolutionised in England by the opening of the Empire Pool in 1934, Earl's Court in 1935 and Harringay in 1936?

**8** Which sport is played on the largest pitch?

**9** What is the lowest weight category in women's judo?

**10** Who won her record fifth Queen Elizabeth II Cup in 1986?

**11** Which sport's first men's and women's champions were Age Hadler and Ulla Lindkvist, in 1966?

**12** How many players are there on a hurling team?

**13** What is the oldest of all the Henley races?

**14** Which nation won their third men's hockey World Cup in 1998?

**15** In which part of London was the All-England Croquet Club formed in 1869?

## *Answers to page 448*

**1** It got lost in the fog, **2** 20 minutes, **3** 1967, **4** Tony Hand, **5** Brian Leadbetter, **6** Single-seater luge tobogganing, **7** Prince Philip Trophy, **8** John Curry, **9** Netherlands, **10** Australia, Great Britain and New Zealand, **11** Karen Briggs, **12** Orange, **13** Rudolf Nierlich, **14** Germany, **15** Bjarne Riis.

# LUCKY DIP - QUIZ 2

*Answers on page 449*

1 How many teams entered the first hockey league in 1903?

2 Which squash player became, in 1967, the first to win both the British Open and the British Amateur title?

3 At which London venue is the final of the All-Ireland Hurling Championships held each year?

4 What did the Boston Braves become in 1933?

5 Which Henley race is regarded as the Blue Riband of amateur sculling?

6 Which year saw the only appearance of croquet at the Olympics?

7 Which Washington Bullets basketball player was, at seven foot six and three quarters, the tallest in NBA history?

8 Who won their second women's hockey World Cup in 1998?

9 At which weight was Britain's Kate Howey 1997 world judo champion?

10 Who won his record fifth consecutive Tour de France in 1995?

11 Who won his third King George V Gold Cup in 1986?

12 What is the surname of Tony and John, both World Fly-Fishing champions?

13 Who won a record second successive men's slalom world title in 1982?

14 Who was 1997 gymnastics All-around women's world champion?

15 Of which game in Three-Cushions a variety?

## *Answers to page 449*

**1** W G Grace, **2** Tommy Simpson, **3** The Refridgerator, **4** America's Cup, **5** Archery, **6** The Derby, **7** Ninepin was banned, **8** Judo, **9** Gina Gogean, **10** Atle Skardal, **11** Fifty, **12** Paul Schockemohle, **13** Graham Sharp, **14** Croquet, **15** Netherlands.

# • LUCKY DIP - QUIZ 3 •

*Answers on page 446*

1 Why did Shamrock III not finish the last race in the 1903 America's Cup?

2 What time limit did the International Table Tennis Federation impose on games in 1937?

3 Which year's badminton Thomas Cup final was abandoned due to crowd barracking?

4 Which Murrayfield Racers ice hockey player was the first to be drafted by an NHL club?

5 Which Englishman won his second World Fly-Fishing Championship in 1991?

6 In which sport did Georg Hackl win a record third world title in 1997?

7 What was show jumping's world team championship renamed in 1985?

8 Which Briton became men's figure skating world champion in 1976?

9 In which country did the sport of yachting originate?

10 Which three countries contest croquet's MacRobertson International Shield?

11 Who won a record fourth women's Under 48kg world judo title in 1989?

12 What colour does a greyhound wear in lane five?

13 Who won a record second successive men's giant slalom world title in 1991?

14 Which nation won their fourth European men's hockey title in 1995?

15 Which Dane won the 1996 Tour de France?

***The official British duration record for Pigeon racing (flying into the UK) is 1,887 km in 15 days by C.S.O, in the 1976 Palamos Race.***

---

## *Answers to page 446*

**1** Badminton, **2** 1984, **3** Sicty seven, **4** Rex Williams, **5** Greg LeMond, **6** White, **7** Ice Hockey, **8** Polo, **9** Under 48kg, **10** Liz Edgar, **11** Orienteering, **12** Fifteen, **13** Grand Challenge Cup, **14** Netherlands, **15** Wimbledon.

# • LUCKY DIP - QUIZ 4 •

*Answers on page 447*

**1** Who became the first president of the English Bowling Association, in 1903?

**2** Who was the first Briton to wear the Tour de France's yellow jersey?

**3** What is American footballer William Perry's nickname?

**4** What was originally called the Hundred Guinea Cup?

**5** At which sport did Hans Deutgen win a record fourth consecutive men's world title in 1950?

**6** What was the first sporting event to be televised in the UK?

**7** Why, in 19th century America, was ninepin bowling developed into tenpin bowling?

**8** In which sport was Britain's Nicola Fairbrother 1993 Under 56kg world champion?

**9** Who was 1997 world champion in the balance beam and floor exercises?

**10** Who won a record second successive men's super G world title in 1997?

**11** How much is the inner bull worth in darts?

**12** Who won a record third consecutive European show jumping title on Deister in 1985?

**13** Who became, in 1939, Britain's first men's figure skating world champion?

**14** At which sport has Nigel Aspinall won a record 11 British Masters titles?

**15** Which nation won their third European women's hockey title in 1995?

---

## *Answers to page 447*

**1** Five, **2** Jonah Barrington, **3** Croke Park, **4** The Redskins, **5** Diamond Sculls, **6** 1900, **7** Manute Bol, **8** Australia, **9** Under 66kg, **10** Miguel Indurain, **11** Nick Skelton, **12** Pawson, **13** Ingemar Stenmark, **14** Svetlana Chorkina, **15** Billiards.

# LUCKY DIP - QUIZ 5

*Answers on page 452*

1. Who was American football's first verified black professional player?
2. Who became, in 1967, equestrianism's first woman chef d'equipe?
3. Who was the first American to wear the Tour de France's yellow jersey?
4. Who took the table tennis world title in 1937 as an Austrian, then three more times as an Englishman?
5. Which country's men's team has won the most archery world titles?
6. In the University Boat Race, what is the Cambridge reserve crew called?
7. Who won his second gymnastics All-around world title in 1987?
8. In which sport did Sharon Rendle win her second consecutive Under 52kg world title in 1989?
9. Which country's show jumping team has won a record four European titles?
10. How many holes are there in a tenpin bowling ball?
11. Which country's hockey team won their seventh Men's Champions' Trophy in 1997?
12. What is known as the 'roaring game'?
13. Who won a record third men's Alpine combination world title in 1996?
14. What is the highest one can score with one dart?
15. What is Canada's most popular sport?

## *Answers to page 452*

**1** 1907, **2** Morning Cloud, **3** Stephen Roche, **4** Eighteen, **5** Cleveland Rams, **6** Leander Club, **7** About 40lb, **8** Pin spotter, **9** Great Britain, **10** Nine, **11** Canada, **12** Isolde Kostner, **13** 1949, **14** China, **15** Uhlenhorst Mulheim.

# • LUCKY DIP - QUIZ 6 •

*Answers on page 453*

**1** Who threatened to ban American football after 8 players were killed and 148 injured in the 1905 season?

**2** Who resigned as president of the International Table Tennis Federation after 40 years in 1967?

**3** Which New Zealander ended Jahangir Khan's five-year unbeaten spell in the 1986 squash World Open?

**4** Which country's hockey team won their fourth Women's Champions' Trophy in 1997?

**5** In which year did American football's NFL attract 1 million spectators for the first time?

**6** What do curlers use to smooth the ice ahead of the stone?

**7** In the University Boat Race, what is the Oxford reserve crew called?

**8** At which venue is the British Show Jumping Derby held annually?

**9** Which sport's World Championships are divided into Kumite and Kata events?

**10** What may be bare, recurve or compound?

**11** Which German won the 1997 Tour de France?

**12** Who won a record second successive women's giant slalom world title in 1989?

**13** What is the weight of a tenpin bowling ball?

**14** Which year saw Britain win their only men's hockey World Championship title?

**15** What colour does a greyhound wear in lane four?

---

*Answers to page453*

**1** 1970, **2** He only had one arm, **3** 300, **4** Black and white stripes, **5** 1907, **6** Pittsburgh Steelers, **7** Canada, **8** Pedro Delgado, **9** True, **10** , **11** USA, **12** Australian Rules football, **13** She was declared a man, **14** Athletic Terrassa, **15** Kendo.

# LUCKY DIP - QUIZ 7

*Answers on page 450*

1 In which year were women's badminton singles matches reduced from 15-up to 11-up?

2 With which boat did Edward Heath win the 1969 Sydney-Hobart race?

3 Who was the first Irishman to win the Tour de France?

4 How many players are there in an Australian Rules football team?

5 Which NFL team moved to Los Angeles in 1945?

6 What is the oldest rowing club in the UK?

7 What is the weight of a curling?

8 What is the machine that picks up the bowling pins called?

9 Which country won a record fifth consecutive men's team world karate title in 1990?

10 What is the minimum number of dart throws necessary to reduce one's score from 501 to zero?

11 Which nation won their fourth women's ice hockey World Championship title in 1997?

12 Who won her second successive super G world title in 1997?

13 In which year did the first Badminton Horse Trials take place?

14 Which country's men's team were 1997 gymnastics world champions?

15 Who won their record eighth consecutive European Club Champions' Cup in hockey in 1995?

***England has at least one sport that it commands. The World Tug of War Championships held biennially since 1986 has been dominated by England, who have won 16 titles in all categories from 1975.***

---

## *Answers to page 450*

**1** Charles W Follis, **2** Pat Smythe, **3** Greg LeMond, **4** Richard Bergmann, **5** USA, **6** Goldie, **7** Dmitriy Bilozerchev, **8** Judo, **9** Great Britain, **10** Three, **11** Germany, **12** Curling, **13** Marc Girardelli, **14** Sixty, **15** Ice hockey.

# • LUCKY DIP - QUIZ 8 •

*Answers on page 451*

**1** In which year was ice hockey's Southern League formed?

**2** What singled out Pete Gray, who appeared for the St Louis Browns 77 times?

**3** What is the maximum score possible in a game of tenpin bowling?

**4** What colours does a greyhound wear in lane six?

**5** In which year was the first International Horse Show held at London Olympia?

**6** Who are the only team to have won the Super Bowl in successive years twice?

**7** Which country has won the most men's and women's curling world titles?

**8** Who won the 75th Tour de France on a technicality despite failing a drugs test?

**9** The University Boat Race course is more than four miles long True or false?

**10** In which county is Badminton House, home of the Badminton Horse Trials?

**11** Which nation won the ice hockey World Cup in 1996?

**12** In which sport did the Adelaide Crows win the Grand Final for the first time?

**13** Why was Erika Schinegger stripped of her 1966 downhill skiing world title?

**14** Who won the men's hockey European Club Champions' Cup in 1998?

**15** Which Japanese swordsmanship martial art was practised by the samurai?

---

### *Answers to page 451*

**1** Theodore Roosevelt, **2** Ivor Montague, **3** Ross Norman, **4** Australia, **5** 1939, **6** Brooms, **7** Isis, **8** Hickstead, **9** Karate, **10** Bows, **11** Jan Ullrich, **12** Vreni Schneider, **13** 16lb, **14** 1936, **15** Black.

# • LUCKY DIP - QUIZ 9 •

*Answers on page 456*

**1** What is the surname of the six American footballing brothers who all played for the Columbus Panhandles?

**2** Who became, in 1982, the first man to win five Boat Races?

**3** Who beat Britain in the only polo world championships, held in 1989?

**4** Who holds the record for the most Australian Rules football goals, with 2,191?

**5** What is the term for knocking down all ten pins with one ball?

**6** In which country did korfball originate?

**7** Which Italian won the 1998 Tour de France?

**8** How many people are there in a University Boat Race boat?

**9** Who rode Golden Willow to become the first Badminton Horse Trials champion?

**10** What are kendo's shiani?

**11** Who won the women's hockey European Club Champions' Cup for a record eighth consecutive time in 1982?

**12** Which country's women's team were 1997 gymnastics world champions?

**13** What trophy is awarded annually to the winning ice hockey team in the NHL play-offs?

**14** Who was 1998 men's overall skiing World Cup champion?

**15** Which sport's world championship was originally called the Scotch Whisky Cup?

## *Answers to page 456*

**1** 1913, **2** Officers and Gentlemen, **3** Wayne Gretzky, **4** Doggetts Coat and Badge, **5** Sweden, **6** Svetlana Khorkina, **7** Lacrosse, **8** Feathers, **9** Federico Bahamontes, **10** Freestyle skiing, **11** Mark Phillips, **12** Netherlands, **13** Madge Syers, **14** Treadle-propelled bicycle, **15** Gillian Gilks.

# • LUCKY DIP - QUIZ 10 •

*Answers on page 457*

**1** Who presented the gold cup at equestrianism's first Nations Cup in 1909?

**2** Who became the youngest NFL coach when he took over the Oakland Raiders in 1869 at the age of 32?

**3** Who won two table tennis world titles for China and has played for England since 1989?

**4** What is a rowing team's pace setter called?

**5** Who won women's hockey European Club Champions' Cup in 1998?

**6** How many greyhounds run in a race in Britain?

**7** Which indoor team sport is played by mixed teams of four men and four women?

**8** Which city houses curling's international governing body?

**9** What is the surname of Frank and daughters Judy and Sue who have 35 All-England badminton titles between them?

**10** Who were the first ice hockey team to achieve the Grand Slam in Britain?

**11** Who became, in 1950, the first Swiss to win the Tour de France?

**12** Who was 1998 women's overall skiing World Cup champion?

**13** What is the term for knocking all ten pins down with two balls?

**14** Who was Badminton Horse Trials champion for a record sixth time in 1984?

**15** Who has won the most men's figure skating World Championship titles, with 10?

---

## *Answers to page 457*

**1** Princess Anne, **2** Phil Taylor, **3** Gold, **4** Hugo Koblet, **5** An end, **6** Cox, **7** Paris, **8** Ninety nine, **9** Ten, **10** 1910, **11** Montreal Canadiens, **12** Eight, **13** Snowboarding, **14** Virginia Leng, **15** Rudy Hartono.

# • LUCKY DIP - QUIZ 11 •

*Answers on page 454*

1 Which year saw the formation of the British Ice Hockey Association - 1893, 1913 or 1933?

2 Which distinction in equestrianism was abolished in 1948?

3 Who became the National Hockey League's most prolific scorer in 1989?

4 What is the oldest sculling race called?

5 Which country has won the most world professional doubles titles at tenpin bowling?

6 Who was women's European gymnastics champion in 1998?

7 Which team sport was originally played by American Indians, who called it 'baggataway'?

8 What were replaced by plastic on shuttlecocks in 1949?

9 Who became, in 1959, the first Spaniard to win the Tour de France?

10 What type of skiing event comprises aerials, ballet and moguls?

11 Who won his fourth Badminton Horse Trials title in 1981?

12 Which country won both men's and women's hockey European Cup-Winners' Cups in 1998?

13 Which Briton won the first two women's figure skating World Championship titles?

14 What was first designed by Scottish blacksmith Kirkpatrick Macmillan in 1839?

15 In 1978, which British woman became All-England badminton singles champion?

---

## *Answers to page 454*

**1** Nasser, **2** Boris Rankov, **3** USA, **4** Peter Hudson, **5** Strike, **6** Holland, **7** Marco Pantini, **8** Nine, **9** John Sheddon, **10** Bamboo swords, **11** Amsterdam, **12** Romania, **13** ,Stanley Cup **14** Hermann Maier, **15** Curling

# • LUCKY DIP - QUIZ 12 •

*Answers on page 455*

1 Who won individual and team golds with Doublet at the 1971 European Three-Day Event championships?

2 Which 100-1 outsider went on to win the 1990 world professional darts title?

3 In archery, what colour is the centre ring?

4 Which Swiss cyclist became, in 1950, the first non-Italian to win the Giro d'Italia?

5 What is the term for a round in bowls?

6 Who steers a rowing boat?

7 In which city was the first cycling race held in 1868, won by Englishman James Moore?

8 What is the only two-figure number from which one can't finish with two darts?

9 How many players are there in a men's lacrosse team?

10 In wiich year were mass attacks banned in American football after another 6 players had been killed?

11 Who won the NHL's Stanley Cup for a record 24th time in 1993?

12 How many greyhounds run in a race in America?

13 Which sport's events include slalom, parallel slalom and halfpipe?

14 As whom did Miss Holgate win her third Badminton Horse Trials title in 1993?

15 Which Indonesian won the All-England badminton men's singles for a record seventh successive year in 1974?

***The fastest greyhound ever recorded was Star Title on the straightaway track in New South Wales, Austalia in March 1994.***

---

## *Answers to page 455*

**1** King Edward VII, **2** John Madden, **3** Chen Xinhua, **4** Stroke, **5** Russelsheimer, **6** Six, **7** Korfball, **8** Edinburgh, **9** Devlin, **10** Murrayfield Racers, **11** Ferdinand Kubler, **12** Katja Seizinger, **13** Spare, **14** Lucinda Green, **15** Ulrich Salchow.

# • LUCKY DIP - QUIZ 13 •

*Answers on page 460*

1 Who won his fourth consecutive All-England title in 1923, and is known as the 'grand old man' of badminton?

2 With which new feature was a squash court first opened in Sheffield in 1971?

3 Which Briton won the 1951 world and European women's figure skating titles?

4 Who became, in 1992, the first Canadian team to win baseball's World Series?

5 What is hockey played on ice but with a ball rather than a puck called?

6 Who skippered the Virgin Atlantic Challenger II when it broke the Atlantic crossing record in 1986?

7 On which horse did Ian Stark successfully defend his Badminton Horse Trials title in 1988?

8 What is the 'most valuable player' in ice hockey's Stanley Cup awarded?

9 In archery, what colour is the ring next to the gold?

10 What is cycling's Tour of Britain now called?

11 Which sport was invented by George Hancock of the Farragut Boat Club, Chicago, in 1887?

12 Which darts star's fans dress up as The Flintstones' Barney Rubble?

13 What is the white ball called in bowls?

14 How many players are there usually in a women's lacrosse team?

15 Who was men's European gymnastics champion in 1998?

---

## *Answers to page 460*

**1** Babe Ruth, **2** Dogsled racing, **3** Badminton, **4** Halyards, **5** Bowls, **6** Kendo, **7** Darts, **8** 300m, **9** Wayne Gretzky, **10** Larisa Latynina, **11** Black, **12** Hashim Khan, **13** Paul Palmer, **14** Isabell Werth, **15** 333m.

# • LUCKY DIP - QUIZ 14 •

*Answers on page 461*

**1** Who was the Chicago Bears' 'Papa Bear', their coach for 40 years?

**2** Who captained the British team that regained the Admiral's Cup in 1971?

**3** What was the surname of the four brothers who have dominated squash since 1950?

**4** Which Ukrainian 15-year-old won the women's world figure skating title at her debut in 1993?

**5** Who became, in 1968, the first Dutchman to win the Tour de France?

**6** In yachting, what is the forward sail called?

**7** In which sport are players given points for goals and 'assists'?

**8** Which woman has won the most All-England badminton singles titles, with 10?

**9** In which year of the 1960s saw Britain's women's team win the lacrosse World Cup?

**10** What is the French equivalent to bowls?

**11** What is the major event of the autumn horse trials season?

**12** How many players are there in a softball team?

**13** Who has won the most men's World Championship gold medals in gymnastics, with 12?

**14** In archery, what colour is the outer ring?

**15** What is the cycling term for standing out of the saddle?

---

## *Answers to page 461*

**1** The Lapham Cup, **2** South Korea, **3** Chris Boardman, **4** Tony Allcock, **5** Epee, foil and sabre, **6** Sheets, **7** Three, **8** Johnny Leach, **9** 4000m, **10** Eric Bristow, **11** Koichi Nakano, **12** Squash, **13** Badminton, **14** Katarina Witt, **15** Wimbledon.

# • LUCKY DIP - QUIZ 15 •

*Answers on page 458*

1 Whom did the Boston Red Sox sell to the New York Yankees for $125,000 in 1921?

2 In which sport was Dick Wilmarth the first winner of the Iditarod Trial in 1971?

3 Which racket sport was named after the Duke of Beaufort's house?

4 In yachting, what are ropes for hoisting called?

5 The modern rules for which sport were drawn up in 1848-9 by Glasgow solicitor William Mitchell?

6 Whihc martial art literally means 'sword way'?

7 Which sport's World Professional Championship is held annually at the Lakeside Country Club, Frimley Green?

8 What distance is the swimming section in the Modern Pentathlon?

9 Whose three-year $255m contract with the LA Kings in 1993 made him the highest-paid sportsman in America?

10 Who has won the most women's World Championship gold medals in gymnastics, with 9?

11 In archery, what colour is the ring next to the white outer ring?

12 Who said he was 35, but was probably 42, when he won the British Open squash title for the seventh time, in 1957?

13 Which British swimmer was 1997 European men's 200m freestyle champion?

14 Who was European dressage champion for a record fourth consecutive time in 1997?

15 What is the common length of an indoor cycling track?

---

## *Answers to page 458*

**1** Sir George Thomas, **2** Glass back wall, **3** Jeannette Altwegg, **4** Toronto Blue Jays, **5** Bandy, **6** Richard Bransone, **7** Sir Wattiy, **8** Conn Smythe Troph, **9** Red, **10** The Milk Race, **11** Softball, **12** Raymond Barneveld, **13** The jack, **14** Twelve, **15** Aleksey Bondarenko.

# • LUCKY DIP - QUIZ 16 •

*Answers on page 459*

1. What was the name of squash's first International competition, first held in 1922 between the US and Canada?
2. Which country dominated the first tae kwon do world championships in 1973?
3. Who became, in 1994, the first Briton since Tommy Simpson to wear the Tour de France's yellow jersey?
4. Who successfully defended his World Outdoor bowls title in 1996?
5. Which three weapons are used in modern fencing?
6. In yachting, what are ropes for trimming called?
7. How many balls are used in billiards?
8. Which English table tennis player won the 1951 singles world title?
9. What distance is the cross-country running in the Modern Pentathlon?
10. Who was World Professional darts runner-up for a record third successive time in 1991?
11. Which cyclist has won a record ten consecutive professional sprint titles?
12. Which sport was first played at Harrow School in 1817?
13. What is the national sport of Indonesia and Malaysia?
14. Who was women's figure skating world champion for two successive years twice in the 1980s?
15. At which British stadium is the Greyhound Derby held?

***The biggest Yachting race, open to all, is the Admiral's Cup. Only three boats are allowed from each nation. Britain holds the record with nine wins.***

---

*Answers to page 459*

**1** George Halas, **2** Edward Heath, **3** Khan, **4** Oksana Bayul, **5** Jan Janssen, **6** Jib, **7** Ice hockey, **8** Judy Devlin/Hashman, **9** 1965, **10** Boules (or Pétanque), **11** Burghley Horse Trials, **12** Nine, **13** Eizo Kenmotsu, **14** White, **15** Honking.

# • LUCKY DIP - QUIZ 17 •

*Answers on page 464*

1 Which NY sporting venue opened in 1923 and was known as 'the house that Roth built'?

2 How many points are needed to win a game of badminton?

3 Who were 1997 European men's 4 x 200m freestyle relay champions?

4 Who was squash player Jonah Barrington's great Australian rival?

5 Which cyclist failed a drugs test to leave the 1991 professional sprint title vacant?

6 Who won her second figure skating World Championship title in 1998?

7 Who has won the most men's individual gymnastics world titles, with 8?

8 Which weapon is used in the fencing in the Modern Pentathlon?

9 Whose record 554 yards pass for the Los Angeles Rams in 1951 still stands?

10 Which year was the first since 1904 to see baseball's World Series cancelled, this time due to players striking?

11 How many hulls does a catamaran have?

12 What is a boblet?

13 Who won a record third consecutive World Indoor bowls title in 1981?

14 Which is the only country other than England to have won the darts World Cup team title?

15 What is the target area when fencing with an epee?

## *Answers to page 464*

**1** Red Grange, **2** Princess Diana, **3** Telemark position, **4** Jocky Wilson, **5** 1954, **6** Wendy Norman, **7** Caroline McAllister, **8** Jennifer and John Nicks, **9** 1953, **10** Vladimir Selkov, **11** Hall Green, Birmingham, **12** Denmark, **13** The opponent's metallic jacket, **14** Skip, **15** Thirteen.

# • LUCKY DIP - QUIZ 18 •

*Answers on page 465*

1 Which sport's Daily Mirror tournament did cricketing legend Jack Hobbs enter in 1923?

2 Which country dominated the first men's tug-of-war world championships in 1975?

3 At which event did James Hickman win Britain's only gold at the 1997 World Short-Course Swimming championships?

4 What is a baseball field known as?

5 Which sport has a Motor-paced category?

6 How many hulls does a trimaran have?

7 Which British couple won their second figure skating World Championship title in 1912?

8 Who won the Embassy World Professional Darts Championship five times during the 1980s?

9 What is the target area when fencing with a sabre?

10 Who, in 1993, won Britain's only ever men's Modern Pentathlon World title?

11 Who was the 1998 World Indoor bowls men's champion?

12 Who won his third consecutive European 200m breaststroke title in 1993?

13 What nationality were both the singles winners in the inaugural badminton world championships in 1977?

14 What is the name for the technique used to right a capsized canoe?

15 Who has won the most women's individual gymnastics world titles, with 6?

---

*Answers to page 465*

**1** New York Yankees, **2** Waterskiing, **3** Fives, **4** Crawl, **5** Sooping, **6** Leighton Rees, **7** Don Larsen, **8** Canadian canoe, **9** Eddie Merckx, **10** Great Britain, **11** The sabre, **12** Michael Gross, **13** Five, **14** London, **15** Herma Jaross.

# • LUCKY DIP - QUIZ 19 •

*Answers on page 462*

1 Which Chicago Bears player was known as the 'Galloping Ghost'?

2 In whose memory was all sport in Britain cancelled on September 6, 1997?

3 Which position is assumed on landing in ski-jumping?

4 Who became, in 1982, the first Scottish World Professional darts champion?

5 Which year saw Soviet Union crews make their Henley regatta debut, winning the Grand Challenge Cup, the Stewards Cup and the Silver Goblets?

6 Who, in 1982, won Britain's only ever women's Modern Pentathlon World title?

7 Who was the 1998 World Indoor bowls women's champion?

8 Who became, in 1953, the last British couple to win the figure skating World Championships?

9 In which year did England win their only table tennis world championship?

10 Who won his third consecutive European 200m backstroke title in 1997?

11 At which English stadium is the greyhound Grand National held?

12 Which country has won the most European team titles in badminton?

13 What is the target area when fencing with a foil?

14 What is a curling captain called?

15 How many Classic cycling races are there?

---

## *Answers to page 462*

**1** The Yankee Stadium, **2** Fifteen, **3** UK, **4** Geoff Hunt, **5** Carey Hall, **6** Michelle Kwan, **7** Vitaliy Scherbo, **8** Epee, **9** Norm van Brocklin, **10** 1994, **11** Two, **12** 2 person bobsleigh, **13** David Bryant, **14** Wales, **15** The whole body.

# • LUCKY DIP - QUIZ 20 •

*Answers on page 463*

**1** For which baseball team did Lou Gehrig start a run of 2,130 consecutive games on June 1, 1925?

**2** In which sport did Mike Hazelwood become, in 1977, the first Briton to win the men's overall world championship title?

**3** In which sport is the ball hit with gloves?

**4** What is the fastest swimming stroke?

**5** In curling, what is the term for sweeping the ice?

**6** Who was the first World Professional darts champion, in 1978?

**7** Who pitched the only perfect game in the history of the World Series for the NY Yankees in 1956?

**8** Which type of canoe is propelled from a half-kneeling position?

**9** Which cyclist holds the record for the most Classic race titles, with 38?

**10** In 1983, which nation won their third consecutive Modern Pentathlon team World title?

**11** Which of the men's fencing weapons is not used by women?

**12** Who won his third consecutive European 200m butterfly title in 1987?

**13** How many sides does baseball's home base have?

**14** In which city was the first greyhound race held, in 1876?

**15** Who is the only figure skater to have been singles and doubles world champion in the same year?

***The largest single angling catch ever was recorded in Australia in 1959. The massive man-eating great white shark was over 16ft 10 inches long.***

---

## *Answers to page 463*

**1**Table tennis , **2** England, **3** 200m butterfly, **4** The diamond, **5** Cycling, **6** Three, **7** Phyllis and James Johnson, **8** Eric Bristow, **9** Above the waist, **10** Richard Phelps, **11** Paul Foster, **12** Nick Gillingham, **13** Danish, **14** Eskimo roll, **15**Daniela Silivas .

# • LUCKY DIP - QUIZ 21 •

*Answers on page 468*

**1** In which year did seven yachts leave Ryde on the inaugural Fastnet Race?

**2** Who won the men's water polo title in the first world championships in 1973 and the first World Cup in 1979?

**3** In which sport is the pitch called the gridiron?

**4** Which sport do the Philadelphia Flyers play?

**5** How many players are in a polo team?

**6** How many innings are there in a professional baseball game?

**7** Who won the first men's hockey county championship in 1958?

**8** Which sport was invented by Major Ernst Killander in 1918 in Sweden?

**9** Which weapon did Grigoriy Kirienko use to successfully defend his fencing world title in 1993?

**10** Who won her third successive European 200m backstroke and 400m individual medley titles in 1995?

**11** Who became, in 1994, the first non-British World Profesional darts champion?

**12** What is the popular name for the August day that sees the start of the grouse shooting season?

**13** How long is the standard outdoor speed skating circuit?

**14** Which sport is divided into categories K1, K2, K4, C1 and C2?

**15** Which greyhound has won a record 32 consecutive races?

## *Answers to page 468*

**1** 1979, **2** Empty hand, **3** James Barr, **4** 1926, **5** Eleven, **6** Darts, **7** Brian Robinson, **8** 5.8km, **9** Foil, **10** Gunda Niemann, **11** John Lowe, **12** 600m, **13** Heike Friedrich, **14** The Bronx Bombers, **15** Pommel horse.

# • LUCKY DIP - QUIZ 22 •

*Answers on page 469*

**1** Which former junior Wimbledon champion won 51 international badminton matches 1926-51?

**2** Who was bowls's first indoor world champion and outdoor world champion?

**3** What did baseball's Brooklyn Dodgers move to become?

**4** In which country were darts first used as a means of self-defence in battle?

**5** Who became, in 1997, only the second Scottish World Profesional darts champion?

**6** What is the length of a game of American football?

**7** Who retired in 1958 after her tenth successive squash British Open title?

**8** Where did the America's Cup go for the first time in 1995?

**9** Over which four distances is World Championship speed skating contested?

**10** Which gymnast won her record third consecutive European title in 1979?

**11** What is the distance of the men's orienteering long event?

**12** Over which two distances are speed canoeing events on still water contested?

**13** Who has won the most European men's swimming gold medals, with 15?

**14** With which weapon did Eric Srecki successfully defend his fencing world title in 1997?

**15** In which sport is play started or restarted with a face off?

---

## *Answers to page 469*

**1** John Hilton, **2** Seven, **3** 1958, **4** One hour, **5** Harold Vanderbilt, **6** Nine, **7** Six, **8** Korea, **9** Fives, **10** Rintje Ritsma, **11** Baseball, **12** Raymond Barneveld, **13** 10.5km, **14** Weightlifting, **15** Twenty five.

# • LUCKY DIP - QUIZ 23 •

*Answers on page 466*

1 In which year's Fastnet race were 15 people killed?

2 What does the word karate mean?

3 Who skippered the Reliance to his third consecutive America's Cup victory in 1903?

4 Which year saw the formation of the All-England Women's Netball Association?

5 How many players are there on an American football team?

6 For which game did Brian Gamlin devise the present numbering system in 1896?

7 Who, in 1958, became the first Briton to win a stage at the Tour de France?

8 What is the distance of the men's orienteering short event?

9 With which weapon did Aleksandr Romankov win a record fifth world fencing title in 1983?

10 Who won a record seventh women's world speed skating title in 1998?

11 Who won his first World Professional darts title in 1979 and his third in 1993?

12 What is the maximum length of a canoe slalom course?

13 Who has won the most European women's swimming gold medals, with 11?

14 What is the New York Yankees' nickname?

15 In which gymnastics event did Zoltan Magyar win his third successive world title in 1979?

## *Answers to page 466*

**1** 1925, **2** Hungary, **3** American football, **4** Ice hockey, **5** Four, **6** Nine, **7** Lincolnshire, **8** Orienteering, **9** Sabre, **10** Krisztina Egerszegi, **11** John Part, **12** The Glorious Twelfth, **13** 400m, **14** Canoeing, **15** Ballyregan Bob.

# • LUCKY DIP - QUIZ 24 •

*Answers on page 467*

1 Who became, in 1980, the first Briton to win the European table tennis singles title?

2 How many players are there in an indoor handball team?

3 In which year did ice hockey's Harringay Arena close after 22 years?

4 Over what time period is the classic cycling speed record set?

5 Who skippered the Ranger to his third consecutive America's Cup victory in 1937?

6 To how many points did Britain change squash's 15-point scoring in 1926?

7 How many points are awarded for a touchdown in American football?

8 In which country did tae kwon do originate?

9 Which sport has Eton and Rugby varieties?

10 Who won his second consecutive world speed skating title in 1996?

11 Which sport is played to Cartwright Rules?

12 Who successfully defended his World Professional darts title in 1999?

13 What is the distance of the women's orienteering long event?

14 At which sport did William Pullum break more than 200 world and British records?

15 How many gates are there in a canoe slalom course?

***The first university boat race was won by Oxford on 10 June 1846. The race ran from Henley Bridge to Hambledon Lock.***

---

*Answers to page 467*

**1** Betty Uber, **2** David Bryant, **3** The Los Angeles Dodgers, **4** Ireland, **5** Les Wallace, **6** One hour, **7** Janet Morgan, **8** New Zealand, **9** 500m, 1000m, 5000m and 10,000m, **10** Nadia Comaneci, **11** 17.5km, **12** 500m and 1000m, **13** Aleksandr Popov, **14** Epee, **15** Ice hockey.

# • LUCKY DIP - QUIZ 25 •

*Answers on page 472*

**1** Which sport's world championships trophy was named after its federation's chairman's mother, Lady Swaythling?

**2** Which number is at the bottom of a darts board?

**3** What is the distance of the women's orienteering short event?

**4** Who won the first single-handed Transatlantic race in Gypsy Moth III in 1960?

**5** How long is each of the four quarters of a game of netball?

**6** Which skater won the 1998 men's World Sprint Championships?

**7** Which sport is divided into single and double-seaters, Standard and 15 metres classes?

**8** What are the dimensions of an indoor handball court?

**9** How many weight categories are there in tae kwon do?

**10** Which sport is played to Harvard Rules?

**11** In whose honour was a memorial erected on Mount Ventoux, after he collapsed and died there during the 1967 Tour de France?

**12** What is the minimum length of a wild-water canoe course?

**13** Who skippered Stars and Stripes to his third America's Cup victory in 1988?

**14** Who won his record fifth World Professional darts title in 1986?

**15** Which city has the White Sox and the Cubs baseball teams?

## *Answers to page 472*

**1** Gordie Howe, **2** The Duke of Edinburgh, **3** Nottingham, **4** 1967, **5** Cross-country, **6** Boston Red Sox, **7** Petanque, **8** Shinty, **9** 12m square, **10** Hungary, **11** Triathlon, **12** Russia, **13** Twelfth, **14** Johan Museeuw, **15** .

# • LUCKY DIP - QUIZ 26 •

*Answers on page 473*

**1** Where were the first table tennis World Championships held in 1926?

**2** In handball, the dimensions of the goal are 3m by 4m True or false?

**3** Which year saw Oxford win the Boat Race by a canvas, the smallest winning margin ever?

**4** Which sport's World Series is confined to North America?

**5** Which yachting event ends in the Fastnet Race?

**6** Who, in 1961, were the first to take the Admiral's Cup away from Britain?

**7** Which British cyclist broke the one hour speed record with 56375km in one hour?

**8** In which Basque sport is a chistera, a wicker basket, strapped to the player's arm?

**9** Who won the first two Super Bowls?

**10** Which sport has synchronised pairs and tumbling events?

**11** What is Three-Day Eventing's first event?

**12** Who won the 1998 women's World Sprint Championships?

**13** Which country has won the women's K1 team title at all four Wild-Water World Championships?

**14** In which country did polo originate?

**15** How high are parallel bars fixed above the floor?

*Answers to page 473*

**1** Jean Aerts, **2** China, **3** Sue Brown, **4** Buffalo Bills, **5** Whitbread Round-the-World Race, **6** Denmark, **7** Banderillas, **8** Black, **9** 5m, **10** Powerboating, **11** Figure skating, **12** Yogi Berra, **13** Chukkas, **14** 1.5km, **15** Show-jumping.

# • LUCKY DIP - QUIZ 27 •

*Answers on page 470*

1 Who retired from ice hockey in 1980 at the age of 52, having played a record 26 seasons?

2 Whose good luck telegram to the 1962 Australian America's Cup team arrived the day after they were beaten?

3 In which English city were the Canoe Marathon World Championships held in 1988?

4 In which year was the Super Bowl first held?

5 What is Three-Day Eventing's second event?

6 Who won baseball's first World Series in 1903?

7 How is boules also known?

8 How is the sport 'camanachd' better known in Scotland?

9 In which size space are floor exercises performed?

10 Which country won table tennis's first Swaythling Cup and all four individual titles in 1926?

11 Which sport is played in the Hawaii Ironman competition?

12 Which nation were the 1997 men's handball world champions?

13 What is the highest possible number Dan in judo?

14 Who won his second successive cycling World Cup title in 1996?

15 Which country won their record ninth Admiral's Cup in 1989?

***The fastest swimmer ever managed, what we might think a measly 5.37 mph, over 50 yards in a 25 yard pool in March 1990.***

## *Answers to page 470*

**1** Table tennis, **2** Three, **3** 5.5km, **4** Francis Chichester, **5** 15 minutes, **6** Jan Bos, **7** Gliding, **8** 20m by 40m, **9** Eight, **10** American football, **11** Tommy Simpson, **12** 3km, **13** Dennis Conner, **14** Eric Bristow, **15** Chicago.

# • LUCKY DIP - QUIZ 28 •

*Answers on page 471*

**1** Which cyclist became, in 1927, the first to win both the amateur and professional titles?

**2** Which country took over from Japan as the dominant force in table tennis in 1961?

**3** Who became, in 1981, the first woman cox in the University Boat Race?

**4** Who were Super Bowl runners-up a record four consecutive times, 1991-94?

**5** What is the longest yachting race?

**6** Who were the 1997 women's handball world champions?

**7** What are the barbed sticks used in bullfighting called?

**8** What colour belt do 1st-5th judo Dans wear?

**9** What is the length of the beam in gymnastics?

**10** In which sport is the Harmsworth Trophy contested?

**11** In which sport might you see a 'loop' and a 'rocker'?

**12** Which New York Yankee played in a record 14 World Series?

**13** What are the sections of a polo match called?

**14** What is the distance of the World Championship Triathlon swimming section?

**15** What is Three-Day Eventing's third event?

---

*Answers to page 471*

**1** London, **2** False - 2m by 3m, **3** 1980, **4** Baseball, **5** Admiral's Cup, **6** USA, **7** Chris Boardman, **8** Pelota, **9** Green Bay Packers, **10** Trampolining, **11** Dressage, **12** Catriona LeMay-Doan, **13** France, **14** Persia (Iran, **15** 195cm.

# • LUCKY DIP - QUIZ 29 •

*Answers on page 476*

1 Which nation won the inaugural netball world championship in 1963?

2 How many cylists competed in the 1986 Tour de France - 110, 160 or 210?

3 Which race was originally the idea of Colonel 'Blondie' Hasler, who came second in the inaugural race?

4 Who won their third successive World Series in 1974?

5 What is the width of the beam in gymnastics?

6 How many attempts are allowed at each lift in powerlifting?

7 In which year were the Harlem Globetrotters founded - 1927, 1937 or 1947?

8 What is the principal show jumping event for male riders in the Royal International Horse Show?

9 Who became, in 1981, the first don to take part in the University Boat Race?

10 How many bulls are killed in a normal bullfight?

11 Which Spanish team won the European men's handball title for the third consecutive time in 1998?

12 What is the distance of the World Championship Triathlon cycling section?

13 Who successfully defended their Super Bowl title in 1974?

14 What colour belt do 6th-8th judo Dans wear?

15 How long is a polo chukka?

---

## *Answers to page 476*

**1** Surfing, **2** China, **3** Plymouth, **4** Veronicas, **5** Dallas Cowboys, **6** Maurice Garin, **7** 1931, **8** Spartak Kiev, **9** Ten, **10** David Broome, **11** Eight, **12** New York Yankees, **13** Red, **14** Horse vault, **15** White.

# • LUCKY DIP - QUIZ 30 •

*Answers on page 477*

**1** In which sport was Danny Millman the first men's world champion, in 1964?

**2** Who became, in 1981, the first wild-card team to win the Super Bowl?

**3** Which sport was invented by Dr James Naismith in 1891?

**4** Who won the European women's handball title in 1998?

**5** What is the distance of the World Championship Triathlon running section?

**6** Who successfully defended their World Series title in 1976?

**7** What colour belt do 9th-11th judo Dans wear?

**8** Which women's sport involves skipping ropes, ribbons, hoops, clubs and balls?

**9** In which year was the Squash Rackets Association formed - 1908, 1918 or 1928?

**10** What colour is the eight ball in pool?

**11** At which London venue is the Royal International Horse Show held?

**12** How many weight categories are there in men's powerlifting?

**13** Which year saw a record 158 finishers in the Tour de France?

**14** A bullfighter's cape is red on one side, and what colour on the other?

**15** At which city does the Whitbread Round-the-World Race start and finish?

---

*Answers to page 477*

**1** Australia, **2** Jahangir Khan, **3** Jack Purcell, **4** Wrestling, **5** Blue and white, **6** Denver Broncos, **7** FIve, **8** The roller skate, **9** A flic-flac, **10** Karate, **11** Picadors, **12** Greg LeMond, **13** Queen Elizabeth II Cup, **14** Newport, Rhode Island, **15** Brooklyn Dodgers.

# • LUCKY DIP - QUIZ 31 •

*Answers on page 474*

**1** In which sport were Australians Bernard Farrelly and Phyllis O'Donnell the first world amateur champions, in 1964?

**2** Which is the only country to have won all seven titles at a table tennis world championship?

**3** At which city does the Single-Handed Transatlantic Race start?

**4** What is the term for the passes a bullfighter makes?

**5** Who successfully defended their Super Bowl title in 1994?

**6** Who won the first Tour de France in 1903 with a record margin of nearly three hours?

**7** In which year was the English Ice Hockey League formed and the Streatham rink opened - 1921, 1926 or 1931?

**8** Which team have won the European women's handball title a record 13 times?

**9** How many weight categories are there in women's powerlifting?

**10** Who won his first King George V Gold Cup in 1966 and his record sixth in 1991?

**11** How many people are there on a tug-of-war team?

**12** Who won the World Series a record fifth consecutive time in 1953?

**13** What colour cap does the goalkeeper wear in water polo?

**14** Which is the only gymnastics apparatus discipline to be shared by men and women?

**15** What colour belt does a 12th judo Dan wear?

---

## *Answers to page 474*

**1** Australia, **2** 210, **3** Single-handed Transatlantic Race, **4** Oakland Athletics, **5** 10cm, **6** Three, **7** 1927, **8** King George V Gold Cup, **9** Boris Rankov, **10** Six, **11** FC Barcelona, **12** 40km, **13** Miami Dolphins, **14** Red and white, **15** 7 minutes.

# • LUCKY DIP - QUIZ 32 •

*Answers on page 475*

**1** In 1965, which nation became the first women's softball world champions?

**2** Who became, in 1982, the first squash player to win a major final without losing a point?

**3** Which Canadian was the first foreign entrant to the All-England badminton Championships?

**4** Of which sport is 'Cumberland and Westmorland' a variety?

**5** Which two colours can be found on the caps worn by non-goalkeepers in water polo?

**6** Who were Super Bowl runners-up for the second year in succession in 1988?

**7** How many of a basketball team's players are on court at any one time?

**8** What was invented by Joseph Merlin of Belgium?

**9** In gymnastics, what is a backward handspring called?

**10** With which martial art was Chojun Miyagi associated?

**11** What are bullfighters on horses called?

**12** Who became, in 1986, the first non-European to win the Tour de France?

**13** What is the women's equivalent to the King George V Gold Cup?

**14** At which resort does the Single-Handed Transatlantic Race finish?

**15** For which baseball team did Ray Campanella play from 1948 to 1957?

***Britain's cycling Prutour came to a grinding halt when 90 leading racers ended up in a parking lot!***

---

*Answers to page 475*

**1** Trampolining, **2** The Oakland Raiders, **3** Basketball, **4** Nieder Osterreich, **5** 10km, **6** Cincinnati Reds, **7** Red, **8** Rhythmic Sportive Gymnastics, **9** 1928, **10** Black, **11** Wembley, **12** Eleven, **13** 1991, **14** Yellow, **15** Portsmouth

# • LUCKY DIP - QUIZ 33 •

*Answers on page 480*

1 Which tycoon's money was used to build Australia II for the 1983 America's Cup?

2 Who became men's squash world No 1 in 1966?

3 What is the length of a croquet lawn?

4 Who won his second successive Single-Handed Transatlantic Race on Fujicolor II in 1996?

5 What is basketball's Wilt Chamberlain's nickname?

6 Which demonstrative show jumper won the 1970 King George V Gold Cup?

7 What is the highest weight category in men's judo?

8 What colour does a greyhound in lane one wear?

9 How many players are there on a water polo team, not including substitutes?

10 On which river was the first known regatta held in 1775?

11 In which year was seeding introduced to the All-England badminton Championships, the names being withheld to avoid insulting the unseeded?

12 Who was the first cyclist to win the Tour de France five times?

13 How many players are there on a volleyball team?

14 What may be rigid-wing or flex-wing?

15 Who successfully defended their Super Bowl title in 1990?

---

## *Answers to page 479*

**1** USA, **2** Leicester, **3** Five and one, **4** Whitaker, **5** Shinty, **6** France, **7** Steven Redgrave, **8** Ivan Ivankov, **9** 1933, **10** Four, **11** 28yds, **12** Michael Jordan, **13** Harness racing, **14** Over 72kg, **15** Two.

# • LUCKY DIP - QUIZ 34 •

*Answers on page 478*

1 Who, in 1966, became the first men's softball world champions?

2 In which city were the first all-glass courts used in the squash World Masters?

3 Which numbers are adjacent to the 20 on a dart-board?

4 What is the surname of John and Michael who between them have won the King George V Gold Cup 7 times?

5 Which 12-a-side game, played with a curved stick and ball, is almost exclusive to the Scottish Highlands?

6 Which country's team has won angling's World Fresh Water Championship most often?

7 Which British rower has won more than 10 rowing gold medals in World Championships and Olympic Games?

8 Who was 1997 gymnastics All-around men's world champion?

9 Which year saw the Tour de France's first King of the Mountains classification?

10 How many substitutes does a water polo team have?

11 What is the width of a croquet lawn?

12 Who was the NBA's leading scorer for a record tenth time in 1998?

13 Which sport's classic for three-year-olds is the Little Brown Jug?

14 What is the highest weight category in women's judo?

15 How many players are there on a beach volleyball team?

## *Answers to page 480*

**1** 1966, **2** Eleven, **3** Water-Skiing, **4** Beattie Feathers, **5** Skiing, **6** Polo, **7** 1994, **8** Under 48kg, **9** Hurling, **10** Six, **11** Blue, **12** Sunsalve, **13** 1983, **14** Bernard Hinault, **15** Shaquille O'Neal.

# • LUCKY DIP - QUIZ 35 •

*Answers on page 479*

**1** Which year saw a resurgence in ice hockey in Britain with the formation of the Northern League?

**2** How many players are there in a hockey team?

**3** Which sport has slalom, tricks and jumping events?

**4** Which Chicago player became American football's first 1,000 yard rusher in 1934?

**5** Which sport has Nordic and Alpine varieties?

**6** Which sport was first played in England by the 10th Hussars in 1869?

**7** In which year was the women's World Fresh Water Championship first held, 37 years after the first men's?

**8** What is the lowest weight category in men's judo?

**9** What is the second most popular traditional sport in Ireland?

**10** How many hoops are used in croquet?

**11** What colour does a greyhound wear in lane two?

**12** Which was the first horse to win both the King George V Gold Cup and the Queen Elizabeth II Cup?

**13** In which year did the NY Yacht Club have to unbolt the America's Cup from their floor and hand it over for the first time in 132 years?

**14** Who became, in 1985, the third cyclist to win the Tour de France five times?

**15** Who was the NBA's leading scorer in 1995?

***"It's difficult to be more laid back (David Gower) without actually being comotose!" Phil Edmonds.***

---

## *Answers to page 478*

**1** Alan Bond, **2** Jonah Barrington, **3** 35yds, **4** Loick Peyron, **5** The stilt, **6** Harvey Smith, **7** Over 95kg, **8** Red, **9** Seven, **10** The Thames, **11** 1932, **12** Jacques Anquetil, **13** Six, **14** Hang gliders, **15** San Francisco 49ers.